W9-BMD-164

Saint Peter's University Library
Withdrawn

Saint Peter's University Library
Withdrawn

SCHIZOPHRENIA
Research and Theory

PERSONALITY AND PSYCHOPATHOLOGY
A Series of Texts, Monographs, and Treatises

1. The Anatomy of Achievement Motivation, *Heinz Heckhausen.* 1967

2. Cues, Decisions, and Diagnoses: A Systems-Analytic Approach to the Diagnosis of Psychopathology, *Peter E. Nathan.* 1967

3. Human Adaptation and Its Failures, *Leslie Phillips.* 1968

4. Schizophrenia: Research and Theory, *William E. Broen, Jr.* 1968

SCHIZOPHRENIA
Research and Theory

WILLIAM E. BROEN, JR.

DEPARTMENT OF PSYCHOLOGY
UNIVERSITY OF CALIFORNIA
LOS ANGELES, CALIFORNIA

 1968

ACADEMIC PRESS   New York   and   London

Permission and Copyright Notice

The selections from Dr. Eugen Bleuler's *Dementia Praecox or the Group of Schizophrenias,* copyright 1950 by International Universities Press, are used with International Universities Press's permission.

Copyright © 1968, by Academic Press, Inc.
All rights reserved.
No part of this book may be reproduced in any form,
by photostat, microfilm, or any other means, without
written permission from the publishers.

ACADEMIC PRESS, INC.
111 Fifth Avenue, New York, New York 10003

United Kingdom Edition published by
ACADEMIC PRESS, INC. (LONDON) LTD.
Berkeley Square House, London W.1

Library of Congress Catalog Card Number: 68-8423

PRINTED IN THE UNITED STATES OF AMERICA

To Carol,
Karen, and Linda

PREFACE

During the past two decades there has been a marked and accelerating increase in experimental studies of schizophrenic behavior. For some time schizophrenia has been a major focus of clinical interest because of its frequency and its seriousness for the individuals involved. The accelerating research interest seems to reflect not only this importance of the problem, but also the stimulation from the increasing understanding, recognition of order, and clarification of additional research questions that has been added by recent results. With order emerging in this important area that had previously been characterized by diversity of opinion and apparent lack of intelligibility, the increasing research emphasis on schizophrenia is not surprising.

This work attempts to clarify the major directions in which the research points and to indicate the consistencies in and the questions raised by the different theoretical attempts to integrate the research. It is intended for investigators, students, and persons in the several professions whose work requires knowledge of recent research on schizophrenia.

The contents of the book were determined by two considerations — that they reflect the emphases in recent research and theory on schizophrenic behavior and underline behavioral processes that are emerging as important in differences between schizophrenics and normals, and as important in differences among schizophrenics. Therefore, much of the discussion is within the broad and interrelated areas of response interference, attention and cue utilization, and physiological arousal and inhibition.

The major acknowledgment for contributions to a book of this type must be made, and is gladly made, to other investigators in this area. Many have contributed not only in the innovations in their own work, but also through personal discussions or correspondence that forced me to clarify my own thinking and made me aware of recent data and integrative ideas that had not then been published. It is a pleasure to acknowledge the stimulation and help from many, including Drs. L. J. Chapman, R. L. Cromwell, J. A. Easterbrook, S. Epstein, R. W. Payne, J. Silverman, and P. H. Venables. Special acknowledgment is due Dr. L. H. Storms, my close colleague for many years. Our joint and disjunct work on schizophrenia has been supported by grants from the National Association for Mental Health, the UCLA Research Committee, the California Department of Mental Hygiene (No. R-61-2-20), and the U.S. Public Health Service (No. R01-MH-12373). It is also a pleasure to acknowledge that this work owes much to the encouraging enthusiasm and constructive criticisms from many students at the Universities of Wisconsin, Massachusetts, and California (Los Angeles), who dealt with a number of the topics covered in seminars and in other discussions with me. The kind cooperation of the numerous authors and publishers who gave permission to quote and reproduce their material is also gratefully acknowledged. The authors are cited within the text. Permission from the following is not acknowledged elsewhere: Academic Press, for material from Volumes 1 and 4 of *Progress in Experimental Personality Research;* the *American Journal of Psychiatry;* the American Psychological Association, for material from the *American Psychologist, Journal of Abnormal and Social Psychology, Journal of Consulting Psychology, Journal of Experimental Psychology, Journal of Personality and Social Psychology, Psychological Review,* and the book, *Research in Psychotherapy;* the British Psychological Society, for material from the *British Journal of Social and Clinical Psychology,* and the *British Journal of Medical Psychology;* the *Journal of Mental Science* (now the *British Journal of Psychiatry,* published by authority of the Royal Medico-Psychological Association); and Harper and Row, for material from *Psychosomatic Medicine.*

I also want to acknowledge, with thanks, the help of Linda Levitz, who cheerfully carried the arduous burden of repeated typing of drafts. Dr. Brendan A. Maher was a tremendous help at all stages of the work. He helped in planning its scope, was encouraging throughout, and critically reviewed the entire manuscript, contributing considerably to the final revision. It should be noted that I have sometimes not acted on his suggestions. Hence any errors and omissions are mine.

To my wife goes my deepest appreciation; her help and encouragement have been invaluable.

WILLIAM E. BROEN, JR.

Malibu, California
October, 1968

CONTENTS

1. Interfering Responses

2. Theories of Response Disorganization in Schizophrenia: Reduced Information

3. Theories of Response Disorganization in Schizophrenia: Greater Interference from Concurrent Response Tendencies

4. Neurophysiological Speculations about Response Interference in Schizophrenia

ix

5. Overinclusion and Heterogeneity in Schizophrenia

6. Differences in Breadth of Cue Utilization

7. Other Accounts of Altered Cue Utilization in Schizophrenia

8. Physiological Arousal in Schizophrenia

9. Concluding Remarks

References

SCHIZOPHRENIA
Research and Theory

1

INTERFERING RESPONSES

"My thoughts get all jumbled up. I start thinking or talking about something but I never get there. Instead I wander off in the wrong direction and get caught up with all sorts of different things that may be connected with the things I want to say but in a way I can't explain. People listening to me get more lost than I do [McGhie & Chapman, 1961, p. 108]."

The speaker is a schizophrenic. His description of his experience reflects an aspect of schizophrenia that has often been emphasized: that ideas with relationships tangential to a main theme intrude, interfering with the organized continuity of the theme. As described by another schizophrenic: "My trouble is that I've got too many thoughts. You might think about something, let's say that ash tray and just think, oh! yes, that's for putting my cigarette in, but I would think of it and then I would think of a dozen different things connected with it at the same time [ibid]."

As is obvious from the clarity of the quotations themselves, the degree of disorganization varies. Often, however, the intrusion of associated ideas lends a particular flavor to schizophrenic language that is hard to describe, yet is fairly distinctive. Bleuler illustrated it with the following quotation from a hebephrenic: "The mountains which are outlined in the swellings of the oxygen are beautiful [1950, p. 19]." Here, as often occurs in the speech of schizophrenics, related terms are used in place of more precise terms in a statement that is, in general, quite similar to normal language. Cameron's (1938) study of schizophrenic thinking also emphasized the same kind of sporadic intrusion of imprecise approximations, as shown in a schizophrenic's explanation of why he is alive: "Because you really live physically because you have menu three times a day . . . [p. 21]."

As would be expected from the two initial quotations where schizophrenics described the degree of disorganization they sometimes experience, the incongruity that results from the intrusion of associated ideas is not always as mild as in the examples in the last paragraph. At times the train of thought may be completely derailed, as in the following interchange with a schizophrenic: " 'Are you very unhappy?' — 'No.' — 'Is something weighing heavily on your mind?' — 'Yes. Iron is heavy' [Bleuler, 1950, p. 19]."

The reason for citing these examples is not to begin to provide data to support any conclusions about schizophrenia. For this, we will focus on experiments; the emphasis in this chapter will be on reporting a large body of research so that our later discussion of theories of schizophrenia will have a good foundation. However, in order to organize the discussion of research, a tentative and gross description of schizophrenic disturbance will be useful, and it is here that the clinical examples that have been emphasized by past writers on schizophrenia enter in. The examples given above and others that will be given soon will point toward a tentative formulation about schizophrenic disturbance that is relevant to much recent research.

In working toward a formulation, one of the questions that can be asked about the associated intrusions in the examples is whether or not these intrusions represent a stable shift in associations. Would the schizophrenic who substituted "have menu" for a more usual way of referring to eating use this same substitution consistently? As Sommer, Dewar, and Osmond (1960) asked in the title of their paper on verbal associations in schizophrenia, "Is there a schizophrenic language?" From the way the schizophrenics who were quoted at the beginning of the chapter characterized their thinking — for example, "jumbled up" among related ideas — it seems quite likely that the answer is no. Also there is suggestive evidence in research results that have shown that, on repeated testing with the same verbal stimulus, schizophrenics are less consistent than normals in their association to that stimulus. Thus, to the extent that we can generalize from instability in verbal associations to instability in the choice of words in sentences, it seems likely that the deviant associations are not stable translations of normal associations. Abnormal intra-individual variability in verbal associations on repeated testing has been found in schizophrenics by Sommer et al. (1960), Storms, Broen, & Levin (1967), and Dokecki, Polidoro, & Cromwell (1965), although in the latter study, abnormal instability was not found in a group of chronic good-premorbid schizophrenics.

That the instability in schizophrenics' associations is an important characteristic that is related to the extent of their deviancy from normal responses is indicated by the correlation between response stability and the normative commonality of responses that was found by Dokecki et al. and Storms et al. It also seems that the relationship between intra-individual variability and deficit is true not only for verbal behavior, but also holds in many other areas. Weckowicz and Blewett (1959) found that in schizophrenics the amount of intra-individual variability in judging sizes of objects was negatively correlated with ability to judge sizes; was negatively correlated with performance on a test of abstracting ability (Goldstein-Scheerer Color-Form Test); and was negatively correlated with ability to select relevant figures from complex backgrounds (Gottschaldt's figures).

A TENTATIVE FORMULATION

The characterization of schizophrenic deficit as unstable, with much of the variability being in intrusions of responses that are associated in some way with the context is illustrated in Figure 1. Normal subjects obviously often have many associations to stimuli, but seem able to focus primarily on single appropriate responses. Schizophrenics, on the other hand, though apparently sharing many of the same response tendencies as normals, seem to have an abnormal equivalence of the alternate response tendencies. Competing associations seem to intrude with much greater frequency, not in a stable fashion, but with a tendency toward unstable randomization among the alternate associates.

If there is any utility to this kind of preliminary formulation, one question is how broadly it should be applied. If an important basic characteristic of schizophrenia is susceptibility to competing response tendencies,

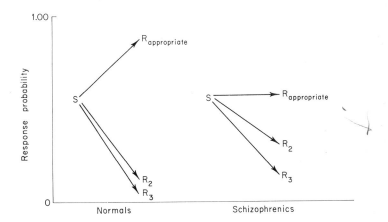

Fig. 1. Theoretical illustration of the probability of occurrence of alternate responses (R) that are associated to a stimulus (S).

does this mean that the responses that intrude are only different associations to a single stimulus? In general, environments are complex. Many stimuli are present and competing response tendencies are evoked by different stimuli.

Clinical examples do suggest that when different concurrent events evoke competing responses, schizophrenics have trouble in maintaining focus on a single line of responding, just as they do when the competing responses are different associations to the same stimulus. For example, Cameron (1938) reports the response of a severely disorganized schizophrenic woman when she was asked to explain how fish can live in water. The important point here is that in addition to being faced with this question, this woman also had a number of preoccupations—religious preoccupations and a concern about physical injuries, such as having her back broken. Thus, a number of concurrent themes are in competition as she is asked to reply to the question about fish. Her reply was, "Because it's learned to swim." When then asked, "What if it couldn't swim?" she replied, "Not naturally it couldn't. Why do certain gods have effect on the seas like that? What does the earth have such an effect to break their backs? The fishes near home come to the surface and break." She was then asked to explain further and continued, "I think it is due to the bodies people lose. A body becomes adapted to the air. Think thoughts and break the fishes [p. 25]." This is a rather extreme and striking example of relatively randomized interpenetration of themes, some stimulated internally and one by a question from another person.

The same inability to hold responding to defined limits when multiple stimuli evoke multiple response tendencies was noticed in early research using concept-sorting tasks with schizophrenics. As part of a series of historically important studies, Cameron (1939) administered the Hanfman-Kasanin sorting test to five seriously disorganized schizophrenics. The test consists of 22 wooden blocks which vary in color, shape, size, and height, and which are to be sorted on the basis of height-size configurations. Cameron presented anecdotal data in support of his conclusion that: "The single most striking characteristic of our schizophrenic patients' attempts at solution was their inability to maintain adequate *boundaries*. Faced with this definite, arbitrary task, they could neither restrict themselves to its limits, nor keep other material from intruding [p. 207]." Cameron then gave examples, such as schizophrenics being unable to confine their responding to the appropriate stimulus characteristics of the task material, and even having response intrusions stimulated by commonalities between task and non-task material, for example wanting to include a yellow pencil in a group with a yellow block.

Many schizophrenics' descriptions of their own experience also emphasize the discontinuous and unfocused responding which occurs when concurrent stimuli evoke alternate thoughts, emotions, and attention tendencies. The following quotations are all from McGhie and Chapman (1961):

"Half the time I am talking about one thing and thinking about a half a dozen other things at the same time. It must look queer to people when I laugh about something that has got nothing to do with what I am talking about, but they don't know what's going on inside and how much of it is running around in my head [p. 109]."

"When people are talking, I just get scraps of it. If it is just one person who is speaking that's not so bad, but if others join in then I can't pick it up at all. I just can't get in tune with the conversation. It makes me feel all open—as if things are closing in on me and I have lost control [p. 106]."

"I can't concentrate on television because I can't watch the screen and listen to what is being said at the same time. I can't seem to take in two things like this at the same time especially when one of them means watching and the other means listening. On the other hand I seem to be always taking in too much at the one time and then I can't handle it and can't make sense of it [p. 105]."

It seems then that it may be well to expand our tentative formulation to include multiple-stimulus situations, as illustrated in Figure 2.

From clinical examples and some early observations about standardized situations, it seems very possible that in both of these types of situa-

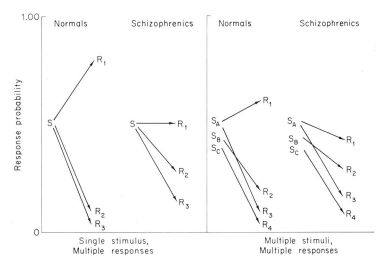

Fig. 2. Theoretical illustration of the probability of occurrence of alternate responses that are associated to the same stimulus or concurrent stimuli.

tions the responding of schizophrenics is more variable among the alternate response tendencies evoked in the situation than is the case for normals. Schizophrenics seem not only to show a tendency toward randomization among associates to single stimuli, but may also tend to be distracted by a wider range of stimuli in multiple-stimulus situations. What may well be basic, or at least what we will consider basic in this tentative formulation, is the susceptibility to competing response tendencies, regardless of whether the stimulation is single or multiple, external or internal.

Now let us see what experimental data tell us about this tentative response-interference model of schizophrenia.

Schizophrenic Deficit as a Function of Stimulus Complexity

The hypothesis that schizophrenic deficit is an abnormal inability to shut out the interfering response tendencies that are evoked in a situation has a number of implications. One is that schizophrenic deficit should be greater when situations are more complex, i.e., contain more stimuli that elicit attention responses or other competing responses, or where single stimuli evoke more competing tendencies. Of course, there may well be limits on this hypothesis, in that schizophrenic variability may be only among a limited subset of all available response alternates, or may occur only in certain conditions. This is said only to emphasize that our goal is not only to test whether or not a model is right or wrong, but also, as we search through studies, to be alert to findings that will require us to modify the initial formulation and point the directions in which change or elaboration is needed.

We first turn to studies which vary stimulus complexity; these studies should be relevant in that an increase in the number of prominent stimuli in an experimental situation should tend to increase the number of response tendencies, whether the response is merely attending to a stimulus or taking some other action signaled by the stimulus.

First let us note a study by Ludwig, Wood, and Downs (1962), which compared schizophrenics and normals (54 in each group) on five different audiometric tests. Four of the tests are relevant here; two of these tests, measuring pure tone threshold and speech reception threshold, were essentially single-stimulus tests; the other two tests used multiple stimulation, and efficient performance required responding to one kind of stimulus and ignoring another. The schizophrenic and normal groups did not differ from each other in pure tone threshold or speech reception threshold.

One of the multiple-stimulus tests was a measure of the signal-to-noise ratio at which subjects could discriminate a signal from noise. The signals were words given at a constant volume 30 db above each subject's speech threshold, while speech noise was gradually increased until the subject could no longer repeat the words. The noise decibel level at which words could not be repeated was the measure used. As can be seen in Figure 3, this measure yielded quite different scores for the two groups, with schizophrenics being unable to respond only to the words at a lower level of background stimulation than was the case for normals.

These results so far seem very much in accord with the initial formulation. In simple situations, schizophrenics can respond to single stimuli and do so as well as normals. However, when irrelevant stimulation is introduced, schizophrenics cannot confine their response only to appropriate stimuli; they are distracted more by irrelevant stimulation than normals.

However, the results of the second multiple-stimulus test used by Ludwig *et al.* seem sharply opposed to this view. This test involved delayed auditory feedback. In it, subjects were first given fourth-grade level material to read, and read it through first without auditory feedback, and then again with their voices returned through earphones at a 70 db level with a .2 second delay. The measure used was the difference in the reading time for the two readings. As is illustrated in Figure 4, different schizophrenics reacted to the multiple-stimulus stimulation in distinctly different ways. While all of the normals read a little more slowly during the second reading where delayed auditory feedback was present, the additional stimulation interfered even more for some schizophrenics. However, other schizophrenics read the passage faster on the second

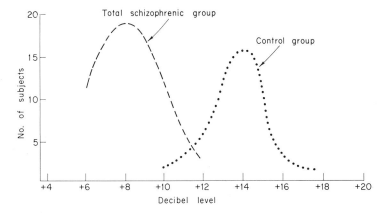

Fig. 3. Increase in noise level at which subjects could no longer repeat words. (From Ludwig, Wood, & Downs, 1962.)

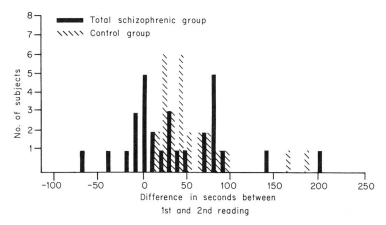

Fig. 4. Retardation caused by delayed auditory feedback. (From Ludwig *et al.,* 1962.)

than on the first reading. The schizophrenic distribution is bimodal and differs significantly from the normals' distribution.

Thus, a number of schizophrenics responded to the additional stimulation as expected, but many did not. The delayed-feedback reading was the second time the subjects read through the passage, so that improvement might be expected if the feedback could be ignored. However, the finding that many schizophrenics were less responsive than normals to the additional source of stimuli means that our formulation is obviously incomplete, at least with regard to some schizophrenics.

One of the multiple-stimulus situations produced results in accord with the formulation, the other did not. What is the difference between them? In the situation where almost all schizophrenics were less able than normals to focus on the appropriate stimulus, appropriate and interfering stimuli were in the same sensory modality. In the other task the interfering stimulation was auditory and the needed stimuli were presented visually.

It should be easier to separate relevant from irrelevant stimuli when the two kinds of stimuli are presented in different sensory modalities. However, there is nothing in what has been said so far that would lead us to expect that any subgroup of schizophrenics would be more focused in the range of categories of stimuli they attend to than normals. Though our formulation cannot account for this aspect of these findings, we will not change it until we have more information about the directions of change that are needed. However, as we continue to use the formulation as stated, we must remember that while it seems to hold for the majority of schizophrenics when multiple stimuli are hard to discriminate, it is incomplete, and may not be accurate for an as yet undefined subgroup of schizophrenics when irrelevant stimuli are in classes distinct from focal stimuli. This possibility will be discussed in considerable detail in later chapters.

Ludwig, Stilson, Wood, and Downs (1963) replicated the Ludwig *et al.* (1962) finding that schizophrenics require higher signal-to-noise ratios than normals. However, the mean performance of schizophrenics did not differ significantly from a group of non-schizophrenic psychiatric patients. This new sample of schizophrenics also did not show the previous bimodal reaction to the delayed-feedback test. Only the tendency toward greater distractibility in schizophrenics appeared, although in this situation where interfering stimulation was from a different modality, the tendency was not significant. Again, the difficult discrimination task, that involving single-modality interference, yielded better discrimination between normals and schizophrenics.

The results of the last two studies may, of course, have been due to some particular sensitivity of schizophrenics to interference from auditory stimuli. In order to test this possibility, Stilson and Kopell (1964) ran an analogous study using visual instead of auditory noise. The subjects' task was to identify geometric shapes which were presented with and without a background of continually moving spots (the "visual noise"). Within each condition, the intensity of the geometric shape was increased until shapes could be recognized. Schizophrenics, non-psychiatric patients, and normals did not differ in recognition thresholds when the shapes were presented without visual noise. However, when visual noise was present, schizophrenics did significantly more poorly than the other two groups. The reduction in performance from the no-noise conditions was significantly greater for schizophrenics than for either non-schizophrenic patients or normals. It does seem quite clear then that schizophrenic distractibility is not confined to any single modality. For both visual and auditory material, when competing stimuli are presented in one modality, schizophrenics are abnormally distracted by irrelevant stimuli.

In the studies that we have looked at so far, the schizophrenics have been rather mixed groups. Weckowicz (1960) separated schizophrenics a little more, comparing acute and chronic schizophrenics, normals, brain-damaged patients, and non-organic non-schizophrenic psychiatric patients on a task entailing ability to select relevant stimuli and disregard irrelevant stimuli presented in the same modality. The task was a hidden-pictures test. The first form of this test consisted of 16 drawings of common objects on which were jumbled lines that crossed the lines of the drawings. The subjects were asked to identify the drawings. Following this, the drawings were shown without the superimposed lines. Scores were based on accuracy of identification of the objects when the irrelevant lines were present, but "only those failures were considered in which the subject failed to recognize the picture in the figure-ground confusion card but recognized it subsequently in the card without the figure-ground confusion [p. 522]." Thus, the score was actually a measure of difference in performance on conditions with and without interfering stimuli. As would be expected from the other studies that we have discussed, schizophrenics were relatively more distracted by additional stimuli than were normals and non-organic non-schizophrenic psychiatric patients. This was true for both acute and chronic schizophrenics. Chronic schizophrenics were even more distracted by the additional same-modality stimuli than acutes. The organics showed most deficit, being significantly more distracted by added irrelevant stimuli than the chronic schizophrenics.

So far, we have looked at only two studies where interfering stimuli were in a different modality than relevant stimuli. The results of this type of interference seem equivocal, with many schizophrenics being more distracted than normals, but it seems that some others may be less distracted by second-modality interference. Two experiments by J. Chapman and McGhie (1962) provide firmer evidence indicating that schizophrenics can be abnormally distracted by stimuli from a second modality. In one task, subjects were to repeat a series of six numbers or letters with different series presented to the subject visually and auditorily. When audio and visual presentations were concurrent and the subjects were to respond selectively only to audio or visual information, schizophrenics did worse than normals and non-schizophrenic psychiatric patients.

In a second experiment, the subjects first turned a wheel at a constant rate that was comfortable for them, and then the task was repeated while the subject heard a variable auditory rhythm. The comparison of the variability in turning rate between the two conditions gave a distractibility index that was greater for the schizophrenics than either normals or non-schizophrenic psychiatric patients.

These two studies give added evidence that schizophrenics can be abnormally distracted by irrelevant stimuli from a sensory modality that is not needed for performing a task. However, they do not help with regard to the question of whether or not any specific group of schizophrenics are better than normals at ignoring identifiable sets of stimuli, e.g., stimuli from a second modality. Chapman and McGhie selected young schizophrenics (ages 17 to 30) and did not include the more chronic patients, but mean duration of illness was still over four years, so their results do not clearly point to a specific group as being distractible by stimuli in a second modality.

We have seen that although many schizophrenics seem to be abnormally distracted by interfering stimuli from a second modality, there may well be a more uniform tendency, or a greater tendency, to be distracted by same-modality stimuli. However, what is it about modality differences that reduces interference? It may well be that the important distinction is not whether relevant and irrelevant stimuli are in different modalities, but rather whether relevant and irrelevant stimuli are in easily discriminable classes, regardless of whether these classes are based on modality differences or other differences.

A third experiment by Chapman and McGhie (1962) points toward the possibility that discriminability, rather than modality differences, may be what is important. This study used the Stroop test, in which subjects are timed while they read aloud a list of names of colors printed in black. Then subjects are timed while naming colors in a list of different colored spots, and finally subjects are given a list of names of colors which are printed in conflicting colors (e.g., the word "Red" printed in green ink) and are asked to ignore the words and say aloud the colors the words are printed in. The difference in speed for the second and third parts of this test is a measure of distraction by stimuli in the same sense modality (visual). The schizophrenics, normals, and non-schizophrenic psychiatric patients did not differ significantly on this task. The differences were in the expected direction, schizophrenics tending to be more distracted. However, this is still the first study we have discussed where distracting stimuli in the same sensory modality as relevant stimuli did not interfere significantly more with schizophrenic than with normal performance.

What is different about the Stroop and the single-modality distraction tasks where clearer differences were found between schizophrenics and normals? Differences were found when intensity of the irrelevant auditory stimuli was increased relative to the intensity of relevant auditory stimuli (Ludwig *et al.,* 1962), when the intensity of relevant visual stimuli was low relative to constant-intensity irrelevant visual stimuli (Stilson & Kopell, 1964), and when irrelevant lines masked relevant lines (Weckowicz, 1960). In each case, discriminability on the basis of intensity and/or type of stimulation was low. In the Stroop test, relevant stimuli are clearly identifiable colors, and though the irrelevant stimuli are also perceived visually, they are words which should be somewhat more discriminable from the relevant stimuli than is the case in the studies where schizophrenics had special difficulty. There are obviously other differences between the Stroop test and the other single-modality interference tests where schizophrenics showed clearer deficit relative to normals. However, from this analysis of the conditions under which increased deficit occurs, it seems quite plausible that distinctiveness between classes of relevant and irrelevant stimuli is at least one of the factors which contributes to schizophrenic deficit. Why the separation of focal and irrelevant stimuli into more distinct classes should affect the differences between the performance of schizophrenics and normals is not yet clear. However, it does seem likely that ease of discriminating relevant from irrelevant stimuli is a more specific characteristic that differentiates between low and high deficit situations for schizophrenics than whether irrelevant stimuli are in the same or different sense modalities.

In that we have suggested that a subsample of schizophrenics may confine their observation to certain classes of cues and therefore may be helped especially by relevant and irrelevant stimuli being from easily discriminable classes, it should be remembered that on any specific test, where relevant and irrelevant stimuli are from classes of stimuli which are clearly different, different samples of schizophrenics may show different amounts of deficit. However, though different groups of schizophrenics may show different amounts of deficit, the most important point here is that in the studies we have looked at where deficit in the same group of schizophrenics has been studied over different conditions, the results have shown that approximation to normal behavior tends to vary with the ease of discriminating relevant from irrelevant stimuli.

It is possible that schizophrenic subjects show greater deficit in situations where interfering stimuli are difficult to discriminate, not only because such situations affect an additional subgroup of schizophrenics, but also, in part, because such situations tend to be more difficult for all groups of schizophrenics. We have been looking at studies where irrelevant stimuli were used, because of the hypothesis that adding irrelevant stimuli should increase the number of competing response tendencies, which should intrude especially in schizophrenics. What has been forgotten is that adding a specific number of irrelevant *stimuli* will not always lead to the same increase in number and strength of competing *responses*. If we analyze the situations where schizophrenics had most difficulty under irrelevant stimulation, it seems that these situations were of a type that would be especially likely to increase the number of strong competing responses for two reasons.

First, greater similarity between relevant and irrelevant stimuli should increase both the number and the strength of irrelevant attention responses because of generalization of attention responses. When task instructions strengthen a tendency to focus on certain kinds of stimuli, then this tendency should be more likely to generalize to irrelevant stimuli that are similar, than to irrelevant stimuli that are dissimilar. Thus, similar irrelevant stimuli are more likely than dissimilar stimuli to have a significant effect in increasing the number of competing responses evoked at more than negligible strength.

Second, when irrelevant stimuli are in the same modality as relevant stimuli and are of relatively high intensity, then irrelevant stimuli will be more likely to mask relevant stimuli, making the relevant stimuli more ambiguous. When, as in several of the studies we have looked at (Ludwig *et al.,* 1962, 1963; Stilson & Kopell, 1964; Weckowicz, 1960), the relevant stimuli are to be identified, the increase in ambiguity should increase the number of alternate responses evoked by the relevant stimulus.

The basic point is that competing *response* tendencies seem to be abnormally intrusive in schizophrenics, and any increase in *stimulus* complexity does not always result in the same increase in *response* complexity.

A study (Venables, 1958) where schizophrenics were compared with normals on tasks with different degrees of stimulus complexity is quite relevant here. The task was a verbal reaction-time task. Subjects were to call out the number of a light that was lit on a stimulus display. The number of lights used in different experimental conditions varied from one to eight. The important aspect of this study was that each light had its number painted on it, so all the subject had to do was to look at the stimulus and read off the correct response. Each stimulus clearly led to a single response, and with stimuli being clearly identifiable and presented one at a time, there was little response complexity, even in the conditions with many different stimuli. As would then be expected from our formulation, there was no interaction between stimulus complexity (the number of different stimuli in a condition) and difference between schizophrenic and normal performance.

King (1954) compared chronic schizophrenics and normals in reaction-time tasks with two levels of stimulus complexity with the stimuli being less clearly tied to specific responses. One task was a simple jump reaction-time task where a buzzer was the signal for a subject to move his finger from a start point to another point. A dual-stimulus task was also used where the subject was to move his finger to one point when a buzzer sounded and to another point when a bell sounded. Because the different stimuli were not as clearly labeled and tied to specific task responses as in the Venables task, we would expect a greater degree of generalization of responses from their appropriate stimulus to the alternate stimulus. In other words, stimulus complexity would be more closely related to response complexity in King's task. As we might expect then, the difference between schizophrenic and normal performances was greater on the dual-stimulus task than on the single-stimulus task. It should be noted that King's results have usually been cited as not showing an interaction between task complexity and relative schizophrenic deficit. This is apparently because the *ratio* of single- to multiple-stimulus performance was the same for schizophrenics and normals. This obscures the actual results which were that, even though schizophrenics were slower than normals in the single-stimulus task, their performance worsened even more than the normals' when the task was made more complex. These results are similar to those in an earlier, similar study reported by Huston, Shakow, and Riggs (1937).

Why, though, should schizophrenics be slower than normals on simple reaction-time tasks? Shakow, who has been associated with considerable reaction-time work on schizophrenics, has suggested (1962) that the schizophrenic is distracted by irrelevant stimuli even when, to the experimenter, the situation is a simple, single-stimulus task. ". . . the phenomenon is perhaps most clearly depicted in the reaction time experiments. Here we see particularly the various difficulties created by *context,* the degree to which the schizophrenic is affected by irrelevant aspects of the stimulus surroundings — inner and outer — which prevent his focusing on the 'to-be-responded-to stimulus' [1962, p. 9]." If this is true, then, as implied by Payne (1961), varying amounts of distraction added to normal variation in reaction time should increase the variability of the schizophrenic group. Schizophrenics do have much greater variability than normals in both simple and choice reaction-time tasks (e.g., King, 1954).

We would also expect that distractibility would tend to affect speed tests more than untimed tests. This is because in untimed tests the momentary irrelevant attention responses, or other momentary responses induced by the irrelevant stimuli, would usually not lead to those specific responses which signal completion of a task. After responding to the irrelevant, the subject can return to the task. We have already looked at several studies where untimed "single-stimulus" tasks showed no difference between the performance of schizophrenics and normals [e.g., the puretone threshold and speech-reception threshold tasks in Ludwig *et al.* (1962) and the shape-recognition thresholds without visual distraction in Stilson and Kopell (1964)].

A study by L. J. Chapman (1956a) combines a number of points we have been discussing. It is an untimed task, with varying numbers of distractors, where the distractors are hard to discriminate and lead to competing responses. The task was a card-sorting task where on each trial a response card was to be sorted with one of three sorting cards. The basis for sorting was a shared concept or identity between a figure on the response card and a figure in the lower right-hand corner of one of the sorting cards. For example, if the response card had a picture of a dress on it, and the first sorting card had a dress in its lower right-hand corner, then the response card was to be placed with the first sorting card. There were four figures on the response card and on each sorting card, but only one figure on the response card was identical to, or shared a concept with, the relevant figure on a sorting card (the figure in the lower right-hand corner). Usually the response card also contained figures which were identical to, or shared a concept with, one or more of the three irrelevant figures on a different (distractor) sorting card. The number of irrelevant (distractor) commonalities between the response card and the distractor sorting card varied from 0 to 3. The third sorting card shared no commonalities with any figures on the response card. Note that this is a task where relevant and irrelevant stimuli are both presented visually; they are the same type of stimulus and they are equally intense. The only way to distinguish relevant stimuli is by position on a card and this is difficult because the positions which are not relevant on the sorting cards are relevant on the response card. Thus, this is a study where schizophrenic deficit should vary as a function of distracting stimuli because relevant and irrelevant commonalities are difficult to discriminate and lead to conflicting responses. Also, because it is an untimed task, when task distractors that would tend to evoke incorrect responses are not present, schizophrenics' susceptibility to competing tendencies would not be an important factor and schizophrenic deficit should be minimal.

The results are shown in Figure 5. When there were no distracting commonalities, the performance of schizophrenics and normals did not differ significantly. However, when a competing response was introduced by an irrelevant commonality, schizophrenics performed significantly worse than normals. This is the main analysis which is relevant to our present discussion, in that the addition of more distractors only increased the tendency to the same incorrect response (using the sorting card which had the distractors on it). However, it does seem that the strength of a competing response may be a factor in schizophrenic deficit in addition to the mere presence of competing responses.

One other point should be noted. We have not discussed responses to the third sorting card, which shared no commonalities with the response card. Responses to this card would be made on the basis of random placements, or other response styles not guided by commonalities; thus, the number of responses to this card could be used as a control for such tendencies. As can be seen from distractor level 0 in Figure 5, which shows the total use of both incorrect sorting cards, there was very little of this type of sorting. Also, when all distractor levels are considered together, on the measure of responses to the distractor card minus response to this control card, the schizophrenics significantly exceeded the normals. In other words, this study provides fairly good evidence that schizophrenics make errors because they respond to the response pull of distracting stimuli, and that these errors in complex situations cannot be just explained as due to responses that are not related to the situation, or low motivation when situations get harder.

In review, these stimulus-complexity studies indicate that schizophren-

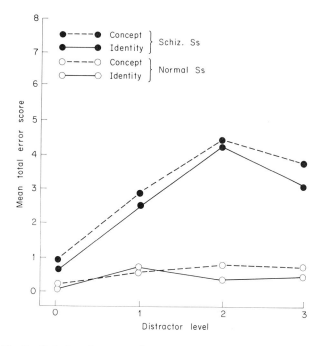

Fig. 5. Relation of errors to distractor level. (From Chapman, 1956a.)

ics are more distracted by irrelevant stimuli than normals, and are usually more distracted than non-organic patients. However, the results of the studies do vary somewhat. Stimulus complexity is only loosely related to the amount of schizophrenic deficit. The important variable seems to be response complexity, which is only imperfectly related to stimulus complexity. When stimuli are easily discriminable, are presented one at a time, and clearly lead to specific responses, then the number of stimuli in a task does not seem to be related to relative schizophrenic deficit. Special schizophrenic deficit occurs when relevant stimuli are made more ambiguous by masking stimuli, thus leading to response uncertainty, and also occurs when concurrent and difficult-to-discriminate irrelevant stimuli evoke competing responses. However, there is also a hint, which will be discussed in a later chapter, that when the competing responses are evoked by classes of stimuli which are easily discriminable, some schizophrenics may ignore the additional stimuli.

We turn now to studies where there have been more direct attempts to study response interference in schizophrenics.

Response Interference Studies

Venables (1965) noted that response complexity was minimized in his stimulus-complexity study. In order to compare schizophrenics and normals on tasks varying in response complexity, he used a card-sorting task with seven different degrees of complexity. Ordinary playing cards were sorted, with sorting complexity varying from a simple red-black choice to a twenty-six choice sort. In the more complex sorts, many of the stimulus characteristics of a card would be appropriate for a number of different responses, e.g., "redness" would be associated with a family of alternate responses. Thus, this is a study where response complexity is varied. Regression lines relating sorting time to task complexity were computed for both groups of subjects. The intercept values (indicating reaction times at minimal response complexity) were not significantly different for schizophrenics and normals. However, the slopes differed significantly, schizophrenics requiring more sorting time per increment in response complexity. Venables concludes, "It would thus appear that in this type of experiment where complexity of response is introduced there is a tendency for the schizophrenic to be relatively imparied in more complex performance [1965, p. 606]."

Schizophrenics also seem to be especially disturbed by response complexity in the form of alternate meanings of words. Faibish (1961) gives several examples of schizophrenics' disorganization that occurs when schizophrenics are asked to define words that have multiple meanings. The disorganization takes the form of fragmented intrusions of the alternate meanings of the words. One of Faibish's examples is a schizophrenic's definition of "mosaic." "I suppose it has to do with Jewish art — Moses, mosaic. Something in reference to a Jewish form of art — mosaic pattern in art. . . . Something in reference to Moses — it's done in tile isn't it? [p. 414]." In order to test whether or not schizophrenics' disturbed use of words is related to the number of possible meanings of a word, Faibish compared schizophrenics and normals on word-association and word-definition tasks where the stimulus words had either one (average 1 plus) or multiple (3 to 5) meanings. The schizophrenics' performance was significantly affected by the number of alternate meanings of a stimulus word. When words had more meanings, their performance was poorer on all four measures used — definition level and disorganization, and word-association delay and deviancy (giving responses only remotely associated and multiword definitions), although on the last measure of difference between performance on single- vs. multiple-meaning words, the difference did not reach significance. Normals also tended to be poorer in response to multi-meaning words on all but the last measure, with the vocabulary-disorganization difference being significant. The deficit from single- to multiple-meaning words was greater for schizophrenics than normals on all four measures, although significantly so only for word-association delay.

Lester (1960) studied verbal response interference by a less direct but very interesting method. Each subject simply listed the alternate responses in a category. There were two forms of this task, listing 40 foods which had been presented on a memory drum, and writing down names of colors. Lester's basic hypothesis was similar to our interference formulation, i.e., that there is more interference, less hierarchical organization, among alternate responses in schizophrenics. Lester specifically applied this hypothesis to hebephrenics, excluding paranoid schizophrenics, whom he felt would exhibit somewhat more response organization. The listing of items in a category was timed. "As a working assumption it was proposed that the rate of depletion [of items in a category] reflects the amount of interference present during the selection of associates for production [p. 226]." Two groups, epileptics and normals, were tested in addition to paranoid schizophrenics and hebephrenic schizophrenics. Both tasks were scored in two ways: (a) counting all responses that were given, and (b) ignoring irrelevant and repetitive responses. The four resulting interference indices (rate of depletion controlled for available supply) were consistently in the following order: normals (least interference), paranoid schizophrenics, hebephrenic schizophrenics, and epileptics. Thus, as expected, the schizophrenics seemed to have more response interference than normals. That the epileptics were the most extreme group recalls Weckowicz's (1960) study where organics were the group most disturbed by irrelevant stimuli. Of course, the response-interference interpretation of this study rests on the assumed relationship between interference and slowed output, but this is certainly a reasonable assumption.

Another method of studying response interference is to vary response competition in accordance with the assumption that those stimuli that elicit both correct and incorrect responses in groups of normals are stimuli which evoke competing responses. The assumption is not quite as obviously true as it sounds, in that it equates the occurrence of different responses in groups with response competition in individuals, but it is nevertheless a very compelling assumption. Chapman (1961) has provided a concept task where normals hardly ever make errors in placing some objects in categories, but make a number of errors with other objects. The objects which elicited more errors were similar to the class of objects where they were incorrectly placed. For example, in one task, fruits, vegetables, and items of sports equipment were to be sorted into fruit and not-fruit categories. Vegetables were usually sorted correctly as "not-fruit" but also were often classed as fruit. Items of sports equipment are quite dissimilar from fruit and evoked almost no competing responses — placements in the fruit category. From our discussion so far, we would expect that schizophrenic deficit would be greater when responding to the objects eliciting most response competition (similar objects), both in comparison with performance with dissimilar objects and in comparison with normal performance. Table 1 gives the results from Chapman's study for the number of objects incorrectly included in a category for the two levels of tasks Chapman used (Level II tasks have broader conceptual categories and more items).

Note that, like normals, schizophrenics made few errors in classifying dissimilar objects. They made most of their errors on similar objects, where response competition, as defined by normals' errors, was greatest. The differences between normals and schizophrenics are also greatest where the response competition is greatest.

As you probably noted in Table 1, Chapman also tested a group of brain-damaged patients, and in contrast to the Weckowicz (1960) and Lester (1960) studies, schizophrenics made more errors than the brain-damaged patients. Although it is a departure from the topic at hand, this is a good place to take note of a suggestion Chapman makes regarding the difference between schizophrenics and organics. Chapman found that most errors by schizophrenics consisted of including incorrect objects in a specified category, but brain-damaged patients' errors were mostly over-exclusions. Brain-damaged patients tended to use narrower categories than schizophrenics. This is, of course, in line with the often-noted "concrete" thought in brain-damaged persons — a tendency to have difficulty in seeing things as belonging together on the basis of shared aspects. It is possible that this tendency may account for the finding in the Weckowicz and Lester studies. Regarding the Weckowicz study, objects that are overlaid with irrelevant lines look somewhat different from the objects themselves, and this, coupled with brain-damaged patients' inability to

TABLE 1[a]

MEAN OVERINCLUSION ERROR SCORES ON THE OVERINCLUSION TASK
FOR ITEMS THAT WERE SIMILAR AND DISSIMILAR TO THE INSTRUCTED CONCEPT

	Schizophrenic	Brain damaged	Normal
Level I[b]			
Similar	9.39	3.23	2.06
Dissimilar	1.18	0	.06
Level II			
Similar	5.56	.10	.33
Dissimilar	1.29	.26	.09

[a] From Chapman (1961).
[b] The Level I scores are doubled to make them comparable to Level II scores.

use partial commonalities, may severely reduce their ability to recognize. Also, relevant to Lester's study, brain-damaged persons may take abnormally long in listing objects in a category because for them the objects do not cluster together as they do for other persons, and are thus recalled only with additional thought and effort. The schizophrenics may often show similar performance but probably for a different reason. For them, the difficulty is too much disorganization and alternation among the competing responses that are evoked.

The studies we have looked at so far in this section have varied the number of alternate responses to a stimulus by using pre-existing differences in the degree of response competitions evoked by a stimulus. An alternate method is to train in competing responses. A number of researchers have studied the effects of response complexity in schizophrenia using this method. We will look first at a study by Lang and Luoto (1962) because it uses some of each method: using pre-existing stimulus-response associations, and training new associations.

Schizophrenics, psychiatric patients with diagnoses of anxiety reaction or anxiety neurosis, and normals were first given part of the Kent-Rosanoff word-association test. Then the subjects learned a 10-pair paired-associate list where the stimulus was a nonsense syllable and the response was one of the stimulus words from the Kent-Rosanoff test. Note that this list involved little response competition in that the stimuli were nonsense syllables, and as such would not have strong associative connections to other responses. Each pair was learned to a criterion of four successive correct trials, and was then dropped from the list. The groups did not differ in ability to learn this list.

The subjects then learned another paired-associate list. This second list had the same stimulus terms as list I, but the response terms were changed. For half the pairs, the nonsense syllables were paired with each subject's own association to the response word which had been the response to that syllable in list I. We will call these mediated pairs. Each subject's own associations to list I responses were also used as responses to the other nonsense syllables, but the pairing was done randomly, with the restriction that each stimulus was assigned a response which was unrelated to its response in list I. We will call these pairs the response-competition pairs. Because of the complexity of this design, the outline of the design of lists I and II on the next page may help. In it, NS refers to a nonsense syllable and KR refers to a stimulus word on the Kent-Rosanoff test.

If this design is now clear in your mind, let us relate it to our thinking about schizophrenia. In this second list, each stimulus is paired with a different response than in the first list. Response competition is greater and so we should expect greater differences between normals and schizo-

LIST I

Stimulus	Response
NS_1	KR_1
NS_2	KR_2
NS_3	KR_3

LIST II

	Stimulus	Response
Mediated pair	NS_1	S's associate to KR_1
Response-competition pair	NS_2	S's associate to KR_3

phrenics. However, judging amount of response competition from normal performance indicates there was somewhat less competition for mediated pairs than unrelated pairs, or at least correct responses were stronger relative to incorrect responses, as would be expected in that old responses mediated correct responses. If schizophrenic deficit is a function of the presence of strong competing responses, schizophrenic deficit should be greater on list II than on list I, with most deficit on the response-competition pairs.

The results were in accord with these expectations. Schizophrenics and normals did differ in performance on this second list, with the major schizophrenic deficit being in learning the response-competition pairs. The anxiety patients tended to perform at a level between that of the schizophrenics and the normals. As Lang and Luoto concluded, "... old response terms interfered differentially in the acquisition by the separate subgroups of the new pairs. The effect of these intruders was most marked for the schizophrenic subjects ... [p. 117]."

Another interesting finding was that, for the second list only, the schizophrenics took an increasing number of trials, relative to the other groups, to learn successive pairs to criterion. "Late in learning these subjects frequently responded to a stimulus syllable with a response term which had already achieved criterion and been dropped from the list. This happened rarely with other groups. For these latter subjects, when a response was eliminated its status as a potential intruder was markedly reduced. The schizophrenics, on the other hand, behaved as if nearly all the competitors remained active, if not phenomenally present, until the very end of the list. In list I the effects might be minimal. However, in list II, where [a stimulus for the non-mediating pairs] ... was always more closely related

to some response other than the one with which it was paired, and intruders from list I could reassert themselves, this might have greatly
retarded the learning of the final few pairs [p. 118]."

This analysis is very similar to Fey's (1951) results and discussion
comparing young schizophrenics and normals on the Wisconsin Card
Sorting Test (WCST). In this test, 64 cards are to be sorted into different
categories. Sorting is guided by reinforcing correct responses instead of
by instructions. First, the subject learns to sort by color until he makes 10
consecutive correct sorts. Then the basis of sorting shifts to form, with
later shifting again through five shifts of criteria for sorting. Because each
basis for sorting is learned to a rather high criterion, and different responses are required in response to a card after a shift, this is obviously a task
with a fairly high degree of response complexity. The most common type
of error was a perseverative response, an error made by sorting on the
basis of the previously correct category. This intrusion of previously correct responses was the only type of error which distinguished schizophrenics from normals. The groups did not differ, for example, on unique
errors (an error not in line with a regular WCST basis for sorting). As
might be expected, perseverative errors were found in both schizophrenics and controls at the beginning of a new basis for sorting. However, perseverative errors also occurred toward the end of a sorting stage. The
most distinguishing difference in performance occurred later in a stage of
sorting, when some correct sorts had been made but the criterion had not
yet been reached. Schizophrenics had an especially high number of sub-
criterion runs of correct responses interspersed with errors. Fey concluded that "The patient group seemed to experience more difficulty in
holding the correct set, once having achieved it, . . . than did the control
group [p. 314]." Or, as Lang and Luoto had said, the schizophrenics "behaved as if nearly all the competitors remained active . . . until the very
end . . . [p. 118]."

In the Lang and Luoto and the Fey studies, the major difference in performance occurred after a period of practice on a new or second response.
This is not surprising in that when a first response has been learned to criterion and a different response becomes correct, both normals and schizophrenics should make many errors at the beginning of the new learning. It
is only when there has been enough learning to lead to dominance of a
new response in normals that this focused responding will clearly differ
from the greater intrusion of competing responses in schizophrenics. Organized and partially disorganized responding can only differ when there
has been a chance to learn organized responding. This is not a complete
explanation of the special schizophrenic deficit on paired-associates
learned later in the Lang and Luoto study because Lang and Luoto were

comparing schizophrenics and normals on pairs which could be learned to criterion in few trials with those that required more trials. Thus, even on the earlier pairs where normals and schizophrenics did not differ, the measures included data from trials which had been sufficient to organize alternate responses appropriately in normals. This special deficit where learning takes longer will be discussed in a later chapter. For now, the important point is simply that if schizophrenic deficit represents a relative equalization of alternate response tendencies, then the deficit from normal performance may require some trials for normals to begin to have appropriate responses become stronger than competing responses. In the next few studies we will cite, training on new responses was continued to the point where most normals learned the second responses quite well. However, there are no data on later trials alone, which might provide clearer differentiation between normals and schizophrenics.

Janet Spence and Lair (1964, 1965) compared normals, acute schizophrenics, and long-term remitted and non-remitted schizophrenics in learning of paired-associate lists which differed in degree of response complexity. The lists were constructed by using the Russell and Jenkins (1954) Kent-Rosanoff norms. The experimental list used responses which were the normatively dominant responses to the stimuli in the list, but the responses were not paired with the stimuli to which they were associated. Thus, there should be considerable response competition on this list. The control list was made up of stimuli and responses with little associative connection, either between or within pairs. Each schizophrenic group was compared with normals in number of correct responses for the two lists. No lists by groups interactions were significant, indicating that the schizophrenics were not relatively more affected by the greater response competition in the experimental list. While these negative results may have been due to insufficient trials as mentioned above (a number of normals and schizophrenics did not reach a criterion of one perfect trial), we still would expect some differences. It is possible that the use of norms based on normals to construct the lists also played a part. Remember that response interference was a function of the strength of normal associative connections between stimuli and incorrect responses. When we consider that Johnson, Weiss, and Zelhart (1964) have shown that the word-association responses that are dominant in normals are less often dominant in psychotics, it seems possible that the associative strength of the competing responses may have been less for the schizophrenics. Less distractor strength in schizophrenics may well have offset a greater susceptibility to distraction.

Kausler, Lair, and Matsumoto (1964) noted that in the first Spence and Lair study, "... associative interference was manipulated extra-experimentally by means of word association norms [p. 584]," and suggested that this technique may be ". . . subject to interactions with other variables, thus obscuring the effect of diagnostic category [p. 585]." Kausler *et al.* felt that results might be clearer if response interference were manipulated within the experiment by means of negative transfer from a paired-associate list that was learned first, to a second list. Both lists contained pairs of words that were initially unrelated. The second list contained three kinds of pairs. One, the highest interference pairs were pairs where stimuli from list I were paired with responses from list I, but the pairing was rearranged. Two, some stimuli from list I were paired with responses that had not been used on list I. Pairs of unrelated stimuli and responses that had not occurred on list I made the third, least interference, type of pair. Chronic schizophrenics and normals were tested. The interaction of groups by type of pair (on errors during learning) was significant. The differences between schizophrenics and normals followed the lines of amount of response competition, being greatest on the first type of pair and least on the third type.

These quite clear results, showing an association between degree of response competition evoked by stimuli and amount of schizophrenic deficit relative to normals, contrast not only with the results of the Spence and Lair studies but also with the negative results in studies by Carson (1958) and Donahoe, Curtin, and Lipton (1961). The two latter studies attempted to vary response competition by varying intralist and interlist similarity, respectively, in serial-list learning tasks. These are, of course, much less direct methods of ensuring that specific stimuli evoke different degrees of competing responses than that used by Kausler *et al.* Thus, when we give most weight to the verbal learning studies that have been more clear and direct in varying response competition, the verbal learning results are in accord with the other response-competition studies we have reviewed.

To summarize this section on studies which have varied the degree of response competition, taken as a whole there is fairly strong support for the idea that schizophrenics show more interference among alternate responses than normals. Response interference seems to be an important aspect of schizophrenic deficit in that relative schizophrenic deficit varies as a function of the presence of competing responses. However, schizophrenics will not always perform more poorly than normals when competing responses are evoked. There can be no relative schizophrenic deficit unless normals are able to respond in an organized fashion. Thus, there are some indications that relative schizophrenic deficit is greater after the initial stages of a complex learning task. The results of one study (Lester, 1960) again pointed to differences among schizophrenics, suggesting that paranoid schizophrenics are nearer normals in ability to subordinate competing responses.

RESPONSE INTERFERENCE AND ENRICHED STIMULUS CONDITIONS

The basic theme has been that schizophrenics are abnormally distracted by the presence of alternate response tendencies. Reasoning along similar lines, Blaufarb (1962) noted that Lothrop (1961) had mentioned that "... some of the present tasks of conceptual thinking, in terms of their ambiguous structure, encourage the production of irrelevant responses." Blaufarb continued, "If one accepts the notion that the abstracting ability of schizophrenics is itself unimpaired, it could be expected that a more precise and amplified structuring of a task stimulus would lead to improved abstracting performance [p. 471]." In other words, elaborating Blaufarb's point in terms of our major theme, if schizophrenics are abnormally susceptible to competing response tendencies, then clarifying and structuring stimuli so that they are less ambiguous and therefore lead more clearly to a single appropriate response instead of several response possibilities, should be especially helpful to schizophrenics.

Blaufarb tested this hypothesis by comparing chronic schizophrenics' interpretation of proverbs under two conditions: proverbs presented singly, and presented in sets of three proverbs where each proverb in the set had the same meaning. Normals were used as a control group. Subjects' responses were rated on a single scale for degree and accuracy of abstraction. Under the single-proverb condition, schizophrenics' responses were significantly inferior to normals' responses. When the proverbs were administered in sets with common meanings, schizophrenics' scores improved significantly and no longer differed from normals' scores. It seems that schizophrenics can benefit from additional stimulation when that stimulation is relevant rather than irrelevant. When single stimuli are ambiguous, additional stimuli that are associated to the same correct response can lessen the degree of response competition and enhance schizophrenic performance.

Hamlin, Haywood, and Folsom (1965) repeated Blaufarb's proverbs tasks with four subject groups: closed-ward schizophrenics, open-ward schizophrenics, former schizophrenic patients who had improved sufficiently to be discharged, and a mixed group of non-schizophrenic psychiatric and non-psychiatric patients. The open-ward and discharged "schizophrenics" improved significantly under the enriched stimulus condition, but the closed-ward schizophrenics and the non-schizophrenics did not. These findings confirm Blaufarb's results in that moderately and mildly disturbed schizophrenics can benefit from the focusing on correct responses and reduced response competition that is made possible by multiple relevant stimuli. However, it also seems that this may not be true of many. severely disturbed schizophrencis. Is it possible that the attention of these schizophrenics is either so disorganized or constricted that they cannot benefit from additional relevant information? Blaufarb's chronic schizophrenic group, which could benefit from added relevant stimulation, was a non-hebephrenic, primarily paranoid group, all of whom were communicative and in fair-to-good contact. This group should be relatively attentive, and from Lester's results concerning paranoids, have relatively good response organization compared to other schizophrenics. Thus, it is not surprising that Blaufarb's results were in accord with those of the more moderately disturbed patients in the Hamlin *et al.* study.

Although the above results seem fairly clear except for more disturbed schizophrenics, the results of two similar studies (Lewinsohn & Elwood, 1961; Lawson, McGhie, & Chapman, 1964) demonstrate that all conditions in which stimulus enrichment is possible will not lessen schizophrenic deficit. In these studies, subjects were to recall lists of words that varied in degree of contextual restraint. The lists varied from words which were randomly chosen, to a sequence from normal discourse. In the lists with high contextual restraint, the recall of each additional word decreases the number of alternate possibilities for the following word. Thus, it might be expected that schizophrenics' performance might be improved, relative to normals', on the lists where there is greater contextual restraint on response possibilities. However, remember that the competing responses are reduced, not by a stimulus which is automatically supplied, but by the subject's own recall. Because correct associates are less frequent in schizophrenics, the prompting effect of additional correct stimuli should be less in schizophrenics, offsetting any relative benefit from reduction in complexity. In both studies, schizophrenics' absolute performance improved somewhat with greater contextual restraint; however schizophrenics did not improve relative to normals. In fact, except for a group of acute patients in the Lewinsohn and Elwood study, schizophrenics' performance worsened relative to normals' performance as contextual restraint was increased.

This study does not change the conclusion drawn from the Blaufarb and Hamlin *et al.* studies. When additional relevant stimuli are *present,* the relative deficit of moderately disturbed schizophrenics is lessened, probably because of the reduction in ambiguity and therefore in response complexity. However, long chains of schizophrenics' disturbed associations cannot be depended on to provide the needed associational prompting.

In sum, these studies, considered together with the earlier stimulus-complexity studies, suggest that added stimulation may increase or decrease schizophrenic deficit relative to normal performance. The important point is not the number of stimuli in a situation, but whether or not the added stimuli increase or decrease response competition. A stimulus which (a) decreases the number or strength of competing responses relative to the strength of appropriate responses, (b) which is prominent enough to be observed by schizophrenics in spite of their distractible attention, and (c) in view of schizophrenics' reduced ability to prompt themselves, is automatically delivered; such a stimulus should be especially good for reducing schizophrenic deficit. This thought will reoccur later in a discussion of the effects of response-contingent punishment in reducing schizophrenic deficit.

DEVIANT-BUT-ASSOCIATED RESPONSES

A number of studies have been presented emphasizing the basic theme of schizophrenics' susceptibility to competing response tendencies and the importance of degree of response complexity in determining amount of schizophrenic deficit. Now we can begin to bring in information on another aspect of the initial formulation—the characteristics of schizophrenic deficit—instead of concentrating only on the conditions which increase or decrease this deficit.

This chapter began with statements by schizophrenics that illustrated the particular deviant-but-associated flavor of response chains that would be expected if competing associations to a stimulus intrude in appropriate responding. However, while selected examples may serve to introduce a topic, well-controlled research is needed for firmer knowledge. But before we turn to research into the question of whether or not the intruding responses that cause schizophrenic deficit are related to task stimuli, some clarification of the rationale may be useful, especially with respect to the question of idiosyncratic responding in schizophrenia.

The basic point in the initial formulation that is relevant here is that in a change from normalcy to schizophrenia, no new stimulus-response associations are added. Thus, in schizophrenics, when competing response tendencies intrude, these intrusions should be the same kinds of associations which are evoked in some strength in normals, though they occur with less frequency in the more focused responding of normals.

If responses are associates to stimuli, what about the often-cited idiosyncratic responding in schizophrenics? In normals as well as in schizophrenics, associations to stimuli are a function of personal experience. Dominant associations are usually the result of common consistencies and are usually shared by members of a culture. In both normals and schizophrenics, associations based on more unique experiences are present, but usually are non-dominant. They are weaker associates because they are the result of less frequent consistency. Thus, the family of alternate responses to a situation may be different from person to person. Normals, with their less variable responding, with very high probability of dominant responses, will exhibit high normative commonality; but schizophrenics, with their greater equalization of competing response tendencies, will respond with a somewhat greater frequency of idiosyncratic associations. However, in the main, schizophrenics' associations should be understandable as associations, although they are very rare normatively. They may reflect either relatively unique personal contingencies or more remote associations that, even though they would rarely, if ever, occur in normal responding, are easily seen as associations by members of a culture. As an example of the latter, Arieti (1955, p. 4) considered the following reply to characterize schizophrenic responding. A schizophrenic is asked, "Who was the first president of the United States?" and he replies, "White House." According to the usual research definition of idiosyncratic responses as responses which are rarely if ever found in a normative sample, this response would be classed as idiosyncratic, though it is understandable as an associate to the stimulus.

Another example of a very idiosyncratic response that can occur as a function of randomization among associates, was a schizophrenic's placement of a rabbit and three matches together in an object-sorting task. His explanation, in addition to showing the associations which determined the grouping for him, also illustrates the pun-like or game-playing quality that listeners sometimes get from the intrusion of deviant associates into a moderately organized train of thought. The reason for the idiosyncratic grouping of three matches with a rabbit was explained by the schizophrenic as follows: "The rabbit being more or less polygamous; polygamous — prolific is what I mean. Three would represent matches or matings. Matings is what I said. Or [the rabbit] could be light on his feet." [Quoted in Cohen, Senf, & Huston, 1954, p. 174.]

Responses to unshared internal events, such as preoccupations, are another kind of competing response, which, when they intrude, would yield idiosyncratic responses and should be more frequent in schizophrenics, although such responses would also effect the performance of normals to a lesser extent.

Thus, an increase in intrusions of the rarer or unique response tendencies, which are evoked in normals as well as schizophrenics, should lead to more idiosyncratic responding in schizophrenics.

However, these intrusions will have little effect on the major kinds of errors that differentiate normals and schizophrenics, which are the focus of the research to be discussed. Idiosyncratic response tendencies are, by definition, not shared, or at least very rare, and according to the initial formulation, any *particular* idiosyncratic tendency should not be any more common in a group of schizophrenics than in a group of normals. In schizophrenics, idiosyncratic responses will intrude somewhat more, but there will not be commonality in the idiosyncratic responses that do intrude. The inappropriate responses that will intrude with the highest frequency in groups of schizophrenics will be the competing associates that are shared by many persons, normals as well as schizophrenics. Hence, when schizophrenics are responding to task stimuli, the type of error responses that will most differentiate schizophrenics and normals will be associates to the task stimuli that are clear, and shared associates to the stimuli. When the method of comparing groups of schizophrenics and normals is in counting the frequency of specific different responses to task stimuli, normals and schizophrenics should be alike in the high frequency responses, the major difference being only that the frequency of the response that is most common in normals, usually the correct response, will be somewhat reduced in schizophrenics, primarily because of an increase in frequency of shared competing associates.

We have already looked at some of the evidence on the question of associated versus unrelated nature of schizophrenic responses. For instance in Fey's (1951) card-sorting task, the only type of error that schizophrenics made significantly more than normals was perseverative responses. These were responses that were associated with the cards which were to be sorted, having been the previously correct responses to the cards. These responses, which most differentiated schizophrenics from normals, were the most common type of error for both normals and schizophrenics. It was also noted previously that Fey counted unique errors, where cards were not sorted on the basis of easily observable commonalities. Schizophrenics and normals did not differ in this type of responding.

Loren Chapman has done more research on this question of associated errors in schizophrenia than any other investigator, and has included an opportunity for non-associated errors in each of his studies on this topic. Thus, each of these studies provides relevant data. We have mentioned one of his studies (1961) where objects were to be sorted on the basis of belonging or not belonging to a specific category (e.g., fruit), and where the objects that did not belong were of two types: objects (e.g., vegetables) that shared similarities with the category and therefore should evoke a competing association with this category, and dissimilar, unassociated objects (e.g., items of sports equipment). A count of the number of unrelated objects placed in the specified category provides a measure of responses that are not associated to the stimulus. For example, if schizophrenics were inattentive to the stimuli, or responded on any other bases that are fairly random with respect to the stimuli, then significant numbers of the non-associated objects (e.g., sports equipment) would be placed in the specified category. As was indicated in Table 1, the incidence of these unassociated errors in schizophrenics is quite low compared to the tendency to make responses that are deviant-but-associated, and the primary difference between normals and schizophrenics was an increase in intrusion of associated responses in the schizophrenics.

The results resemble those of another study which used similar sorting tasks (Chapman & Taylor, 1957). Table 2 shows again the tendency for the major schizophrenic sorting errors to be the placing of objects in associated incorrect categories.

Loren Chapman has also used tasks where an object is to be sorted with one of three other objects on the basis of a designated commonality (Chapman, 1956a, 1956b, 1958). In each of these studies, the intrusion of competing response tendencies that are evoked either by irrelevant aspects of the objects, or competing associations to the objects, provides a commonality between the sorting object and one of the other two objects that would mediate an incorrect sorting. For example, in one case, the word horse is to be sorted conceptually with one of three other words (mule, shoe, or bottle). The response that is correct and most common in both normals and schizophrenics is to place "horse" with "mule." However, the word horse not only evokes conceptual commonalities with "mule," but, due to past environmental contingencies in the word horseshoe, also evokes an incorrect association with the word shoe. In addition to including opportunities to sort on the basis of such associative distrac-

TABLE 2[a]
MEDIAN AND MEAN NUMBER OF INCLUSION ERRORS ON SPECIES SORTINGS

Groups	Similar objects	Dissimilar objects
Normal		
Median	0	0
Mean	.54	.33
Schizophrenic, moderate		
Median	6.00	0
Mean	7.33	.29
Schizophrenic, severe		
Median	6.00	0
Mean	8.20	1.33

[a] Adapted from Chapman & Taylor (1957).

tors, each of these studies also included the possibility of sortings not based on the intrusions of competing associations (e.g., sorting "horse" and "bottle" together). The results were similar in all three studies and indicated again that schizophrenic errors are primarily associated responses. Schizophrenics did more poorly than normals, the major difference being that they made more incorrect sortings based on associative commonalities. Few unrelated objects were placed together.

If a major factor in the errors that schizophrenics make in responding to stimuli is the intrusion of competing associations, then schizophrenics' use of words should be at times disturbed by the intrusion of opposite meanings, in that one type of shared association to words is a word with opposite meaning (Russell & Jenkins, 1954). Burstein (1961) gave schizophrenics and normals a multiple-choice task where subjects were to pick the one of three response words that had the same meaning as a stimulus word. In addition to the correct responses (synonyms), the choices included an antonym and an unrelated word. Schizophrenics' error responses were predominantly antonyms, as expected, rather than unrelated words, and the primary difference between schizophrenics and normals was in the higher frequency of these associated errors in schizophrenics.

In the same study, Burstein used a similar task with homonyms being the associated error possibility instead of antonyms. Again, schizophrenic errors were primarily the associated errors, homonyms, rather than unrelated words.

An interesting relationship between the discussion here and the Freudian discussion of schizophrenia can be seen in that Burstein's hypothesis about the tendency to use antonyms and homonyms as synonyms in schizophrenia came, not from a theory of response interference in schizophrenia, but from Freud's suggestion that "primary process" thinking should determine schizophrenics' use of words. As Burstein emphasizes, the treatment of antonyms as synonyms and homonyms as synonyms have been seen as two aspects of Freudian theory about "primary process" thinking.

Another aspect of Freudian theory concerning schizophrenia that is relevant here is the regressive nature of schizophrenic responses. Responses that are preferred in childhood may later be replaced as dominant responses. If this happens, the child-preferred (regressive) responses should still be associated to the situation, although they may seldom occur in the focused responding of normal adults. From the discussion thus far, we would expect that in schizophrenics there would be greater equalization of the probabilities of the different responses that are associated to a situation. Thus, over a number of trials, schizophrenics should show more equal frequencies of the previously preferred responses and the usual adult responses. In other words, regressive responding is seen as another form of the intrusion of deviant-but-associated responses. It should also be noted that this way of viewing regressive responding makes it the same as perseverative responding, as in the earlier discussion of Fey's results, except for a greater time difference between old and new learning.

In a study of regressive responding which is relevant here, Gottesman (1964) used a forced-choice word-association test to measure schizophrenics' use of adult-preferred versus child-preferred associations. In terms of our discussion, a major point is that a third, unrelated association was also included as a possible response. For normals, the mean numbers of adult, child, and unrelated associations were 31.12, 18.56, and 1.31, respectively. The comparable figures for schizophrenics were 23.44, 25.00, and 1.88. Thus, for schizophrenics, the alternate associated responses (adult and child preferred) were quite equal in probability, with irrelevant associations rarely chosen.

Together, the studies in this section indicate that, as the beginning formulation suggests, schizophrenics' errors in responding to task stimuli are mediated by the intrusion of responses which are normal associates evoked by the task situation, rather than schizophrenic responding being characterized by the addition of new and abnormal stimulus-response associations. Schizophrenic responding is abnormal and changed, but apparently a primary factor in this change is disorganization among the family of associated responses which are also evoked in normals. These studies indicate that schizophrenic error tendencies can be predicted on the basis of a prior classification of responses, by normals, as responses that are associated or not associated to a stimulus. The major difference between schizophrenics and normals is in the increase of incorrect associated responses that intrude sporadically in a general context of correct responses in schizophrenics.

OVERINCLUSION AND OVEREXCLUSION

We have seen a number of instances where schizophrenics overinclude similar-but-inappropriate objects in sorting categories. The particular studies we have discussed were chosen because they provided good discriminations regarding the particular kind of objects which were and were not overincluded. There are a number of other studies which indicate that schizophrenics include too much in categories. These studies reflect the importance that has been attached to overinclusive responding in the literature on schizophrenics.

Epstein (1953) presented schizophrenics and normals with stimulus words (e.g., Man) followed by five other words (e.g., head and hat), with instructions to underline those words that are required for the complete thing denoted by the stimulus word. Schizophrenics underlined more words than normals. In discussing the particular responses that were more frequent in schizophrenics, Epstein noted that schizophrenics responded abnormally to neologistic stimulus words, selected more responses that were loosely associated (e.g., clang associates), and selected more other associates such as words that were examples of a stimulus concept instead of being necessary for it. Epstein noted that, "As the Inclusion Test contains a great number of associationistic choices, this type of response contributed heavily to the schizophrenic score [p. 386]."

Payne, Matussek, and George (1959) found that on Epstein's test, schizophrenics also overinclude more than neurotics. Payne *et al.* also totaled the number of responses underlined to neologistic stimuli (e.g., "Topitch") and the number of responses that were neologisms. On this measure, schizophrenics were also higher than neurotics. Payne *et al.* concluded, "The significant difference on this score suggests that the over-inclusive concepts formed by schizophrenics can incorporate words which are meaningless, but which have features in common with everyday words [pp. 644-645]."

Other results that show overinclusion in schizophrenics were found by Moran (1953) using a test similar to Epstein's, and by Payne *et al.* (1959), who also measured overinclusion by the number of objects included in a single category in the "handing over" part of the Goldstein-Scheerer Object Sorting Test. On the other hand, Sturm (1965) did not find that schizophrenics were more overinclusive than controls on a test similar to Epstein's. However, in Sturm's scoring method, if one necessary part of a concept was not included, then overinclusions in that concept were not counted as overinclusive. In sum, there is quite a bit of support for the position that schizophrenics overinclude, which we have interpreted as due to schizophrenics' special susceptibility to interfering responses evoked by task stimuli.

However, overinclusion should be only part of the picture. A "susceptibility to competing-response tendencies" interpretation of schizophrenia should also predict over*exclusion* under some conditions. If objects that should be included in a concept are associated to other categories or are similar to objects that go in other categories, then there should be competing exclusion tendencies to which schizophrenics should be especially susceptible. (It should also be remembered that there was a suggestion from some of the stimulus complexity studies we discussed that some schizophrenics may be abnormal in that they react less to some sources of stimulation. This possibility is relevant here in that it could lead to exclusion of relevant stimuli in multi-stimulus tasks, but without better support for this possibility than we have now, it will not as yet be emphasized.

Also the majority of the tasks we are discussing are tasks in which one stimulus at a time is prominent, in which case reduced observation must not be as important as disorganization among the associates evoked by that stimulus.) In the Moran (1953) and Epstein (1953) studies, schizophrenics did not overexclude words that belonged to the concept in question, but these studies did not include alternate concepts requiring alternate responses that might be generalized to objects that belonged in the primary category. For example, in Epstein's test, the stimulus word Man is followed by the response words, arms, shoes, hat, toes, head, none. The items that are parts of man are arms, toes, and head. These are closely associated to "Man" but have no association to other test categories. The major associational pulls in these tests are unidirectional, in the direction of inclusion.

A concept-sorting task used by Chapman and Taylor (1957) did include objects belonging to alternate classes, to which subjects were to make a specific alternate response. For example, in one of their tasks, cards designating alcoholic beverages (the designated category) were to be placed in one slot in a box and other cards were to be placed in a second slot. Cards with names of non-alcoholic beverages and insects were included as objects to go in the second slot. This study provides practice in a specific exclusion response (placement in the second slot), that, because of similarity to objects that are supposed to be excluded, may be generalized to the objects that belong in the designated category. The objects to which this competing response is learned are similar to the objects in the designated category in several ways. Both classes of objects were words typed on cards, and, probably most important, there is a mediated similarity between the two kinds of beverages. As we would expect if a competing exclusion response generalized to objects which should be included, schizophrenics, both moderately and severely disturbed groups, excluded objects that belonged in the designated category significantly more than normals.

Chapman and Taylor also used tasks (genus sorting rather than species sorting) where generalization should be less in that all the objects with mediated similarity were included in the designated category. On tasks where, for example, all beverages were to go in the first slot, there was less difference between schizophrenics and normals. In fact, moderately disturbed schizophrenics did not make significantly more exclusion errors than normals, although severely disturbed schizophrenics still did. Chapman and Taylor noted that the greater association between categories in the species sorting led to more errors in schizophrenics relative to normals than when mediated generalization was reduced in the genus sorting. "One of the interesting results of the genus sorting in general was the fact that schizophrenics made so few errors of any type, inclusive or exclusive. In a sense the comparative adequacy of the schizophrenics' performance further confirms the findings of the species sorting: when faced with separating categories of items that are dissimilar (as in the genus tasks), schizophrenics differ comparatively little from normals; when the correct items are relatively similar to some of the incorrect, schizophrenic performance suffers although that of normals does not. Related to this is the unexpected finding that schizophrenics showed a more pronounced tendency to exclude correct items from the designated category in the species than in the genus sorting [p. 122]."

Another study by Chapman (1961) that has been referred to in a different context impels caution in the kind of interpretation that is being made here. In contrast to the results of the Chapman-Taylor (1957) study, schizophrenics made somewhat more exclusion errors on tasks similar to the Chapman-Taylor genus sortings than on species-sorting tasks where similarity in terms of broader concepts than those that were to be used would seem more likely to evoke exclusion errors. Although the difference is not extreme when the data are corrected for opportunity to make exclusion errors, and data on statistical significance were not presented either for schizophrenics across the two kinds of tasks or relative to the same difference in normals, the data should be considered. However, a striking aspect of the Chapman (1961) data is that again in contrast to the Chapman-Taylor (1957) results where data corrected for the number of chances to make exclusion errors showed a decrease in exclusion errors in genus sortings in normals; in the Chapman (1961) study, normals also showed an increase in exclusion responses from the species to genus tasks. Based on this increase in incorrect exclusion responses in normals, it seems very likely that significant competing exclusion tendencies were, for some reason, more frequently evoked in the genus-sorting tasks. Therefore, the results of both these studies are alike if the probability of exclusion errors in normals is used as an index of the extent to which different tasks evoke competing exclusion tendencies. When this assumption is made, and it does seem quite tenable, then both studies suggest that across situations which differ in the extent to which they evoke competing exclusion tendencies in normals, these tendencies will intrude more in schizophrenic responding, leading to an exacerbation of the pattern of normal exclusion errors.

In further support of the implication that schizophrenics' susceptibility to competing response tendencies should at times lead to abnormal overexclusion, it should be remembered that the three other Chapman sorting studies we have mentioned (1956a, 1956b, 1958) are also relevant here. In each of these studies, schizophrenics were abnormally exclusive in that schizophrenics often sorted on the basis of competing associations rather than placing objects where they belonged. Remember from our previous discussion that the sorting errors (overexclusions) varied with the number or strength of competing associations (1956a, 1958).

In contrast to the emphasis in the literature on overinclusion, it then seems quite possible that schizophrenics do not seem to carry around with them any general abnormal tendency to be overinclusive and not overexclusive. The direction of their difference from normals in specific situations seems to be guided, at least in part, by the competing responses evoked by the particular task which faces them. When competing associations are few, schizophrenics categorize objects in about the same way as normals do (Chapman, 1956a; Chapman & Taylor, 1957). When task materials elicit more or stronger competing associations, schizophrenic conceptual errors increase, becoming either overinclusive or overexclusive (or both for different stimuli in a task), depending on the direction of pull of the competing responses. The reason for the emphasis on overinclusion in the literature is possibly due to the use of tasks which have, in general, loaded the competing tendencies in the direction of inappropriate inclusions.

Stimulus Generalization

Special susceptibility to competing response tendencies should also affect schizophrenics' performance in stimulus generalization or discrimination tasks, and the answer to the question of whether schizophrenics will show overgeneralization or undergeneralization again should depend on the presence and nature of competing response tendencies.

If different responses are trained to fairly similar stimuli, competing response tendencies should generalize to, and be evoked by, stimuli where they are not appropriate. These competing response tendencies should interfere with dominant response tendencies more in schizophrenics than in normals. In general, because responses are dominant to stimuli where they have been trained and are appropriate, schizophrenics should show *reduced* frequency of a response at its training stimulus, and *increased* frequency of a response primarily at more remote generalization stimuli where the response is inappropriate and is non-dominant in normals.

One difficulty in making predictions from a general hypothesis of increased susceptibility to competing tendencies in schizophrenia is that at training stimuli and more remote generalization stimuli, where it is easiest to predict that specific responses will clearly be dominant, it is also true that generalized competing response tendencies are weakest. Thus, at these stimuli, response competition may be negligible, in which case differences between schizophrenics and normals would be negligible, at least if response interference is all that is considered.

From these considerations, it follows that schizophrenics will not always differ from normals in stimulus generalization tasks. Differences are not likely to occur if response competition evoked by task stimuli is minimal. However, if differences do occur, our beginning formulation suggests that the exacerbation of competing responses in schizophrenics should lead to a reduction in responses at or near training stimuli, with an increase in responses to stimuli where they are non-dominant, resulting in a flattening of stimulus generalization gradients.

When differences between normals and schizophrenics have been found in stimulus generalization studies, the results have generally been as suggested above. Often, however, differences are not found.

Mednick (1955) tested generalization of a response from the center to the periphery of a horizontal row of lamps. Subjects were instructed to hold a reaction key down and release it quickly when the center lamp was lit but not to respond to other lamps. Schizophrenics tended to give more generalized responses than normals; the only significant difference between these groups being a greater number of schizophrenic responses to one of most peripheral lamps. Responses at the training stimulus were not reported.

Knopf and Fager (1959) used a similar position-generalization task, but in their task response competition was increased in that two different responses were required to training and generalization stimuli, and reinforcement of these responses was probabilistic. If subjects pushed a switch forward when the center lamp lit, they were informed 80 per cent of the time that they had made the correct response. On 20 per cent of the trials, pulling the switch backward was the correct response. The reinforcement probabilities for the two responses were reversed for peripheral lamps. The distributions of push responses (dominant to the central lamp) did not differ significantly for schizophrenics and psychotic depressed subjects, so these groups were combined. The combined psychotic group did differ from normal subjects and from neurotic subjects in the directions we would expect. The psychotics had significantly flatter gradients of stimulus generalization (GSG) with fewer push responses to the center lamp and more generalized push responses.

Brain-damaged groups were used in both this study and the Mednick study, with inconsistent results. In Mednick's study, brain-damaged patients generalized less than normals or schizophrenics. The opposite happened in the Knopf and Fager study.

Garmezy (1952) trained schizophrenic and normal subjects to pull a lever in response to one tone and push the lever to other tones. In this condition there was no difference in the generalization gradients of schizophrenics and normals. In a second condition, pull responses to the most different generalization tone were then censured.

Consider what this censure should do. At the stimulus where pull responses were censured, pull responses were competing responses, and it is not surprising that the inhibition of competing responses improved the performance of both schizophrenics and normals. (Actually, as we will discuss in later chapters, censure and other stress-inducing stimuli may have general response-energizing effects and when increased stress is used to inhibit competing responses, the predictions of what should happen in schizophrenics relative to normals are quite complex.) The prediction about what should be the effect of censure at the stimulus where pull responses were appropriate is quite clear. Here, pull responses were dominant. Hence, the generalized effects of censuring pull responses should be to increase response competition, and it is here that the results were most clear. Schizophrenics showed the most deficit relative to normals, as would be expected from their special susceptibility to increased response competition.

The results of a study by Dunn (1954) provide another instance showing that stimulus generalization is not disturbed under all conditions in schizophrenics, being disturbed primarily when response competition is increased. In Dunn's study, subjects were to pull a lever if a picture was identical to a standard, and push the lever to indicate different pictures. Schizophrenics and normals were not different in ability to discriminate variants of scenes of a mother feeding a child and variants of scenes of a house and tree. Two other types of scenes, a mother scolding a child and a mother whipping a child, had aversive content, which can be thought of as evoking a tendency to withdraw from the scene. If a tendency to avoid a scene is evoked while attempting to discriminate variants in a succession of similar pictures, this is a competing response which should interfere with maximal attention. If schizophrenics are especially susceptible to competing responses, schizophrenics' ability to discriminate differences in the task stimuli should be especially reduced. The effect of the intrusion of withdrawal tendencies should be to flatten generalization gradients as the push or pull responses will be more randomized, not guided by appropriate attention. This abnormal flattening in schizophrenics was not significant on the whipping scene. Although there was a tendency for schizophrenics to make fewer pull responses where they were appropriate, there was no difference in responding to the stimuli where push responses were appropriate. On the other aversive scene, schizophrenics' GSGs were significantly flatter than normals', with both pull and push responses reduced, relative to normals', at the stimuli where they were appropriate.

Rodnick and Garmezy (1957) have explained schizophrenics' deficit in the above two studies as due not to an abnormal susceptibility to competing responses that are evoked in both normals and schizophrenics, but rather to the special nature of certain stimulus conditions that, because of schizophrenics' life histories, evoke stronger withdrawal responses in schizophrenics. They suggest that schizophrenics will have abnormally strong withdrawal tendencies when faced with censure conditions. This is certainly a very tenable explanation of these studies. However, as we have seen, schizophrenics also seem to be especially bothered by response competition in non-censorious situations. Therefore a more general response-interference formulation is used here because it applies to a broader range of findings, in addition to the differences in normals' and schizophrenics' reactions to censure conditions.

Aversive Conditions

We have seen that censure can increase schizophrenic deficit, and have interpreted this deficit as due to increased response competition from avoidance tendencies stimulated by censure. Actually, any aversive condition should have this same tendency to increase avoidance responses, and we now turn to a more general discussion of the effect of aversive conditions on schizophrenic deficit, basing our discussion on two postulates: first, the obvious observation that human beings tend to avoid aversive conditions; and second, the theme of this chapter, schizophrenics are especially susceptible to competing response tendencies.

If we think through the likely effects of aversive conditions on task-irrelevant (competing) responses, it is clear that aversive conditions do not always increase irrelevant responses. Punishment of undesirable responses can, of course, decrease the frequency of those responses. On the other hand, when aversive conditions can be avoided by avoiding task-relevant responses, the avoidance tendencies compete with appropriate responses. Thus, aversive conditions may either increase or decrease competing responses.

The Garmezy (1952) and Dunn (1954) studies showed poorer performance in schizophrenics under censure conditions because censure could be avoided by avoiding one of the discriminative responses (only pull responses were punished in the Garmezy study), or by avoiding the task stimuli (the stimuli to be discriminated provided the censorious content in Dunn's study). In both cases, a specific type of avoidance — avoidance which could interfere with appropriate performance — was encouraged by the particular pattern of censure.

The alternate possibility—decreasing competing responses by censure—is demonstrated in a study by Meyer and Offenbach (1962). The ability of normal grade school children to learn a conceptual block-choosing task was studied under three conditions: (a) verbal reinforcement ("right") for correct responses and nothing said following incorrect responses (right-nothing); (b) nothing said following correct responses with censure tied directly to competing responses by saying "wrong" after incorrect responses (nothing-wrong); and (c) a right-wrong condition, where correct responses were reinforced and incorrect responses were censured. Each subject was shown two blocks at a time, and was to pick one. The correct choice was always on the basis of position, but different numbers of irrelevant stimulus dimensions (color, shape, height) were used to vary task complexity. The subjects learned as well under the nothing-wrong condition as under the right-wrong condition, and learning was faster under these conditions than when correct responses were reinforced but no censure was given. In other words, censure can be an effective method of improving performance if censure is tied directly to competing responses.

Because we have discussed schizophrenia as a condition of an increase in response competition, the relation between effectiveness of reward and censure in improving performance as a function of task complexity, is also important. Meyer and Offenbach found that the effectiveness of censure, relative to reward, was greater under increased task complexity. Their discussion of this result is quite relevant if schizophrenia is seen as a condition of increased response complexity. "Acquisition for the punishment group occurs as incorrect tendencies are eliminated. The effect of punishment is to make it very clear to the [subjects] . . . that a particular mode of responding is incorrect or inadequate. Acquisition for the reward-alone group occurs when a particular response set is confirmed. However, it must be remembered that all dimensions, relevant and irrelevant, are present in one of each pair of stimuli presented to the [subjects]. . . . When [a right-nothing subject] . . . makes a rewardable response in this situation, it is highly probable that an incorrect response set will be confirmed and thus strengthened. Eventually learning occurs as the [subjects] . . . , in an effort to maximize reward, respond to a different dimension. For the situation, then, where the task involves at least two irrelevant dimensions, the elimination of incorrect sets, as provided by punishment is superior to the confirmation of sets, provided by reward [p. 533]."

If the nature of schizophrenic deficit is increased response competition —more competing responses intrude than is the case with normals—then Meyer and Offenbach's results suggest that (a) schizophrenic performance may be benefited by censure, and (b) benefited more by censure than by reward if, in contrast to the Garmezy and Dunn studies, the only way to escape censure is to stop making inappropriate responses. In addition, if schizophrenics have more interfering responses than normals, (c) punishing interfering responses should be more beneficial for schizophrenics than for normals.

Two experiments by Cavanaugh, Cohen, and Lang (1960) bear on the first and second implications. In both experiments, chronic schizophrenics performed a disjunctive reaction-time task, being timed in how fast they responded to the lighting of one of two signal lamps by moving their hands to the appropriate one of two telegraph keys. In the first experiment, the results of pre-information trials were used to place subjects into three groups matched on reaction time. In the second, or information, phase of the experiment, the subjects in a censure group were told, "That was bad — too slow" if their performance was below their own median reaction time for the previous 7 trials. In other words, if a subject was looking at something other than the signal light, or responded in any way that led to poor performance, the result was censure. A second group was given a mild non-verbal censure following reaction times which were slower than their own median. A tone, which the subjects had been told meant they had been too slow, sounded. For the third, or control, group, there were no changes from the pre-information trials. After the information trials, the continuance of effects was tested in a series of post-information trials.

The results were that both the censure and the non-verbal censure groups improved significantly more than the control group in the information trials, and the censure group maintained this superiority in post-information trials. As expected, it seems that censure arranged so that it follows interfering responses can significantly improve the performance of schizophrenics.

The second Cavanaugh *et al.* experiment was the same as the first, except for the information trials where an approval or reward group was used and compared to censure and control groups — defined as in Experiment I. After fast responses, schizophrenics in the approval group were told, "That was good — very fast." The reward and censure groups received approximately the same number of messages. The results are shown in Figure 6.

The schizophrenics performing under response-contingent censure did significantly better than the approval and control groups and maintained this superiority in post-information trials. The approval and control groups did not differ significantly from each other. Thus, as was suggested by a combination of Meyer and Offenbach's results and considering schiz-

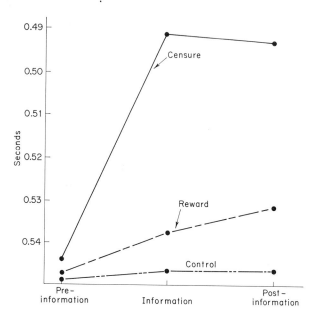

Fig. 6. Schizophrenics' mean reaction times in censure, reward, and control conditions. (Adapted from Cavanaugh *et al.,* 1960.)

ophrenic deficit to be a result of intrusion of competing responses, schizophrenic performance does seem to improve more under response-contingent censure than under approval.

The third implication, that if schizophrenics are especially susceptible to competing response tendencies, the inhibition of these tendencies through punishing them should benefit schizophrenics more than normals, has also been supported experimentally. In one relevant study, Pascal and Swenson (1952) trained schizophrenics in a complex reaction-time task where different patterns of position and color of signal lights indicated which of two switches were to be pulled. After training for 60 trials, asymptotic performance seemed to be reached, with schizophrenics' reactions significantly slower than normals'. At this point, 116 db white noise was delivered through headphones with the onset of the ready signal and the only way to stop the noise was to pull the correct switch. This level of noise is fairly aversive. Thus, after the first 60 trials, incorrect responses were punished by the continuation of aversive white noise. This condition was continued for two sets of twelve trials each, and for the second set of trials, brought schizophrenic performance to a level not significantly different from normal performance. One additional finding is quite interesting. The initial effect of the noise was to worsen schizophrenics' performances relative to normals'. This demonstrates again the dual role of an aversive condition. When used over a number of trials to punish interfering responses, it can be especially effective with schizophrenics, improving their performance more than that of normals. However, initially such conditions will only be another irrelevant stimulus leading to irrelevant responses to which schizophrenics are especially susceptible.

All three implications we have drawn from Meyer and Offenbach's results and our formulation of schizophrenia were supported in two experiments by Atkinson and Robinson (1961). Both studies used the same experimental task, paired-associate learning under reward, punishment, or control conditions. When reward or punishment was given, it followed closely after each correct (or incorrect) response was made. In one experiment, fairly acute female schizophrenics were compared with normals. In the second experiment, the only subjects were male schizophrenics. For both male and female schizophrenics, response-contingent punishment improved performance significantly more than response-contingent reward. Normal subjects showed the opposite effect—their performance improved most with reward. The differential effects of punishment versus reward for schizophrenics and normals was highly significant.

Thus, the five experiments we have looked at where schizophrenics have been tested under response-contingent aversive conditions show that schizophrenic performance improves under these conditions. For schizophrenics, punishment of incorrect responses is more effective than rewarding correct responses, as we would expect if the problem is not the lack of a correct response tendency, but is rather in a concurrent tendency toward competing responses. Also, schizophrenics benefit more from punishment of incorrect responses than normals, which fits with the formulation that schizophrenics are especially bothered by interfering response tendencies.

None of this implies that rewarding correct responses will always benefit normals more than schizophrenics. Reward does seem to be more effective when there are fewer interfering responses, but as we have seen in earlier sections, tasks can be arranged so that they evoke little response competition. In such situations, schizophrenic performance approaches that of normals, and rewarding correct performance should yield comparable results for the two groups. A study by Stotsky (1957) shows that as task complexity is reduced, the greater benefit of reward for normals than schizophrenics is reduced. Stotsky gave simple and disjunctive reaction-time tasks before and after praise. For schizophrenics, the praise was a five-minute praise and exhortation session with the schizophrenic's therapist. Only those therapist-patient pairs where the therapist felt there was a good relationship were used. Normals had their praise and encouragement session with the experimenter. This procedure may have resulted in more powerful rewards for the schizophrenics, so before and after effects cannot be compared directly. However, comparing schizophrenics and normals on the difference in effect of this reward between single and disjunctive reaction-time tasks is still meaningful. Schizophrenics should be especially effected by the response complexity of the disjunctive reaction-time task; the schizophrenic versus normal difference in interfering responses should be greatest on this task; the reward should be relatively ineffective for schizophrenics on this more complex task. This is the way the results turned out. Here the main point for our discussion is that as task complexity increased, reward became relatively less effective for schizophrenics than normals, as is expected if task complexity is exacerbated in schizophrenia and rewarding correct responses is relatively less effective in improving performance when task complexity is greater.

Returning to discussion of aversive conditions, note that we have stressed that the relatively greater benefits from punishment for schizophrenics depends on tying punishment to incorrect responses, but we have looked only at response-contingent studies and compared their results with the Garmezy and Dunn studies where censure could be avoided by avoiding the task. In order to know if the important variable is close tie-in of punishment and competing responses, we also need to look at studies where punishment can provide task-relevant motivation, but is not closely tied to competing responses as they occur.

Studies by Olson (1958) and Goodstein, Guertin, and Blackburn (1961) are of this type. In both studies, schizophrenics and normals were first tested on tasks (timed digit symbol and disjunctive reaction-time tasks, respectively). Then subjects were given an evaluation of their performance, either positive or negative, or there was no evaluative feedback; the subjects were then retested. In these studies, negative evaluation was not used as a stimulus for interfering responses, but also did not directly punish specific competing responses. It is not surprising then that neither study showed a significant interaction between type of evaluation and the performance of different diagnostic groups. The differential trends that did occur were different for the two studies, schizophrenics tending to perform relatively better following positive evaluation in the Olson study, and relatively better following negative evaluation in the Goodstein *et al.* study. When compared with the other studies in this section, these studies support the conclusion that the important factor underlying the beneficial effect of punishment in schizophrenics is in the immediate punishment of interfering responses. When this direct punishment does not occur, the special facilitative effects for schizophrenics are not as clear.

A good final study for this section is a study by Karras (1962), which clearly illustrates both beneficial and deleterious effects of an aversive condition in schizophrenics in a single study, thus emphasizing that it is the way that aversive conditions are used that is important. Chronic schizophrenics were tested in a disjunctive reaction-time task with white noise used either to punish slow responses or as an irrelevent stimulus. The response-contingent conditions were much like in Pascal and Swenson—the noise came on with a light that signaled that a response should be made, and the noise remained on while incorrect responses were made and could be terminated only by a correct response. Both low-intensity (47 — 51 db, apparently not unpleasant) and high-intensity (91 — 94 db, unpleasant) noise were used this way in different groups. These noise groups will be called the "low-escape" and "high-escape" groups, respectively. Two other schizophrenic groups performed under medium- (79 — 82 db), and high-intensity noise, respectively, with the noise left on throughout the task. These latter groups, where noise was an irrelevant stimulus, will be called the medium- and high-stimulation groups. A control group of schizophrenics did not hear white noise.

The results are shown in Figure 7. All groups except the low-escape

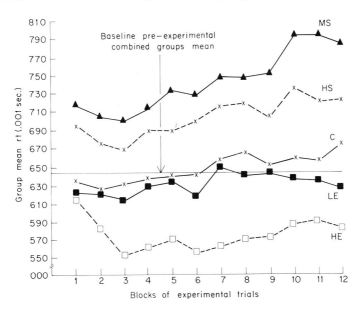

Fig. 7. Mean of the medians of each group for each of the 12 blocks of the experimental condition. KEY: MS = Medium Stimulation, HS = High Stimulation, LE = Low Escape, HE = High Escape, C = Control. (From Karras, 1962.)

group differed significantly from the control group. The high-escape group performed best, and the groups where noise was an irrelevant stimulus did worst. The medium-stimulation group did worse than the high-stimulation group, which is difficult to interpret without considering possible homeostatic factors controlling high-intensity stimulation, as suggested by Reynolds (1962), which are outside the discussion at this point. The lack of significant difference from controls for the low-escape group is not surprising in that the level of noise in this condition was not judged to be aversive and thus should have only minimal effects.

In spite of a need for such interpretive comments about some of the details of the results, the major results that are relevant to our discussion are very clear. With the high-escape and irrelevant-stimulation groups performing significantly differently from controls in opposite directions from each other, these results clearly indicate that aversive stimulation may be either beneficial or deleterious for schizophrenics. The difference seems to depend simply on whether or not the aversive conditions decrease or increase irrelevant responses. This conclusion can be trusted more when, as in this study, both effects occur in one study, and task differences other than the arrangement of the aversive conditions are controlled.

One possible alternate interpretation of some of these studies is that response-contingent punishment provides the most additional information about the task when it is needed, i.e., when responses have been incorrect, and this information, not a more general suppression of incorrect response tendencies, is what is needed. With the stipulation that schizophrenics need more knowledge about task requirements than normals because of their disturbed attention responses which should, for example, affect the use of task instructions, this explanation is in line with our general formulation and would explain some of the results. However, the special intrusion of interfering responses in schizophrenics seems to affect performance much more broadly than only leading to attentional and informational deficits, and it does seem that what is needed is a general suppression of any interfering response tendency, rather than there being only a need for additional task-relevant information. In the studies by Atkinson and Robinson (1961), information about correct answers was given after each response, with punishment of incorrect responses still having a relatively greater effect than reward for schizophrenics than for normals. A study by Losen (1961) also suggests that the locus of effect is, in general, suppression of interfering responses rather than specifically in improved knowledge about what is wanted in the task.

Losen compared normals and good premorbid schizophrenics, matched on a pretest, on an arithmetic task under no-censure conditions, conditions where incorrect responses were censured, and an information condition where correct answers were given to the subjects after each response. Correct answers were given following incorrect responses only in the information condition. The conditions interacted significantly with diagnostic categories. Normals were not affected differently by the conditions, but the schizophrenics were aided more by censure of incorrect responses than by knowing what had been the correct response. An additional schizophrenic group that was censured only on every other incorrect response was also used. The results from this group also point to the locus of effect as response suppression in that while the 50% censure group performed non-significantly poorer than the 100% censure group during training (but significantly better than the information group), the effects for the 50% group were more permanent on follow-up tests. The 50% group received less information than the 100% censure group, so these results are best interpreted as due to the utility and relative permanence of periodic, as compared to 100% punishment, in surpressing interfering response tendencies.

There are a number of additional relevant studies [for most of them see Silverman (1963)] but reviewing them would add little to the points that have been raised, and would not lead to different conclusions. The trend of results in this area has been quite consistent.

Summary and Concluding Remarks

We have now looked at quite a bit of research, and the simple beginning formulation has held up surprisingly well. The formulation is obviously incomplete, especially regarding heterogeneity in schizophrenia. However, the basic idea, that the alternate response tendencies evoked in a situation are especially intrusive for schizophrenics, does seem to be an important aspect of schizophrenia. When tasks are complex, with a number of different response tendencies present, schizophrenics seem to have reduced response focus. The resulting disorganized fluctuation between appropriate and competing responses gives a special "flavor" to schizophrenic deficit, made up of appropriate responses, errors that are primarily deviant responses having some association to the task, and abnormal variability. This process seems to be quite important. Important first in that its consequences are so pervasive—the relevant research we have looked at has included verbal associations, shape recognition, reaction time, concept formation, and stimulus generalization—and important because when interfering response tendencies are reduced, schizophrenics may approximate normal performance. The presence of interfering

responses is the important point, and should be distinguished from stimulus complexity. Situations that do not seem to be complex on the stimulus
side may still evoke multiple responses. On the other hand, an increase in
number of irrelevant stimuli will not increase schizophrenic deficit unless
the stimuli increase response competition. Added stimuli may, in fact,
reduce schizophrenic deficit by decreasing task complexity through reducing task ambiguity or by punishing interfering responses. It should
also be remembered that all alternate response tendencies are not potential interfering responses. Tasks vary in the extent to which different responses interfere with performance. For example, on some tasks many irrelevant responses may be made without affecting performance because
responding is not timed and only a limited number of specific responses
are counted as incorrect. On the other tasks, e.g., reaction-time tasks,
many kinds of responses may interfere with performance.

The major theme — the importance of lack of response focus in schizophrenia — seems fairly well established. The evidence also suggests differences in subgroups of schizophrenics which, without more relevant data,
must be tentative. These suggestions are that:

1. Paranoid schizophrenics seem to have more focused, more organized, responding than hebephrenics (Lester, 1960).
2. It is possible that after the early acute stage, schizophrenics with
   good-premorbid histories are less troubled by response interference
   than poor-premorbid schizophrenics (Dokecki, Polidoro, & Cromwell, 1965).
3. When response complexity comes from multiple stimuli, predicting
   increased deficit is difficult because some schizophrenics (un-
   identified as yet) may ignore some sources of stimulation more
   than other schizophrenics.

The intention in this chapter has been to present an extensive body of
research which is relevant to the hypothesis that response interference is
an important aspect of schizophrenia. Although our review of the literature has been extensive, it has not been exhaustive. The goal has been to
present studies that illustrate an important direction in which the broader
body of research points, together with literature that raises some additional questions. The selection of material always raises the possibility of
a selection biased in favor of certain trends, even though the goal has been
to represent the trends fairly, with a conscious bias only toward experiments which provide better illustrations of the trend of the broader literature. Hence, it may be useful to quote some of the conclusions from a
very extensive overview of recent laboratory studies of schizophrenic
deficit (Buss & Lang, 1965; Lang & Buss, 1965).

"The mechanism that appears in all studies of deficit concerns the initiation of responses to selected stimuli and the inhibition of inappropriate responses. All intelligent behavior represents a compromise between the demands of the immediate environment and a previously established set of the organism, but the schizophrenic makes a uniquely poor bargain. External stimuli, associational and biological 'noise,' routinely suppressed by normal subjects, intrude, and responses to the appropriate stimuli are not made.

"These facts suggest that researchers in schizophrenia should concentrate on the processes by which stimuli adapt out or habituate and response competition is resolved [Lang & Buss, 1965, p. 98]."

We have begun by pointing toward something that is fairly well substantiated and important in schizophrenia. Many questions remain. Elaboration of causes and effects of lack of response focus in schizophrenia is needed, but is as yet much less certain than the major emphases in the material we have discussed. However, a number of theoretical accounts of response disorganization in schizophrenia make suggestions that go beyond our discussion to this point and have some empirical support. These accounts, to which we now turn, are important both for the way they integrate other variables and other research, and for their implications for future research.

2

THEORIES OF RESPONSE DISORGANIZATION IN SCHIZOPHRENIA:

Reduced Information

In the last chapter a tentative theory was used to organize the presentation of a body of research. Now we turn to other theories that are relevant to that research. Some of these theories will be quite different; some, to be considered in the next chapter, are essentially elaborations of the response-interference formulation that has been used. Each of the theories that we will look at can account for all or major parts of the research that has been discussed. Their theme is that schizophrenic behavior is characterized by response disorganization—appropriate responses are often given, but other responses, often associated-but-deviant responses, intrude sporadically. It is not surprising that different theories about schizophrenia predict similar kinds of behavior. For example, if disorganized intrusion of associated responses is important in schizophrenia, theories of schizophrenia must deal with it. However, the implications of the theories go beyond this common core, leading to new, and sometimes opposing predictions. These predictions will lead us to research not covered in the last chapter.

To oversimplify somewhat, the theories are of two major types. First, response disorganization is seen as due to changes in the influence of cues on behavior. In these theories, schizophrenic responses are deviant because they are based on reduced and, in one theory, fluctuating, information. The second type of theory, which will be discussed in the following chapter, emphasizes competition among simultaneously evoked responses; the alternate responses interfering with each other more in schizophrenia. Though the theories in which reduced information plays a central role differ the most from the formulation that was used in the last chapter, they will be discussed first, partly to emphasize the contrast in theories which overlap in the data they attempt to account for, and partly to conform historically, in that a theory based on reduced information was proposed first.

WEAKENING OF ASSOCIATIVE THREADS — BLEULER

Bleuler's "Dementia Praecox or the Group of Schizophrenias" was published in 1911 (English translation, 1950). This remarkable monograph presents description and theory which foreshadows much of the research presented in the last chapter. As we will see, Bleuler's theoretical ideas are also quite close to the somewhat more precise elaborations of several recent theorists.

As the title of Bleuler's book suggests, one of Bleuler's concerns was an adequate name for the disturbance he described. "I call dementia praecox 'schizophrenia' because (as I hope to demonstrate) the 'splitting' of the different psychic functions is one of its most important characteristics [1950, p. 8]." "In every case we are confronted with a more or less clear-cut splitting of the psychic functions .... The psychic complexes do not combine in a conglomeration of strivings with a unified resultant as they do in a healthy person; rather, one set of complexes dominates the personality for a time, while other groups of ideas or drives are 'split off' and seem either partly or completely impotent .... Thus, the process of association often works with mere fragments of ideas and concepts. This results in associations which normal individuals will regard as incorrect, bizarre, and utterly unpredictable [1950, p. 9]."

Bleuler's basic postulate is that in schizophrenia some of the cues that normally organize and guide thinking (e.g., ideas and "drives") lose much or all of their influence. In normals, thinking is focused, and is channeled by a number of concurrent influences acting together to lead to appropriate behavior. The guidelines must be complete in order for thought to be appropriate. "The direction of our associations is determined not by any single force but by an almost infinite number of influences. In the thought process of schizophrenia, however, all the associative threads ... whether singly or in haphazard groupings, may remain totally ineffective [1950, p. 17]."

For Bleuler, the loss of guidance by total context is important because so many different possible thoughts are associated with the same situation, and it is the context that determines the occurrence of the appropriate from among the many potential associations. For example, "The idea of water is quite different depending on whether it refers to chemistry, physiology, navigation, landscape, inundation, or source of power. Each of these special ideas becomes connected with the other ideas by a special set of threads. No healthy person thinks of crystal water when his house is being swept away by a flood; nor will he think of water as a medium of transportation when he is thirsty [1950, p. 17]." When the associative guidance provided by total context is absent, different members of the family of potential associates may occur, depending on which of the associative threads have been weakened and which remain.

Associated meanings are not the only kinds of associations. Associative threads may also be formed on the basis of habit, similarity, subordination, causality, and many other relationships. This is why there is such a family of potential associations to most situations. "But in the normal mind only those part concepts dominate the picture that belong to a given frame of reference. The others exist only potentially or at least retreat into the background so that we cannot even demonstrate their influence [1950, p. 17]." When in schizophrenia some of the guiding associative threads provided by total context become weakened, then responses based only on the remaining associative threads may appear. A quotation given earlier is an example of an association that is deviant because it is not guided by total context (" 'Is something weighing heavily on your mind?' — 'Yes. Iron is heavy' [1950, p. 19]." *"Even where only part of the associative threads is interrupted, other influences which under normal circumstances are not noticeable, become operative in the place of logical directives* . . . . All these thought-connections are not foreign to the normal psyche either. But they occur only exceptionally and incidentally, whereas in schizophrenia they are exaggerated to the point of caricature and often actually dominate the thought processes [Bleuler's emphasis, 1950, p. 23]."

The main point here is that the schizophrenic's deviant associations are related to the stimulus situation. The basis of the relationship is likely to be bizarre when the context is considered, but the association is there. "It looks as though ideas of a certain category . . . were thrown into one pot, mixed, and subsequently picked out at random . . . [*ibid.*, p. 16]." The schizophrenic's responding is guided by the same kinds of associations as are present in the normal. However, because many of the normal's associations are gone, those that remain to influence the schizophrenic may be unimportant, incidental relationships. We have seen that research tends to support this implication of Bleuler's theory. Schizophrenics' errors tend to be associated rather than unrelated responses (Burstein, 1961; Chapman & Taylor, 1957; Chapman, 1961; Fey, 1951; Gottesman, 1964).

To complete the picture, it should be noted that Bleuler suggests that, on occasion, all associative threads may be lost for a time. When this happens, there will be a complete disruption in the stream of thought. There will be a blocking of thought instead of loosely associated responses.

Another clear implication is that, as a group, schizophrenics should be more variable than normals. Schizophrenic responses are determined by "apparently haphazard" [1950, p. 22] subgroups of the total complex of associative threads that lead to normal responses. [The "haphazard" applies to those associative threads in a situation that will be weakened. However, different situations are not affected haphazardly. Emotionally toned situations are more affected. Why this is thought to be so is not spelled out (1950, p. 74)]. Because the subgroups of associative threads that remain are haphazard, they vary from schizophrenic to schizophrenic, leading to considerable within-group variation. There has probably been no more consistent research finding than the support for this implication.

Bleuler also strongly implies that within-subject variability should be greater in schizophrenics than in normals. As was quoted earlier, he refers to specific subgroups of associative threads as influencing schizophrenic responses "for a time" and most of his examples imply changes in the determining associative links over fairly short time intervals, although he also gives a few examples that indicate the influence of the same subgroups of links over longer periods. Regardless of the time interval involved, behavior that is determined by changing subgroups of associative links will be more variable than behavior that results from the total context. This is, of course, consistent with the evidence of less response stability in schizophrenics than normals (Sommer, Dewar, & Osmond, 1960; Storms, Broen, & Levin, 1967).

Bleuler's theory also presents a straightforward account of schizophrenics' tendency toward overly broad or too-narrow concepts. When part of the associative links normally generated by a stimulus are missing, the remaining partial associations determine the entire meaning. Thus, words denoting different things may be seen as having identical meaning simply because their partial meanings remain identical. In the same way, two distinct concepts may be identified as one on the basis of one common component. On the other hand, if the missing associates involve important common meanings, objects that are conceptually alike may be thought of as quite disparate because the remaining partial meanings have little in common. ". . . ideas are thought of in entirely haphazard fragments which frequently retain far-fetched connections and miss the closer related ones [Bleuler, 1950, pp. 77-78]." These statements are certainly in accord with, and provide a somewhat different way of accounting for, the research on overexclusion and overinclusion discussed in the previous chapter (Epstein, 1953; Moran, 1953; Payne et al., 1959; Chapman & Taylor, 1957; Chapman, 1961).

Bleuler's theory has another important implication that was not emphasized in Chapter 1. Relative schizophrenic deficit should increase when more guidance from context is needed, is available, and is useful to normals. The greater the number of useful associative threads that are available, the greater the likelihood that useful associative threads will be missing in schizophrenics. Two studies (Lewinsohn & Elwood, 1961; Lawson *et al.*, 1964) which have been discussed, can be interpreted in a way that is relevant here. In these studies, schizophrenics did worse, relative to normals, in memorizing lists of words, where the words provided context that should be useful in recall. We interpreted this as due to schizophrenics' response-interference acting to lower the appropriate contextual information they supplied themselves. However, the results can also be interpreted simply in terms of schizophrenics' reduced ability to note and/or use a broad range of cues, regardless of the source of these cues. Other studies will be cited in later chapters when we discuss more recent theories that elaborate this basic and important idea that many schizophrenics are unable to profit from a broad range of contextual cues. However, from the research already discussed in Chapter 1, it does seem that a simple theory of reduced cue utilization in schizophrenia would have to be modified to account for differences in use of different kinds of information, and for heterogeneity among schizophrenics in breadth of cue utilization.

In addition, although Bleuler's theory is clearly in accord with the results of much recent research on schizophrenia, there are two other fairly important trends in recent evidence which, although not necessarily contrary to his theory, would not seem to be easily encompassed by it. These trends indicate that (a) schizophrenics have special difficulty when alternate responses are trained to single stimuli, and (b) schizophrenics are especially helped when competing responses are punished. In that Bleuler's theory of schizophrenia focuses on a loss of needed associative links rather than a special susceptibility to interference from incorrect associations, these results would not seem to be implied by the theory. Bleuler's theory is a theory of susceptibility to interfering responses, not in any competitional sense, but only in the sense that inappropriate responses based on partial links may appear when needed associational links become impotent. Associational links that specifically mediate incorrect responses should be as likely to disappear as needed links. Thus, there is nothing here that necessarily implies that training new competing associations or punishing incorrect responses would change the degree of deficit from normal performance.

While these related areas of research — differential use of different kinds of information between groups of schizophrenics, heterogeneity in range of cue utilization among schizophrenics, relationship of deficit to (a) number of competing responses and (b) punishment of interfering responses —

cannot be accounted for by Bleuler's theory, this does not mean at all that Bleuler's general way of thinking about schizophrenia is not very important. We have seen that this remarkable theory, proposed over 50 years ago, is in accord with a considerable amount of research evidence. Also, although this type of theory does not directly imply some of the results that are easily encompassed by theories about increased susceptibility to interfering response tendencies, as we shall see in the next theory to which we turn, further elaboration of Bleuler's type of theory easily handles other recent data that are not easily encompassed by straight response-interference theories.

OVERINFLUENCE OF DOMINANT MEANING — CHAPMAN AND CHAPMAN

Although Bleuler discussed schizophrenia as a process wherein different associative threads were weakened in a rather haphazard fashion, there does seem to be more predictability about the kinds of errors schizophrenics will make than is implied by Bleuler's formulation. In general, when more than one kind of response is incorrect, the particular errors that normals make most are also the prominent error responses for schizophrenics. Chapman (1958) showed this in a task where words were to be sorted according to concepts, and Gottesman and Chapman (1960) also obtained this kind of result in a multiple-choice test of syllogistic reasoning. If, as seems to be the case, schizophrenic errors can be predicted from error patterns made by normals, then if loss of associative links is the reason for schizophrenic deficit, this loss would not seem to be as haphazard as Bleuler implies. There must be some underlying principle about which associative links tend to be lost and which links are not lost.

Chapman and Chapman (1965), having for some time thought of schizophrenic errors as an exacerbation of normal association biases, sought to find a principle that would explain deviant schizophrenic associations. They began by presenting pairs of words to schizophrenics and normals and asking if the word pairs meant the same thing, and found that schizophrenics judged similar words to have identical meanings more than normals. By itself this does not deviate from Bleuler in that, as we have seen, partial meanings of similar words are more likely to be seen as identical than total meanings, even if the loss of associative links is haphazard. However, an interpretation of this phenomena which would indicate greater lawfulness was suggested by spontaneous comments by subjects about the word pairs. "One item asked if 'bicycle' means the same as 'wagon.' The schizophrenics often said things like 'You can ride on a bicycle, and you can ride in a wagon, so they mean the same.' Normal subjects would say something like, 'You can ride on both a bicycle and in a wagon, but a bicycle has two wheels and a wagon has four so they don't really mean the same' [Chapman & Chapman, 1965, pp. 138-139]." The same partial meanings ("you can ride on it") were given first by both the schizophrenics and the normals. The difference was that the schizophrenics sometimes used only this dominant meaning and the normals considered additional meanings. It seems that the associative links that are lost in schizophrenia may tend to be those that occur later in a sequence of normal thought, the primary meanings being retained.

The theory can be stated more explicitly as follows (from both Chapman & Chapman, 1965, and Chapman, Chapman, & Miller, 1964):

1. A person responds to a word with a hierarchical sequence of meaning responses, each of which expresses an aspect of the denotative meaning of the word. These meaning responses are hypothetical inner events that mediate a person's overt response to a word.
2. The hierarchies of meaning responses are essentially the same for schizophrenics and normals.
3. "... schizophrenics' misinterpretations of overt responses to words arise in part from mediation of overt responses to words by their strongest meaning responses with a relative neglect of their weaker meaning responses, while the interpretation of words by normal persons reflects the use of the weaker as well as the stronger meaning responses [Chapman et al., 1964, p. 53]."
4. Normals are able to use weaker meanings when a task calls for it, but they are not overinfluenced by them. When a correct response is mediated by a dominant meaning, then normals will make the correct response as often as schizophrenics.
5. Meaning responses to words are not the only response mediators. Context also provides mediating cues. "The theory states that schizophrenic performance deficit arises from an excessive reliance on the strongest mediating responses whether the mediating responses are aroused by the word itself or by a contextual cue [Chapman et al., 1964, p. 68]."

Chapman and Chapman apply this theory only to the use of words. However, because this theory is basically concerned with schizophrenics' deviant use of mediators, it has extremely broad implications. As we shall see later, the basic generalized idea that schizophrenics focus on dominant information has been used independently by several other investigators working with other kinds of research tasks. For now, we will concentrate on the specific implications of the theory as used by Chapman and Chapman, both looking at the compatibility of the theory with the major lines of evidence from Chapter 1 where discussion of denotative meanings is relevant, and considering other research that is relevant to the implications of this theory.

First, consider statement 2 from the previous list, which is a striking assumption in view of widespread differences between schizophrenics and normals. Chapman *et al.* (1964) reported a pilot investigation of this assumption. Twenty chronic schizophrenics and 22 normals of similar age and education were asked to state the meanings of 15 multi-meaning and 5 single-meaning words. For 19 of the 20 words, the most frequent meaning for normals was also the most frequent meaning for schizophrenics. Also, using the 15 multi-meaning words only, each subject was given a score equal to the number of times his first meaning statement was the most frequent meaning for the normal group. Mean scores were 13.9 for the schizophrenics and 13.7 for the normals — a non-significant difference. Thus, in accord with statement 2, the meanings that normals and schizophrenics give to words, at least the dominant meanings, seem quite similar.

Next, the theory is clearly in accord with the considerable evidence we have discussed that indicates that schizophrenics' errors in using words will be associated rather than irrelevant responses. On this point the explanation is the same as with Bleuler's theory. If schizophrenics respond to partial meaning of words, their responses are, of course, associated to the stimulus words.

The theory also provides a precise account of schizophrenics' tendency to form concepts which may be overinclusive and/or overexclusive (e.g., Chapman & Taylor, 1957; Chapman, 1961). If two words are conceptually different, but have the same dominant meaning, schizophrenics, being overinfluenced by these dominant meanings, will tend to view the words as identical. On the other hand, when words belong in the same concept on the basis of non-dominant meanings that are the same and dominant meanings are different, then schizophrenics will view the words as quite different and as not belonging together. This formulation is quite consistent with the kinds of associated conceptual errors schizophrenics make. It is more specific than the evidence we have reviewed, and more specific research in this area, where predictions are made on the basis of meaning hierarchies, is certainly called for.

Chapman, Chapman, and Miller (1964) reported one study that is specifically relevant here. This study confirms the theory's implication that when words belong in a conceptual group because of non-dominant meanings, then schizophrenics will not include these words as often as normals will. Conceptual overexclusion is predicted. In this study, subjects were to sort cards with names of objects on them into two boxes—those belonging to a named conceptual class in one box, and those that did not belong in the other. For example, in one task, "things that have a head" were to go in one box and "things that do not have a head" in the other. The response cards were of three kinds: animate and inanimate things that have heads (e.g., dog and pin, respectively), and things that do not have heads (e.g., napkins). Three other similar tasks were used based on sorting objects in accordance with having legs, teeth, and skin. Animate and inanimate objects that should be included as having the specified characteristics were included in each task along with irrelevant objects.

The hierarchy of meaning responses to each of the four concepts was studied by having students in an introductory psychology course give statements of meaning for head, legs, teeth, and skin. Animate meanings were clearly dominant. From the theory then, schizophrenics' sorts would be overly influenced by this dominant meaning of the concept, while normals would also consider the weaker, inanimate meaning. Thus in this task, schizophrenics' concepts should be narrow, with inanimate objects excluded, while normals should be less likely to exclude inanimate objects.

Chapman *et al.* (1964) wanted to remove the influence of factors such as lack of attention and carelessness from their data and did so by the following procedure. Lack of attention and carelessness should result in random placements, which could be measured by the number of placements of irrelevant objects in the designated concepts. These random placements were corrected for by subtracting the number of irrelevant objects that were placed in the designated conceptual class from the number of animate objects and from the number of inanimate objects that were incorrectly excluded from the concepts. These corrected scores clearly showed that the chronic schizophrenics who served as subjects were influenced by the dominant (animate) meanings of the concepts, but tended to ignore the non-dominant (inanimate) meaning more than normals. Using these corrected scores, the mean number of exclusions of animate objects was .16 for schizophrenics and .19 for normals, while an average of 11.61 inanimate objects were excluded by schizophrenics compared to 3.81 for normals.

In this case, conceptual overexclusion apparently resulted from schizophrenics' abnormal tendency to ignore non-dominant meanings. As was mentioned earlier, overdependence on dominant meanings may also lead to overinclusion—treating different words as meaning the same thing. When words are moderately similar, the hierarchies of meaning responses to these words should have differences as well as commonalities. If subjects are asked to judge whether or not such words mean the same thing, then normals, being influenced by all the meanings to each word, should rarely judge the words as having the same meanings. Considering only the dominant meanings, which are what are hypothesized to overinfluence schizophrenics, in a pair of moderately similar words these dominant meanings will occasionally be identical. Thus, schizophrenics should treat moderately similar words as *identical* more often than normals. On the other hand, when subjects are to judge whether or not two words are *similar*, normals will be influenced by many of the meaning responses that are in both meaning hierarchies and will tend to rate the words as similar. Schizophrenics will specifically overfocus on dominant meanings, and when these are different, schizophrenics will not rate the words as similar even though there is considerable overlap in non-dominant meanings. The hypothesis that follows from all this is that, in judging moderately similar words, schizophrenics should judge the words to have the *same* meaning more than normals, and will judge the words to have *similar* meanings less than normals. An additional implication is that, across a set of word pairs, judgments of sameness and similarity will be more closely related for schizophrenics than normals. This is because the dominant meanings to the two words are either identical or they are not. So schizophrenics' responses should be quite dichotomous in contrast to the responses of normals, whose judgment may reflect the different degrees of overlap of hierarchies of meaning responses.

Chapman and Chapman (1965) provided data concerning each of these implications from their theory. In one task, chronic schizophrenics and normals judged whether or not pairs of words were the same in meaning. In another task, using the same word pairs, subjects judged whether or not the words were similar in meaning. The judgments were made using a multiple-choice format. For example, the similarity of "automobile" and "wagon" were judged in the following item (from Chapman & Chapman, 1965, p. 140):

" 'Automobile' is similar in meaning to
  a. Pail
  b. Wagon
  c. Neither of the above "

In each item an unrelated word (e.g., pail) was included in order to measure "random" responding. The number of judgments of similarity for each subject was corrected for "random error" by subtracting the number of unrelated objects that were judged to be similar, from the number of related words (e.g., wagon) that were judged to be similar. The format was the same for judging sameness as for judging similarity except, of course, for instructions to judge sameness.

The pairs of words had previously been rated for degree of similarity by college students, so the differences between judgments of the schizophrenics (chronics) and normals (maintenance workers and unemployed) who served in the experiment could be studied as a function of degree of similarity between the words in a pair. The results are presented in Figure 8.

Compared to normals, schizophrenics judged significantly more pairs of words to mean the same. Schizophrenics also tended to judge fewer word pairs as similar, although this difference fell short of significance. The tendency for judgments of same and similar to be more closely related in schizophrenics than normals can also be seen in Figure 8.

Chapman and Chapman noted that, in some contrast to previous results they had obtained, ". . . at the A point, which is the point of highest similarity, the schizophrenics marked fewer pairs than the normals as meaning the same ($z=3.10$, p < .01). This can probably be attributed to a greater degree of disorganization in the patients used in Experiment II, with a resultant variability of response [1965, p. 141]." An implication is that, although a tendency to use a specific and abnormally narrow range of meanings can account for some aspects of schizophrenics' deviant behavior, a second process, which is related to abnormal response variability, is also a factor in schizophrenic behavior.

The major trends of the results of this experiment are in accord with the Chapman and Chapman theory, but would also have been expected from Bleuler's theory. Any account that says that schizophrenics tend to use

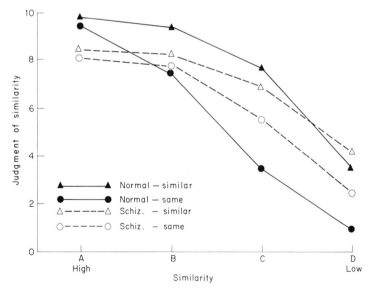

Fig. 8. Mean judgments of sameness and similarity. (From Chapman & Chapman, 1965.)

partial meanings would imply these results. However, further analysis supported predictions from the Chapman theory that could not be made from Bleuler's theory. The intent of the analysis was to relate differences between schizophrenics and normals in judging sameness of meaning to whether or not the dominant meaning responses were identical. The prediction is that "... those word pairs on which schizophrenics exceed normal subjects in judgments of sameness are more often those for which the strongest meaning responses are identical for the two words [Chapman & Chapman, 1965, p. 142]."

In order to study this prediction, college students were asked to list the meanings for each word that had been used in the study and then a second group of college students ranked these meanings as to importance for telling what the word meant. The top-ranked meaning for each word was assumed to be its dominant meaning. Then word pairs that had been used in the experiment were dichotomized according to the number of judges who gave the same meaning first rank for both words. Word pairs where the same meaning was given top rank by 16 or more (of 50) judges are called Type I pairs (19 pairs). Type II pairs (19 pairs) were given the same top meaning by 13 or fewer judges. The number of "same" judgments given these two types of words in the experiment is shown in Table 3.

The Type I – Type II scores in Table 3 are significantly different for schizophrenics and normals.

As expected, schizophrenics' tendency to judge more word pairs as meaning the same thing is primarily found in Type I pairs – pairs of words that have the same dominant meaning. The tendency shown in Table 3 for schizophrenics to exceed normals on judgments of "same" for both types of pairs is unexpected. However, this tendency may be due to differences in meaning hierarchies for different people, in that the judgments by college students of which meanings were dominant were not unanimous. Individual differences in hierarchies would also be expected for schizophrenics. Therefore, some of the Type II word pairs may have also had the same dominant meanings for individual schizophrenics. This com-

TABLE 3[a]

MEAN NUMBER OF WORD PAIRS JUDGED AS SYNONYMOUS FOR TYPE I AND TYPE II ITEMS

Group	Type I	Type II	I – II
Schizophrenics	4.40	3.50	.90
Normals	1.90	2.43	−.53

[a] From Chapman & Chapman (1965).

monality of dominant meanings should, of course, be less for Type II words than Type I words however, giving rise to the special tendency for schizophrenics to judge Type I word pairs to mean the same thing.

In general then, the specific overinclusion-overexclusion predictions made from the theory have been supported. Compared to normals, schizophrenics exclude abnormally many words from concepts when the reason for including the word in the concept is mediated by a non-dominant meaning, and schizophrenics overinclude words—judge different words as meaning the same thing—primarily when dominant meanings are the same.

The theory can also handle some aspects of the evidence relating amount of deficit to the number of alternate associations evoked by a stimulus word. The specific predictions made by the theory go beyond the data we have discussed. When verbal material is ambiguous—evoking different meanings that mediate different responses—then schizophrenics *may* do worse than normals. They *will* do worse than normals if non-dominant meanings aid performance. Schizophrenics will perform more like normals if the stimuli evoke only one meaning or if dominant meanings are all that are needed for correct responses. These predictions are compatible in a general way with the evidence from the studies of interpretation of proverbs and words discussed in Chapter 1 (Blaufarb, 1962; those parts of Faibish's 1961 research concerned with definitions; Hamlin et al., 1965), although the specifics of the predictions are not really tested by these studies. Chapman et al. (1964) have, however, reported relevant data.

In contrast to the usual studies that show that schizophrenics tend to do relatively worse when competing responses are elicited, Chapman et al. (1964) found, in accord with the Chapman theory, that chronic schizophrenics could interpret multi-meaning material as well as normals if dominant meanings mediated correct responses. Schizophrenic deficit was found only when weaker meanings needed to be used, and dominant meanings mediated incorrect responses.

In the first of two relevant studies, multi-meaning words were used in a context that indicated that one meaning was correct, but the context left some ambiguity. Subjects were to select the correct meaning from among several choices that were presented. There were parallel items that required using stronger and weaker meanings of the same word. For example (from Chapman et al., 1964):

"When the farmer bought a herd of cattle, he needed a new pen.
This means:
    a. He needed a new writing implement.
    b. He needed a new fenced enclosure.
    c. He needed a new pick-up truck."

Here the context is intended to suggest alternate "b" although, from judgments of students in introductory psychology, "writing implement" is a stronger meaning response to "pen" than "fenced enclosure." Thus, here an incorrect response is mediated by a stronger meaning. Alternative "c" is an unrelated choice intended to be used as a measure of "random" responses. The parallel item, where the incorrect response is mediated by the weaker meaning of "pen," is:

"The professor loaned his pen to Barbara.

This means:

    a. He loaned her a pick-up truck.

    b. He loaned her a writing implement.

    c. He loaned her a fenced enclosure."

The test consisted of 19 such pairs of items. For both stronger and weaker meaning misinterpretations each subject's score was the number of misinterpretations, minus the number of unrelated choices. The mean corrected misinterpretations made by chronic schizophrenics and normals (City of Chicago firemen) are given in Table 4.

The strong minus weak score was significantly greater for schizophrenics than normals, indicating that schizophrenics' misinterpretations are influenced primarily by the stronger meanings.

However, again schizophrenics also tended to exceed normals in selecting misinterpretations mediated by weaker meanings (even when the use of weaker meanings is corrected for "random" selection). This is not in accord with the theory. Chapman *et al.* (1964) suggest that this was due to individual variations in dominance of meanings. To test this, they divided the items where weaker meanings mediated incorrect responses into two sets: 10 items where judges had had high agreement on which was the stronger meaning and 9 items where there was less agreement. Table 5 shows the misinterpretations made on these subsets.

On items where there is good agreement about which meanings are weaker, in accordance with the theory schizophrenics did not signifi-

TABLE 4[a]

MEAN NUMBER OF MISINTERPRETATIONS MEDIATED BY STRONGER AND WEAKER MEANING RESPONSES

	Total groups	
	Schizophrenic	Normal
Stronger	3.80	.89
Weaker	1.24	.44
Strong minus weak	2.56	.45

[a] From Chapman *et al.* (1964).

TABLE 5[a]

MEAN NUMBER OF MISINTERPRETATIONS MEDIATED BY WEAKER MEANINGS FOR
10 ITEMS WITH HIGH AGREEMENT ON RELATIVE STRENGTH AND 9
ITEMS WITH LOW AGREEMENT

	Schizophrenic	Normal
Low agreement	1.00	.22
High agreement	.24	.22

[a] From Chapman *et al.* (1964).

cantly exceed normals in misinterpretations mediated by these weaker meanings.

The results of this study show the kinds of reactions to multiple meanings that the theory implies: (a) when weaker meanings mediate correct responses, schizophrenics do less well than normals; (b) when stronger meanings mediate correct responses, normals and schizophrenics perform alike (after corrections for random responding). Schizophrenics' inferior performance with multi-meaning materials seems to be more specifically a relative tendency to under-use weaker meanings.

In another study, Chapman *et al.* (1964) showed that weaker meanings of words are not lost for schizophrenics even though, in general, they do not use these meanings sufficiently. Their theory states that context also has a mediating influence, and this study shows that strong contextual cues can enable schizophrenics to make responses mediated by weaker meanings of words. Presumably, stronger context, in contrast to the somewhat ambiguous context in the previous study, can make the weaker meaning dominant in that context. In this study, pairs of multiple-choice items were again constructed with either stronger or weaker meanings (determined by other judges) mediating correct responses, except that the incorrect meaning was not included as a choice. Chapman *et al.* (1964) state that the presence of a correct meaning, with the incorrect meaning not presented, makes for a strong context making the meaning that is presented the stronger meaning. An example of a pair of items in this study is:

"The word *bear* may mean: The word *bear* may mean:
   a. to carry   a. a sharp end
   b. to command   b. an animal
   c. neither of the above   c. neither of the above
   d. I don't know.   d. I don't know."

The incorrect responses for chronic schizophrenics and normals are presented in Table 6 (vocabulary score was related to performance on this task so the groups were matched on vocabulary).

The scores for the schizophrenics and normals were quite similar on this task, and the differences between the groups on scores of stronger meaning items minus weaker meaning items was not significant. As the theory suggests, this indicates that strong contextual cues enable schizophrenics to be near normal in using meanings that would be relatively weak out of that context. These results have some similarity to Blaufarb's (1962) results and the results found by Hamlin et al. (1965). Each of these studies indicates that schizophrenics benefit more than normals from strong context when the basic stimulus material is ambiguous [at least schizophrenics who are not the most extremely disturbed can benefit (Hamlin et al., 1965)] The Chapman and Chapman theory and the group of studies by Chapman et al. (1964) go further in specifying the nature of an underlying process and are much more specific about when schizophrenics will do well in interpreting ambiguous material and when they will not do as well as normals.

The theory is less able to handle the response variability which seems to characterize schizophrenic performance. This may not be a relevant point in that there is very little evidence about schizophrenics' instability in tasks that are based on denotative meanings. However, the Storms et al. (1967) study found that when acute schizophrenics and normals were asked on two occasions to name members of categories (e.g., "diseases"), schizophrenics showed less response stability. Anecdotal reports of schizophrenics' use of words also suggest variability, and disorganized variability, in what words mean to them. A good example is another quotation cited by Faibish (1961), where a schizophrenic was asked to define "regard" and replied, "An honest emotion . . . . In regard to this matter— in regard to this honest matter; in other words, in honest reference to this matter. Like best regards . . . [p. 414]." This abnormal variability of meaning would not be expected from a tendency to focus on a single dominant meaning. However, Chapman and Chapman do not imply that focus on dominant meaning is the only variable affecting schizophrenic performance. Other factors, such as reduced attention, variable attention, or lack of cooperation, are seen as influencing performance and possibly

TABLE 6[a]

MEDIAN ERROR SCORES ON ITEMS FOR WHICH STRONGER AND WEAKER
MEANING RESPONSES YIELD CORRECT ANSWERS

	Schizophrenic	Normal
Stronger	.79	.70
Weaker	2.07	2.21

[a] From Chapman et al. (1964).

contributing to abnormally variable behavior in schizophrenics. This is why a correction for "random" responses is used in their studies. Thus, abnormal response variability in schizophrenics is outside the scope of the theory; it does not contradict the theory.

This point is mentioned primarily because a rather minor elaboration of the theory would specifically handle response variability and would provide a better fit with some of the Chapman and Chapman (1965) data.

The theory implies, but does not explicitly state, that the order of meaning responses to a word changes as a function of context—the order of meaning responses is a joint function of word and context. It is then not inconsistent to view the dominance of a specific meaning response as probabilistic rather than stable for each subject. The dominant meaning for a subject can be defined as the meaning that is usually, but not always, dominant. If individuals' meaning hierarchies do change, then responses that are mediated principally by dominant meanings will change more than responses mediated by all the meanings. This is because the meanings do not change, just their hierarchical order. For schizophrenics, the meaning that influences them most will change if the dominant meaning changes. Normals, who tend to consider all meanings, will not be as influenced by change in the order of meanings.

Thus, the specific assumption that changes in context (which includes changes in addition to intended experimental manipulations of context) cause some variations in a person's meaning hierarchies over time, can account for abnormal variation in schizophrenics' use of words. The changes can occur over quite short time intervals. For example, as a person talks he is the changing context of variation in what he sees, variations in his own thoughts, and his own words.

This same assumption would also account for schizophrenics' tendency to respond to weaker meanings more than normals in some experiments (see Tables 3 and 4). To illustrate this, consider a specific theoretical situation that is intended to be similar to the experiment described earlier in this section where schizophrenics and normals were asked to indicate whether or not pairs of words meant the same thing. Remember that the pairs were of two kinds: (a) Type I, where the strongest meanings to the two words tended to be the same; and (b) Type II, where the strongest meanings tended not to be the same. Assume that the situation is explicitly as follows: (a) each word has three meanings; (b) the dominant meaning has a .4 probability of being in first position in the hierarchy, and the two other meanings each have a .3 probability of being in first position; (c) for Type I pairs, the dominant meanings are the same and one of the other meanings are the same; for Type II pairs, each word has the same two non-dominant meanings; (d) schizophrenics are influenced only by dominant meanings while normals are influenced by all meanings. The last statement is an overstatement of the Chapman theory, but, except for specifying probabilities for strongest meanings, the situation is analogous to the Chapmans' discussion of the experiment. The expected probability of "same" judgments can then be computed. For schizophrenics the probability that the same meanings will be dominant for a pair of words is:

Type I words; $(.4 \times .4)$ plus $(.3 \times .3) = .25$
Type II words; $(.3 \times .3)$ plus $(.3 \times .3) = .18$

These are the probabilities of "same" judgments for schizophrenics. Normals, in scanning the whole meaning hierarchies will note that one of the meanings of words in a pair do not match and will not judge words to be the same. The pattern of these results: schizophrenics giving more "same" judgments than normals for both types of words, but exceeding normals most on Type I words, is closer to the results of the experiment (Table 3) than the expectations from the basic theory. It has been noted that schizophrenics may seem to exceed normals on judgments influenced by weaker meanings only because the normatively weaker meanings were stronger for a specific subject. The elaboration of the theory says this explicitly, adding that there is also within-individual variation in the order of meanings. Note also that words that evoke meaning hierarchies with dominant meanings having very high probabilities of being in first position will also have the order of their meanings judged more consistently. Thus schizophrenics will not be as overinfluenced by normatively weaker meanings on words where judgments about meaning order are very consistent (see Table 5).

The probabilistic changes in order of meaning responses has been attributed to changing context. Uncontrolled changes in context would have most effect when the experimental conditions do not provide strong mediation leading to a single dominant response. However, when experimentally manipulated context is strong, this strong context would tend to override other contextual effects and hold the same meaning dominant. Thus, in experiments where a single invariant context is strong [e.g., the last Chapman *et al.*, (1964) experiment that was discussed], the meaning that influences schizophrenics should not vary much. Therefore, their performance should not be abnormally variable and schizophrenics should not be abnormally influenced by normatively weaker meanings sporadically becoming dominant. Note that in the Chapman *et al.* (1964) experiment where the context provided by the experimenters was strong, schizophrenics did not exceed normals in their use of normatively weaker meanings.

The elaboration of the theory we have been discussing is one possible minor elaboration that is consistent with the emphasis of the rest of the theory. The basic Chapman and Chapman theory is what is important, and this theory is a very valuable and stimulating development in thinking about schizophrenia. The theory deals with a very important area, the meaning of words; the predictions are more specific than has been the case in many theories about schizophrenia; and the predictions have received good experimental support. The role of contextual influence may require elaboration other than the suggestions made above, because if schizophrenics ignore some aspects of context (some meanings), then it seems likely that not all contexts that can make meanings that are usually non-dominant become dominant for normals will do the same for schizophrenics. However, the basic theory is very promising and certainly deserves further experimental attention.

In judging the utility of theories that emphasize a loss of information in schizophrenia, two main points stand out. First, these theories, especially when made specific about what information tends to be lost, account for evidence that response-interference theories, such as that used in the first chapter, cannot handle. On the other hand, especially when the predictive power is increased by suggesting consistent overuse of prominent information, formulations based on reduced information have some difficulty accounting for the response variability which seems to occur in schizophrenia, even when the necessary context is as simple as a single word. In addition, research results that indicate excessive distractibility by irrelevant stimuli in some schizophrenics, and research results that indicate that rewarding correct responses is less effective than response-contingent punishment of competing responses, would seem to be much easier to handle within response-interference theories than within theories which focus on loss of information.

In sum, though our beginning response-interference formulation and theories about reduced information seem to overlap in ability to handle some of the research data; each also seems able to account for data that the other cannot. It is possible that the different types of theory reflect different processes that are important in schizophrenia.

3

THEORIES OF RESPONSE DISORGANIZATION IN SCHIZOPHRENIA:

Greater Interference from Concurrent Response Tendencies

The theories that we will look at in this chapter view schizophrenic disorganization as a consequence of an inability to select appropriate responses from other competing response tendencies. In contrast to the theories in the previous chapter, these response-interference theories are basically the same as the formulation used in Chapter 1, but they elaborate on that formulation.

RESPONSE DISORGANIZATION BECAUSE OF LOSS OF SOCIAL MOTIVATION AND/OR ABILITIES — CAMERON

Cameron's theory (1938, 1939) is a good bridge from the theories that emphasize the loss or reduced use of association links to the theories that say that the trouble is increased interference from competing associations. Cameron's theory is really similar to each type. For Cameron, the schizophrenic is left with unorganized, competing thoughts because of a loss of the organizing factors that are inherent in the need to communicate with others. Cameron's basic assumption seems to be that the natural tendency in thinking or speaking is for loosely related ideas to occur together, and that appropriate selection is learned or occurs only because of a desire to make oneself understood by others. As Cameron (1939) said, his research and discussion on schizophrenia has "... emphasized the loose cluster-form of organization and the peculiar use of inexact approximations. Our subjects seems to throw in, more or less indiscriminately, elements that could be loosely thought of as belonging to the general subject, but which lacked the closer organization one would expect of an adult .... Any normal adult must be able to define his terms to a reasonable degree upon demand. That is, he must be able to become more exact by limiting the reference of a term or a phrase he uses, and to accomplish this end he must be able to discard whatever is unimportant or only partially relevant. Such capacity is just what is absent in schizophrenic disorganization [1939, p. 265]." Without appropriate organization and selection from among loosely related thoughts, the schizophrenic is often unintelligible to others. ". . . yet he is quite satisfied with his product and indicates no uneasiness concerning his own unintelligibility. This is the core of the problem [1938, p. 23]." In other words, the normal subordination of competing associations to appropriate, socially clear thoughts does not occur. The normal cultural organization in the use of language does not appear because the schizophrenic either does not realize or does not care that he is not understood. He is socially apart and does not have adequate role-taking skills (Cameron, 1944).

Cameron (1938) listed three kinds of disturbance in schizophrenics' use of language that reflect increasing degrees of disorganization and loss of socialization: asyndetic thinking, metonymic distortion, and interpenetration of themes. Each of these is essentially the same—unorganized fluctuation between related ideas.

Cameron arrived at the notion of asyndetic thinking from the study of schizophrenics' responses to questions about causation. For example, in response to a question about why the sun comes up in the morning, one schizophrenic said, "because it's a gas." Another responded, "Sun and light and heat." To another question a schizophrenic responded, "I have fair hair because I brush it." [These three quotations are from Cameron, 1938, p. 17.] From many such examples, Cameron concluded, "First, of all, our material shows surprisingly little real irrelevance . . . . The relatedness of the material is, however, often very distant . . . . In short, we find the schizophrenic offering, in place of an integrated functional whole, something that is a collection of fragments. In asyndetic reasoning something has been lost—the capacity for organization . . . . Competing terms cannot be completely discarded, there is a spurious equivalence given to several terms in a given cluster, and the product remains a more or less unorganized conglomerate [1938, pp. 17, 18]." Cameron (1938) also notes that this disorganization is not irreversible. He presented one patient's answers to questions about causes, both during a severe phase of schizophrenia and after the patient had partially recovered, which showed a marked change in ability to select the appropriate from competing associations. For example, during the more disturbed phase, the patient responded to the statement, "My hair is fair because . . ." with "Because of something else; it's on my head; it comes from my mother." After partial recovery, the response was, "Because I inherited it from my parents" (both quotations, p. 19).

Metonymic distortion is the substitution of a related but deviant term for a more precise term. "It is related to asyndesis in that it is also in part the outcome of an incapacity for selecting, restricting, and eliminating. The consequence is that here also the schizophrenic attributes a false equivalence to several terms or phrases which in the normal person might belong to the fringe of his conceptual structures [1938, p. 20]." An example given by Cameron that has been quoted previously was a schizophrenic's substitution of "have menu" for "eat."

Interpenetration of themes is the same alternation among conflicting thoughts, but here the disorganization is even greater. In addition to inability to subordinate inappropriate elements that are associated to a single theme, as in asyndetic thinking and metonymic distortion, here there is inability to even subordinate one theme to another.

In that the basic implication of the theory is that schizophrenics tend toward disorganized intrusion of concurrent response tendencies, Cameron's theory is the same as the theory used in Chapter 1, and it is compatible with much of the evidence presented in that chapter. The similarity of the thinking and the relevance of the evidence in Chapter 1 to Cameron's theory is not surprising in that Cameron's ideas stimulated a fair amount of the thinking and research discussed in that chapter, especially the research on conceptual overinclusion. The major elaboration in Cameron's theory that goes beyond the thinking discussed in Chapter 1 is Cameron's emphasis on loss of social motivation and loss of the ability to put oneself in the place of another as the major factors leading to disorganized thinking.

Cameron's emphasis on deficiency in social motivation and skills has stimulated research on the differential ability of schizophrenics on tasks using social versus non-social material. Although one possible interpretation of Cameron's theory is that social deficiencies lead to a general deficiency in organized thinking, his theory has been interpreted as implying that in schizophrenia there is a selective impairment in conceptual ability, with ability to form social concepts being more disturbed than other conceptual abilities (Moriarty & Kates, 1962; Whiteman, 1954).

Whiteman (1954) compared schizophrenics and normals, matched on the basis of age, education, and Wechsler-Bellevue intelligence, on ability to select from a set of cards those cards that portrayed a social concept. For example, on one item three cards depicted various kinds of "rescue" scenes, one person rescuing another, and one other card showed two children on sleds sliding toward a busy intersection. The correct response was to select the three "rescue" cards but not the other card. Scores on the social-concept test were corrected for differences in scores on verbal analogies and a non-social-concept test. Even with this adjustment to match the groups' performance on non-social performance, the schizophrenics did significantly poorer than the normals on the social-concepts test. This difference could still be due to a lower general conceptual ability in schizophrenics if the social test is considerably more difficult than the other tasks, however subsequent analysis showed that the social-concept task was not more difficult.

Davis and Harrington (1957) and Moriarty and Kates (1962) also found that schizophrenics showed greatest deficit, relative to normals, on problems requiring the use of information from pictures depicting persons. Although Nelson and Caldwell (1962) found no difference between normals and schizophrenics in a depth-perception study involving human and non-human content, the trend of evidence does seem to support the hypothesis of special schizophrenic deficit in selecting and using information from a social context.

Cameron's theory clearly states that schizophrenics are deficient in social motivation and that lack of social concern is basic. If the lack of social motivation is meant to apply only to having little concern about intelligibility, there is little relevant research evidence. However, there is considerable evidence about the power of social motivators, both positive and negative, in influencing schizophrenics' behavior. In Chapter 1 we discussed the consistent evidence concerning the effectiveness of social censure in changing schizophrenics' behavior. Regarding the influence of positive social motivation, Shakow (1963) reported a study by Radlo and Shakow which indicated that schizophrenics perform better under both competitive and cooperative motivation than without such motivation. In this study, sixty cards, each with five digits on it, were to be sorted according to whether one of the digits was a 1, 2, or 3. The score was sorting time. Control schizophrenics, who sorted with no special social motivation, improved on the first two repetitions of the task, but then their performance leveled off on succeeding repetitions. A second group of schizophrenics worked in interindividual competition on some of the trials. These schizophrenics worked individually in separate rooms on the first four trials and then for trials 5 and 6 were brought together in groups of three, and competition between the members of the group was emphasized. Performance improved significantly on these competition trials. These schizophrenics then returned to their original rooms where they worked individually for four more trials. Without competition, their performance worsened significantly from trials 6 to 7 and then leveled off. A third group of schizophrenics worked in individual rooms for eight trials, and were then brought together in teams of three to work together against another team for four trials. The performance of these schizophrenics improved from trials 8 to 9 and from 9 to 10 and then leveled off at a level that was better than the plateaus for the later individual trials for the other two groups.

It then seems that individual competition, and teamwork against another team are able to influence schizophrenics positively, and, referring back to the censure studies, schizophrenics can be considerably influenced by evaluative feedback from other persons. So there must be some doubt about loss of social motivation being the basic cause of schizophrenic behavior.

A distinction may be needed here, however. Cameron (1938) emphasized that schizophrenics simply are not concerned about other persons' reactions to them. The censure and competition research suggests that schizophrenics do care about their impact on others and care about their performance as compared to others, so stating the basic problem as "the schizophrenic doesn't care" may be inaccurate. However, in other places, Cameron (1938, 1939) emphasized schizophrenics' lack of ability in social situations, saying that schizophrenics are unable to take the role of another person—to understand their own impact and so to modify their behavior as needed. This inability is different from lack of desire. The view that schizophrenics are not able to respond adequately to the complex cues of interpersonal relationships is in accord with the evidence we have discussed. Schizophrenics may withdraw socially simply because they realize their inability, do care about it, but do not wish to continue with their social failures. Their inability probably would be exacerbated by this withdrawal. This is in accord with Cameron's emphasis on the cumulative effect of social inability on the use of language (1944). Thus, lack of ability to respond adequately to the complex situations that social situations are may lead to withdrawal from these situations. This is a form of loss of social motivation and it is likely to lead to further deficit, such as loss of information about social interactions. However, this is not a lack of social concern, and when social interactions are forced on schizophrenics, the social incentives and punishments may still have a very significant influence on their behavior.

Although there is a question about the causation being in lack of social concern, it must be emphasized that Cameron's description of schizophrenic behavior is a very important contribution. The emphasis on fragmented interpenetrations of concurrent associations—the inability to disregard associations that are peripheral—has stimulated considerable research and is in accord with considerable evidence.

We cannot leave this theory without noting that, with its emphasis on schizophrenics being overinfluenced by competing associates, this theory seems, at first, to be in conflict with Chapman's theory which emphasizes reduced influence of non-dominant meanings. We will attempt to put these two kinds of theories together later. For now, we only note that the associated-but-deviant responses which seem to characterize much schizophrenic behavior may come either from the loss of associative threads that guide the specific correct response, or from relatively great strength in non-dominant associates that then disrupt a more specific and correct focus. Before attempting some integration of different ways of accounting for schizophrenic behavior, we first must be clear about the different types of accounts, their implications, and the research supporting each type. Thus, we continue by discussing other theories that are near to the Cameron type of theory.

INABILITY TO EXCLUDE THE IRRELEVANT. FOCUS ON THE IRRELEVANT MOTIVATED BY INFANTILE NEEDS—SHAKOW

Shakow's (1950, 1962, 1963) description of schizophrenics' behavior is very similar to Cameron's, although Shakow arrived at his through study of quite different types of behavior: motor and physiological responses, instead of language. Both Cameron's and Shakow's descriptions emphasize the numerous response tendencies evoked in many situations, and schizophrenics' inability to exclude those responses that are not appropriate. One difference is that Cameron emphasized disorganization among concurrent associations or ideas, while Shakow, although mentioning interference from ideas, emphasizes competing attention tendencies. "It is as if, in the scanning process which takes place before the response to a stimulus is made, the schizophrenic is unable to select out the material relevant for optimal response. He apparently cannot free himself from the irrelevant among the numerous possibilities available for choice. In other words, that function which is of equal importance as the response *to* stimuli, namely, the protection *against* the response to the stimuli, is abeyant [Shakow, 1962, p. 9]." The similarity to Cameron and to the response-interference theory presented in the previous chapter can be seen in Shakow's description of why schizophrenics have difficulty in responding quickly to a demand from the environment. In context, the following quotation is intended to speak broadly of this difficulty, although it is put in the terms of reaction-time studies. "If the stimulus follows too quickly upon the warning, the schizophrenic subject finds difficulty in choosing among the numerous (in the context of the task, irrelevant) associations which the stimulus arouses. If the stimulus does not come quickly enough after the warning, then there is the opportunity for irrelevant stimuli to obtrude and delay the reaction [Shakow, 1963, p. 297]."

The major difference in the Cameron and Shakow theories is in statements about causation, although even here there is overlap. Like Cameron, who views the learning of normal language as in great part learning to exclude associated terms that are imprecise, Shakow also emphasized the need to learn to exclude that which is irrelevant, saying that internal mechanisms, which may be mostly inhibitory (Shakow, 1963), enable normals to organize experience appropriately, to learn to disregard irrelevant stimuli, and so to maintain a readiness to respond efficiently to relevant stimuli. Shakow calls this ability to attend appropriately an ability to hold a "major set." For Shakow, "The main point I wish to make is that in schizophrenia one sees a distinct weakening of the control center that serves the integrating and organizing function and provides for what I have called 'generalized' or 'major sets' [Shakow, 1963, p. 303]." This inability to maintain a major set is thus very similar to Cameron's statement that ". . . selection and elimination is just what the schizophrenic is often unable to do [Cameron, 1938, p. 29]."

The greatest difference between Shakow's and Cameron's views on schizophrenia lies in Shakow's view that the intrusion of material that is task irrelevant is motivated. "Actually, this inability to keep a major set is, I believe, a secondary result of a positive characteristic, a primary *need to establish* minor sets, to segmentalize both the external and internal environments [Shakow, 1950, p. 387]." Shakow speculates that schizophrenics are so motivated by needs that have been fulfilled for normals but not for them, that they are ready to respond in ways that will meet these immature needs, and so are not guided by the set that would be optimal for meeting external requirements. So schizophrenic behavior may be organized, but the organization is inappropriate. Of course when motivation to select appropriately from experience is lacking, this must affect the development of the response systems by which normals learn to organize the way they meet the world. Thus, normal ability to organize (select appropriately from) experience may be underdeveloped because of cravings that are not in line with task requirements, or may break down because of these conflicting needs. Variations in these needs mean that "In the defensive goal-seeking of the schizophrenic one may have a range of integration from almost total disintegration to highly organized, integrated, though *localized* patterns of behavior, but rarely total integration. . . . [Shakow, 1962, p. 14]."

Thus, Shakow sees schizophrenia as characterized by intrusion of inappropriate responses, but these intrusions are motivated; motivated by the schizophrenics searching among stimuli and among alternate responses to stimuli for those experiences and meanings which will meet unfulfilled needs. "Perhaps I can best sum up what I have been trying to say in this way: As grown-up human beings we have a job to do and get on with it more or less directly and effectively. The schizophrenic does not. In fact, sometimes we get impatient with him for the devious manner in which he goes about doing his *schizophrenic* job. We see so many ways in which he could accomplish this so much more quickly and efficiently! Can it be that this he really knows better and that our attitude merely reveals how little we know about schizophrenia? [Shakow, 1950, p. 389]"

PARTIAL COLLAPSE OF RESPONSE HIERARCHIES—BROEN AND STORMS

Like the Cameron and Shakow theories, a theory suggested by the present writer and his colleague, L. H. Storms (Broen & Storms, 1961, 1966, 1967), views schizophrenic behavior as due to greater equivalence of appropriate and competing responses resulting in disorganized response patterns. Equivalence is, of course, an ambiguous term. In our theory, equivalence of alternate responses means that response tendencies have equal strength, and when this occurs, the probability of the alternate responses are equal. For normals, when a stimulus evokes more than one response tendency, the appropriate response tendency is much stronger than competing response tendencies and therefore will usually occur. The competing, inappropriate responses will occur infrequently, if at all. The meaning of "normal behavior" is that response tendencies that are simultaneously evoked are hierarchically ordered in accordance with appropriateness, and with considerable increments between the strengths of appropriate and inappropriate response tendencies. Becoming schizophrenic is not seen as changing the content of response hierarchies in individuals, or the hierarchical order of the response tendencies, but in schizophrenics the hierarchies tend to be partially collapsed. The strengths of dominant and competing responses are more nearly equal. Near equivalence in strength leads to response occurence being more random. This also means equivalence in Cameron's sense—another member of a family of associates to a stimulus is likely to occur instead of the appropriate associate.

Like several other theories, this theory is basically the theory used in Chapter 1 except that we have attempted to go a little further in specifying the nature of "susceptibility to interfering response tendencies" and the conditions under which it will be observed.

When susceptibility to interfering response tendencies is seen as a partial collapse of response hierarchies, this change in formulation suggests that in order to aid understanding of response interference in schizophrenics it may be helpful to look at research on normals that has been concerned with the factors that are relevant to changes in the increments of strength between dominant and competing responses. One extensive area of research of this kind is the research on word-association hierarchies in normals that has been done within the framework of Hull-Spence theory.

In Hull-Spence theory, if two or more response tendencies (reaction potentials or Es) are present at the same time, the likelihood that the dominant response (R_D) will occur is a function of the difference in strength between dominant and competing response tendencies [$\%R_D=f(E_D-E_C)$]. Two of the variables that affect strength of response tendencies are (a) habit strength (H), which is a function of variables such as the number of trials where the stimulus has been followed by the response, and (b) drive (D), a general response-energizing factor which is increased by a number of conditions (e.g., stress conditions, emotional excitation). Specifically, the strength of a response tendency is a function of habit strength multiplied by drive [$E=f(D \times H)$]. Thus, when dominant and competing associations are evoked at the same time, the difference between their strengths, which is positively related to the probability of the dominant response, is given by the following formula: $E_D-E_C=f[D(H_D-H_C)]$. In sum, drive variables such as high anxiety multiply differences in habit strengths between alternate responses in response hierarchies, and are therefore predicted to increase the probability of dominate responses. There is considerable evidence supporting this prediction (e.g., Taylor, 1956).

Applied to word association studies, one prediction is that highly anxious subjects will give more normatively dominant responses than subjects with low anxiety. If two or more words are associated to the same stimulus word and an attempt is made to increase the probability of the dominant response through training, high anxious subjects should give more dominant (correct) responses than low anxious subjects. Of course, if training proceeds to the point where the dominant response is learned so well that there is not significant response competition, both high and low anxious groups should perform equally well at 100% correct responses. However, in paired-associate learning studies, the results have not been quite this straightforward.

A look at one study (Spence, Farber, & McFann, 1956) that was done to test the theory will point out the conditions under which the theory works and where it runs into some difficulty. In this study, an anxiety scale was used to select subjects (Ss) who were high and low on level of emotional response, which is a response-energizing (drive) variable in the theory. The prediction was that because drive multiplies habit strengths, thus energizing dominant responses more than competing responses, high anxiety Ss should be superior to low anxiety Ss in a paired-associates learning task where the associative connections between the paired words were strong at the beginning of learning and competing associations were weak. As predicted, high anxious Ss did better throughout the learning trials. It does seem that under these conditions anxiety does seem to strengthen dominant responses (the correct responses in this study) more than competing responses.

However, in a second experiment reported in the same article, anxiety did not seem to increase consistently the probability of dominant responses. In this second experiment, two different kinds of word-pairs were to be learned. In one, the correct response was relatively strong at the beginning of learning and in the other, the correct response was relatively weak at the start. Another difference from the first experiment was that for both kinds of word-pairs, incorrect associates were stronger.

If anxiety facilitates dominant responses more than other responses, then on the word-pairs where the correct response was relatively weak at the beginning of learning, high anxiety should increase the probability of the incorrect associates. As expected, high anxious subjects did worse at the beginning of learning. However, later in learning when correct responses become dominant, high anxiety should facilitate performance. Instead high anxious Ss did worse than the low anxious Ss throughout.

It seems that two conditions may define situations in which anxiety will not facilitate dominant responses: toward the end of training, and in an experiment where competing responses have been strengthened. That the lack of facilitation of dominant responses by anxiety under these conditions is not an isolated instance is shown by what happened on the other kind of word-pairs in this experiment. On these word-pairs, the correct associations were relatively stronger from the beginning of learning. As would be expected from the theory, high anxious Ss did do better than low anxious Ss at the beginning. However, in later trials, where correct associates were even stronger, a crossover took place, with high anxious Ss doing worse than low anxious Ss. This same crossover has been replicated in three other studies where competing associates had significant strength (Lovaas, 1960; Ramond, 1953; Spence, Taylor, & Ketchel, 1956). This repeated finding that, although high drive facilitates dominant responses at the beginning of learning, the facilitative action does not hold to the end, suggests that in terms of the basic formulation the facilitating effect does not hold when habit strength is high.

We (Broen & Storms, 1961) attempted to account for these results by postulating a response-strength ceiling lower than maximum drive times maximum habit strength. This means that when the habit strength of the dominant response (H_D) is low, the multiplicative influence of drive favors the dominant response, but when H_D is high, the response-strength ceiling may limit the multiplicative effect of drive on the dominant response. When the strength of the dominant response is at ceiling, the only effect of increased drive will be to increase the strength of responses lower in the response hierarchy, thus tending to collapse the response hierarchy and increase the probability of incorrect responses. Table 7 gives a theoretical illustration of the reversal in relative performance for high and low anxious groups as training progresses. In our theory, better performance is indicated by greater differences between the strengths of the dominant, correct responses and the strength of competing responses, $RS_D - RS_C$.)

Parenthetically, it should be noted that these considerations regarding the different effects of drive variables at different stages of learning overlap Meyer's (1953) incisive discussion of the effects of muscular tension at different stages in learning. Meyer noted first that muscular tension can increase the magnitude of other responses through ". . . the convergence of simultaneous patterns of neural impulses [p. 205]." Considering only the effect of the stimulus in a learning situation, it is noted that early in learning a specific response may be dominant; not always occurring following a stimulus, but with more neurons that contribute to that response being at or near firing threshold than is the case for other responses. Because the largest subgroups of those neurons that are slightly below firing threshold are those that contribute to the dominant response, a moderate level of excitation added by muscular tension may facilitate the dominant response more than other responses. However, once learning has progressed to the point that a stimulus is itself quite efficient in its effects, the

TABLE 7[a]

THEORETICAL ILLUSTRATION OF THE DIFFERENT EFFECTS
OF DRIVE AT THE BEGINNING AND LATER STAGES OF LEARNING

| | | Response strength (RS Ceiling = 6) | |
| | | Low D Ss ($D = 5$) | High D Ss ($D = 10$) |
Stage	H		
Beginning			
Correct R	.5	2.5	5.0
Incorrect R	.4	2.0	4.0
$RS_D - RS_C$		.5	1.0
Later			
Correct R	1.0	5.0	6.0
Incorrect R	.4	2.0	4.0
$RS_D - RS_C$		3.0	2.0

[a] Adapted from Broen & Storms (1961). Inhibition of competing responses was not taken into account in these calculations but would only increase the cross-over effect since competing responses would be inhibited more rapidly in the low-drive group because of greater frequency in this group early in learning.

results of added tension become different. "Obviously, the effects of induced tension cannot be the same throughout practice. If an input cap-
tures an optimal population, added excitation triggers only neurons which
contribute to the production of errors [*ibid.*, p. 210]."

In the paired-associates studies we have been discussing, it appeared
that a limit on the facilitative effect of high drive would be noticed as habit
strength was increased. Response-strength ceiling effects should also
occur if habit strengths of dominant and competing responses are consistent but drive varies. The theoretical effect of drive in such a situation is
illustrated in Figure 9.

At low drive levels, the multiplicative effect of increased drive is not
restricted by the ceiling and the dominant response is facilitated by increased drive. Distance B, the difference between strengths of dominant
and competing responses, increases. When the strength of the dominant
response reaches ceiling, further increases in drive can only facilitate the
competing response. The probability of the dominant response is a function of distance B. Thus, dominant response probability is expected to
increase through moderate drive levels, and then decrease. The competing response never becomes dominant, but at extreme drive its probability
may approximate that of the dominant response. Note also that there will
be no decrement in the probability of the dominant response if there is no

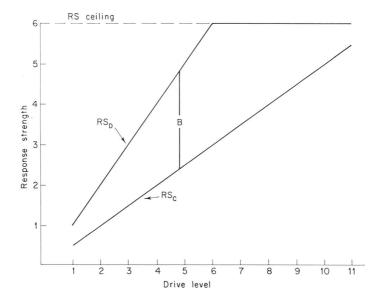

Fig. 9. How RS ceiling and the multiplicative effect of drive combine to make $RS_D -$
RS_C an inverted U-shaped function of drive. (From Broen & Storms, 1967.)

competing response. The strength of the dominant response is not assumed to decrease as a function of drive. Its probability may decrease, but only because drive favors competing responses when dominant response strength is restricted at ceiling level.

In sum, this theory suggests three conditions that should aid in defining situations in which response hierarchies are likely to be partially collapsed: high drive; the presence of competing responses that have high habit strength; and when dominant responses also have high habit strength.

This theory was intended to organize available data and generate predictions about a behavioral process — partial collapse of response hierarchies — which seemed to occur in both normals and schizophrenics, although in more extreme form in schizophrenics. Thus, it followed one line of thinking that will reoccur in this book: that the factors that affect behavioral processes in schizophrenics are likely to be the same factors as are important in normals' behavior; and that instead of the basic processes being quite different, the differences in behavior are more likely to be only because the relevant conditions are more extreme in schizophrenia. It then seemed quite relevant to test the theory with normal subjects as well as with schizophrenics in order to see if the theory's predictions about the conditions favoring partial collapse of response hierarchies had merit. We will first review some of the experiments done with normal subjects before turning to experiments with schizophrenics.

Research with normal subjects

To us it seemed that one of the more unlikely implications of the theory was that increased stress (drive) is more likely to cause response hierarchies to begin to collapse (reduce the frequency of the dominant response) when the dominant response has high habit strength than when H_D is low. At least common sense views of stress as a condition that leads to response interference because it brings new interfering response tendencies into the situation suggest the opposite — that these new responses could not compete as effectively with well-learned responses.

In a pilot study done in collaboration with H. U. Schenck [described in detail in Broen & Storms, (1967)], we tested the prediction that a drive condition would lead to a greater collapse in a response hierarchy where the dominant response had been most practiced. Of course, for this prediction to hold, other conditions, such as the degree of response competition in different response hierarchies, should be controlled.

Therefore, different groups of female college students were trained to press two buttons, with different numbers of training trials used so that the habit strength of the dominant and competing responses varied from low to high, while the level of response competition in the different hierarchies remained equivalent. After training, each of three response hierarchies was tested under 30 low-drive (no shock) trials, or under 30 high-drive (shock) trials, with reinforcement continued as during training.

The attempt to keep the level of response competition equivalent across hierarchies seemed successful in that under low drive, the groups trained in the different hierarchies did not differ in the frequency of their presses of the dominant buttons. However, as predicted from considering where ceiling effects should most restrict the energizing of dominant responses, there was a significant tendency for high drive to cause the most decrement in the response hierarchy where the habit strength of the dominant response was greatest. The effects of drive tended to be in opposite directions for hierarchies with low versus high habit strengths, with drive tending to facilitate the frequency of dominant responses when H_D was low and reducing $\% R_D$ when H_D was high. The average R_D changes from low to high drive were: 2.3 for the low H_D hierarchy, -0.7 for the middle H_D hierarchy, and -3.6 for the hierarchy with highest H_D.

Note that the R_D decrement would not seem to be accounted for by postulating that stress brought new distracting tendencies into the situation. Any new distractors that shock brings into the situation should act the same way on each of the dominant responses. The dominant responses were the same response in each hierarchy, the only difference being the number of training trials. Yet here the effects of stress tended to be differential, with the tendency for shock to reduce the probability of dominant responses being greatest where habit strength was highest, as was predicted from consideration of the effect of a response-strength ceiling.

This theory also predicts that even response hierarchies where the dominant response has high habit strength will not show major collapse under increased drive when competing responses are weak. If competing responses are weak, the multiplicative effect of increased drive will not increase their strength very much, and even if dominant responses are restricted at ceiling strength, increased drive will do little to narrow the difference between dominant and competing responses.

To test the prediction that R_D decrement under increased stress will be greatest when both H_D and H_C are high, in a second experiment (Broen, Storms, & Schenck, 1961), response hierarchies were trained where, unlike in the last experiment, the strength of the dominant response was not correlated with the strength of the competing response. Using a lever-pressing task, three two-response hierarchies were trained, each in a different group of male college students. By varying reinforcement probabilities, one hierarchy was trained to have dominant and competing responses at high strength (*HH* hierarchy); another, a high-strength dominant response, but a competing response of low strength (HL hierarchy); and the third hierarchy with both responses at low strength (LL hierarchy).

The hierarchies were then tested under high stress, induced by 121 db white noise. In accordance with the theory, the HH hierarchy collapsed the most under increased drive.

It should specifically be said that in the last two studies we have discussed, the results were not due to response omissions, which were rare. Rather, a decrement in a dominant response was accompanied by an increase in the frequency of a competing response as "collapsed response hierarchy" means. Thus, it does seem that research on normal subjects suggests that the greater equivalence of alternate response tendencies, which has seemed important in schizophrenia, is exacerbated by the conditions suggested by this theory: increased drive, and dominant and competing responses at high strength. It should also be noted that these studies did deal with decrements in appropriate responses. In both of these studies, the dominant responses were appropriate in that they had the highest probability of reinforcement. We have then been talking about increased interference from competing, less-appropriate responses, which is the focus of this chapter.

One final study using normal subjects will be cited because it deals with regression to responses that had been learned earlier, and regression to earlier response patterns is sometimes considered to be one aspect of schizophrenia. Competing responses may, of course, be responses that had previously been appropriate and dominant, but have been replaced as dominant responses by new responses learned more recently. When this is the case, partial collapse of response hierarchies will imply an increase in regressive responses. A study by Levin (1965) shows a specific kind of relationship between drive and frequency of a regressive response that is expected from the account. In the first part of the experiment, subjects learned to associate numbers to colors. Then the correct associations were changed and the associations were tested under different amounts of drive (induced muscular tension). At the time of testing, the regressive responses (the previously correct responses) were the strongest of several incorrect responses. If you consider the theory carefully, you will realize that when only incorrect responses are considered, the multiplicative effect of the increased drive will favor the dominant error until it is at ceiling strength, but beyond this point additional drive can only increase the proportion of other competing responses. The data were in accord with the curvilinear expectation. The proportion of errors that were regression errors (the dominant error tendency) increased from zero to low to medium tension, and then decreased under high tension. It seems that the theory has utility for accounting for intrusions of competing responses whether the responses are learned concurrently or consecutively.

Broen-Storms theory as applied to schizophrenia

In our later theoretical articles, which emphasize response interference in schizophrenia rather than in normals (Broen & Storms, 1966, 1967), we made two changes in the theory. The first is a change in terminology, a change from using the term "drive" to using the term "arousal" to indicate a state that is thought to produce fairly general response-activation, and which is assumed to be higher in schizophrenics than in normals, on the average. This change was made because the term "arousal" has physiological implications that should aid in defining conditions that the theory would expect to increase response strength. In theoretical formulas, "arousal" (A) is substituted for "drive" (D) without other change. The only difference is that from the time of this substitution, only those experimental conditions that had been shown to lead to relatively general arousal of physiological systems were used as conditions that would be expected to increase response strengths in experiments. As will be detailed later, we have used induced muscular tension repeatedly in our later experiments because this is a controllable variable for which there is good evidence that it does tend to lead to fairly general bodily activation (Pinneo, 1961). In addition to the physiological activation, it has been found that induced muscular tensions acts like a classic drive variable in its effects on association hierarchies (Lovaas, 1960). [See also Meyer's (1953) brilliant analysis of the interaction of muscular tension and other responses.] Experiments with "white noise" would also be considered as relevant to the theory because of their demonstrated qualities of physiological activation. [See evidence cited in Berlyne, Borsa, Hamacher, & Koenig (1966).] In the theory, the term arousal, and the defining of arousing conditions by their physiological effects, was not at all intended to suggest that whenever an increase in activation of any physiological system is noted this means that general energizing of response tendencies is expected. It is clear that physiological systems are activated by many conditions, only some of which have the relatively general effects that are implied by our use of the term arousal. The term arousal is only used to help define those conditions that are relevant to the theory in that they do tend to have fairly diffuse energizing effects. This use is distinct from the argument as to whether or not stimuli usually cause the same kinds of changes in different physiological variables, and whether or not one physiological variable is in general a good predictor of another. These questions will be discussed in a later chapter. The point is that although changes in physiological systems have multiple causes, many of which cause different changes in different systems, there do seem to be some conditions that have fairly general energizing effects. These particular conditions are seen as relevant to the theory, taking the place of the "drive" variables.

The second change is that the level of response-strength ceiling is considered to be a variable on which individuals differ, and schizophrenics as a group are considered to have a lower average response-strength ceiling than non-schizophrenics, although considerable within-group variation and between-group overlap is expected. The effects of two levels of ceiling are illustrated in Figure 10.

We (Broen & Storms, 1967) used this figure to illustrate differences in the effects of arousal on average schizophrenics and normals in the theory, with the left and right halves of the figure intended to apply to the response-interference process we have been discussing in normals and schizophrenics, respectively. In the situation depicted, dominant responses are assumed to be well-practiced responses.

Note several things. First, at all levels of arousal above fairly low levels, if dominant responses are well practiced, schizophrenics' response hierarchies are predicted to be more collapsed than normals'. The collapse is illustrated by less difference between dominant and competing responses (distance B). The theory states explicitly (*ibid.*) that this partial collapse is the basic difference between normals and schizophrenics. From Figure 10 it can be seen that the content of the hierarchies, including which specific response is in which position in the hierarchy, is not thought to be changed by the variables that are involved in the collapse.

For us, the use of response-strength ceiling as an individual difference variable is in part meant to underline the likelihood that abnormal arousal is only one of the factors that causes response hierarchies to collapse in schizophrenia and these other factors interact with arousal to exacerbate the collapse of response hierarchies. It is predicted (*ibid.*) that, because the stress in standard experiments is at least as high as in ward environ-

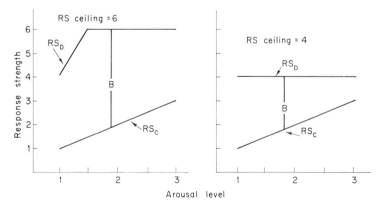

Fig. 10.   Arousal has different relationships to $RS_D - RS_C$ in normals (left) and schizophrenics (right). (From Broen & Storms, 1967.)

ments where schizophrenics show schizophrenic behavior, this schizophrenic behavior — this abnormal collapse of response hierarchies — will
be found in all experimental situations that test on familiar or well-
practiced material, except where special attempts are made to lower the
stress level, thus reducing the adverse effects of low response-strength
ceilings, or where competing responses are not evoked in any significant
strength. This last consideration is not based on circular reasoning in
that the presence of competing response tendencies can be observed in
normals' response frequencies.

Like other theories in this chapter, the most basic statement from the
theory — the statement that schizophrenics have partially collapsed response hierarchies — is, in many respects, only a restatement of the guiding principle in Chapter 1: schizophrenics are abnormally susceptible to
interference from competing response tendencies. Therefore, it is not
surprising that this theory is also consistent with the research that was
reviewed in Chapter 1. What is different in this theory is its degree of
specification about the nature of response interference in schizophrenia
and the conditions under which it will be noted.

Research with schizophrenic subjects

As for the nature of response interference in schizophrenia, the emphasis in the theory is that there should be a surprising similarity in the behavior of schizophrenics and normals. Groups of schizophrenics and normals
should exhibit the same responses and the rank order of the frequencies of
alternate responses should be the same. Only the increments between
the frequencies should be different. Of course, as we have emphasized,
". . . in speaking of similarities we are speaking of average data. Among
individuals, normals as well as schizophrenics, there is considerable variation in the content of response hierarchies, especially in the non-dominant associates which reflect more unique, infrequent experiences.
Hence, if response hierarchies are partially collapsed in schizophrenia,
the competing responses that intrude more often will, at times, reflect
idiosyncratic experience. However, this does not change the predictions
regarding average data [Broen & Storms, 1967, p. 283]."

The similarities and differences in hierarchies of response frequencies
between normals and schizophrenics that this theory predicts should be
most easily observable in tasks where the material that is focused on
evokes a number of fairly strong competing response tendencies. A syllogistic reasoning test used by Gottesman and Chapman (1960) provided a
situation of this type. Normal subjects made a great many errors of different kinds. The test was presented in a multiple-choice format with five

possible responses to each syllogism: the four possible forms of conclusions to syllogisms (e.g., Form A, "All pots are black"; Form E, "None are"; Form I, "Some are"; Form D, "Some aren't"); and the fifth type of alternate, "None of these conclusions is proved."

One reason why this study is described here is that although the valid conclusion for each experimental syllogism was the conclusion that "None is proved," normals showed quite a bit of variation in the hierarchical order of their responses to different syllogisms. This allows us to see if, across different tasks, schizophrenics' hierarchies change in the same ways as normals' hierarchies.

The results for normals and schizophrenics, who were matched with the normals on estimates of premorbid intelligence, are given in Figure 11. The data from different items are grouped according to the type of reasoning error that was strongest for normals.

Though there are some differences in the rank order of the responses between schizophrenics and normals, as might be expected to some extent even in different samples of normals, Figure 11 shows fair similarity between the order of the alternate responses. The major difference seems to be only that the frequencies of the alternate responses are closer together for schizophrenics — their response hierarchies are more collapsed.

Results of this kind could be explained as due to many schizophrenics responding exactly like normals, with the partially flattened average hierarchies occurring because some schizophrenics were unmotivated and simply chose responses at random. However, as was emphasized in Chapter 1, it seems fairly clear from a large number of studies that the major differences between schizophrenics and normals are not due to randomization among all the possible responses available in a task; rather, there is a tendency toward "randomization" only within those response tendencies that are also evoked in some strength in normals. This is, of course, what is meant by "partial collapse of response hierarchies."

That schizophrenics are not especially disturbed by intrusions of those response tendencies that are not in normals' response hierarchies could not be demonstrated in the Gottesman and Chapman study in that each alternate seemed to be a significant competing response for normals. However, research described previously indicates that when a task includes response possibilities having negligible strength for normals, these responses are not the errors that most differentiate schizophrenics and normals. That schizophrenics do not simply tend toward randomization among all response possibilities available in a task was emphasized by Chapman in discussing the results he found in his study of word classification errors in schizophrenia. In his discussion, he noted that, "Similarly, in each of three previous studies [Chapman, 1956a, 1956b;

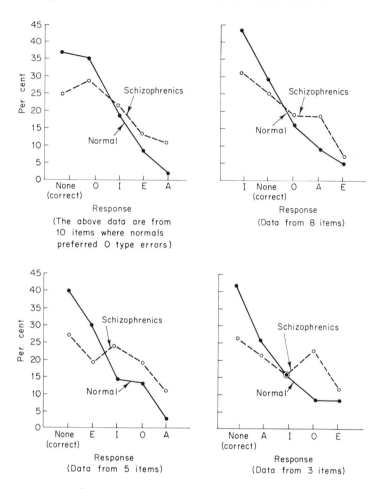

Fig. 11. Normal and schizophrenic response hierarchies by type of error preferred by normals. (From Broen & Storms, 1967, based on data from Gottesman & Chapman, 1960.)

Chapman & Taylor, 1957] the specific kind of error which accounted primarily for the difference between schizophrenics and normals tended consistently to be committed more often by normals than other types of errors which had an equal opportunity to occur by chance [Chapman, 1958, p. 278]." Also, remember that this pattern of results was again confirmed in Chapman's (1961) study of conceptual errors in schizophrenia, and in Gottesman's (1964) word-association study. The errors that most differentiate schizophrenics and normals seem specifically to be those that would be expected from describing schizophrenics' response hierarchies as normal response hierarchies that are partially collapsed.

Another area of added specificity in this theory lies in the conditions under which collapsed response hierarchies are expected. Most specifically, as in normals, increased response interference in schizophrenics should be a joint function of the presence of competing response tendencies, levels of arousal, and the habit strength of the dominant response.

We (Broen, Storms, & Goldberg, 1963) tested these predictions in an experiment where stimulus generalization was used to vary the strength of dominant responses. The specific predictions in the experiment can best be understood by referring to Figure 12 to illustrate the theoretical considerations.

The stimuli at the ends of the stimulus continuum—S_{TL} and S_{TR}—refer to stimuli to which different and conflicting responses have been trained. In the experiment, Ss were trained to press a lever to the left in response to a small gray square (S_{TL}), and to the right in response to a large gray square (S_{TR}). After training, response choices to the two training stimuli and to six intermediate stimuli were tested. Figure 12 illustrates the generalized response strengths expected for the two opposing responses during testing.

Consider only responses to one-half of this symmetrical situation—the left half. (In the results to be discussed later the data concerning responses to experimentally analogous stimuli were combined. Thus, all

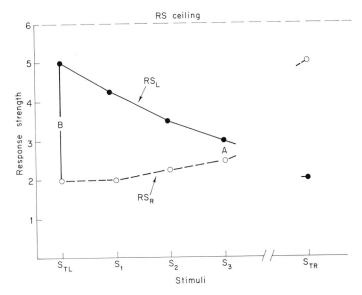

Fig. 12. Hypothetical generalization of response strength for left and right lever presses that have been trained to stimuli at opposite ends of a continuum. (From Broen & Storms, 1967.)

discussion can be in terms of one-half of the theoretical situation.) The response that is dominant at the training stimulus should be dominant through the three of the six generalization stimuli that are most similar to the training stimulus, with the probability of this response highest at S_{TL} where the difference between the strengths of the competing responses is greatest, and decreasing to some value that is still over 50% at S_3.

The basic theoretical question is what will happen if arousal is increased—say doubled. Assume a response-strength ceiling arbitrarily chosen to be 6 in this example, and double all response strengths as doubled arousal would do in the theory. At S_3, the dominant response strength can be doubled and doubling both RS_L and RS_R increases distance A. Thus, because the difference in strength between competing responses is increased, the probability of the dominant response should increase. However, at the training stimulus, where the dominant response is stronger, its strength cannot be doubled. Under doubled arousal, its strength can only increase to the ceiling—6—while the strength of the competing response is doubled from 2 to 4. The net result is that distance B is decreased from 3 to 2; the response hierarchy is partially collapsed; and the probability of the dominant response is decreased.

In the first experiment reported in Broen *et al.* (1963), the subjects were a group of young psychiatric outpatients. No formal diagnosis had been made, but from tentative diagnoses and psychological test results, in most cases a schizophrenic reaction seemed fairly clear.

The condition used to increase arousal was increased muscular tension induced by squeezing a hand dynamometer. When response preference was tested under low arousal (no squeeze), the main theoretical conditions required for the prediction seem to hold in that dominant response probability (% R_D) was maximum at the training stimuli and decreased to S_3, although remaining over 50% at S_3. When the required grip on the dynamometer was increased to $\frac{1}{4}$ maximum grip, and to $\frac{1}{2}$ maximum, there was consistent facilitation of the dominant response at S_3, where the response strength of the dominant response was least and ceiling effects were not expected. At S_T, the intermediate increase in arousal did not cause any significant change, and the $\frac{1}{2}$ maximum grip led to a significant decrement in the frequency of the dominant response.

In a second experiment (Broen *et al.*, 1963), which was designed only to test the consistency of the % R_D decrement at S_T, with hospitalized schizophrenics as subjects, $\frac{1}{2}$ maximum grip again led to a significant decrement in the probability of the dominant response at its training stimulus.

Thus, these two experiments provided replicated evidence that conditions that increase arousal do cause response hierarchies to begin to collapse, but, as predicted from the theory, this collapse occurs only where ceiling effects are expected — where dominant responses have fairly high strength. When the strength of dominant responses is less, and ceiling restrictions are therefore not expected, the full facilitative effect of arousal can take place, which favors dominant responses more than competing responses.

Note again that these results would not seem to be explainable in terms of new distractor responses brought into the situation by the arousal conditions. The same arousal conditions held when subjects were responding to S_T and S_3, and the same response was dominant at both stimuli. Yet the effect of arousal was opposite at the two stimuli, as predicted from ceiling effects, but not as would be expected from a distraction tendency, which should cause dominant responses to decrease in probability toward the 50% level at both stimuli.

Another specific prediction from this theory is that, although low-arousal conditions may be arranged in which schizophrenics' response hierarchies are not collapsed more than normals' hierarchies, an increase in arousal from this low point that is sufficient to lead to a significant collapse in schizophrenics' response hierarchies will, because of normals' higher ceilings, lead to less decrement in normals' responding. To test this, we (Broen & Storms, 1964) trained hospitalized schizophrenics and normals (hospitalized general medical and surgical patients) to move a lever to the left in response to one stimulus and to the right in response to a second, similar stimulus. Because of generalization, the training resulted in two two-response hierarchies, with each of the two responses dominant at its training stimulus. In order to be able to have large numbers of schizophrenics learn the task, special care was taken to keep stress in the basic situation low. Neutral stimuli were used (variants of a silhouette of a house and a tree); the responses were nonverbal; and reinforcement was impersonal (green light).

Under these conditions, approximately the same proportion of schizophrenics learned the task to a criterion as normals. This was not a major point in the study. The major point is that while the normals and schizophrenics who met the criterion did not differ significantly when performance was tested under low arousal, when arousal was increased by gripping a dynamometer at $\frac{1}{2}$ maximum grip the reaction was different for the two groups. From low to high arousal there was a significantly greater reduction in the frequency of dominant responses at both training stimuli in the schizophrenics than in the normals.

Two things that apply to all three experiments in this series of studies should be noted here. During testing, reinforcement continued as during training. Thus, in terms of likelihood of obtaining reinforcement, these decrements at training stimuli are decrements in appropriateness of responding, as well as decrements in the degree of dominance of dominant responses. Also, as in studies discussed early in this section, the decrement in dominant responses is due to intrusions of competing responses, not response ommissions. We are clearly talking about a greater equivalence of dominant and competing responses — a collapse of response hierarchies under increased arousal, with competing responses interfering more with dominant appropriate responses. Thus, the final study in this series indicated that, as predicted by the theory, in normals and schizophrenics who are performing equivalently in a well-learned task under low arousal, the introduction of a condition that increases arousal causes a greater collapse in response hierarchies in schizophrenics than in normals.

Another area of research in which the implications of this theory go somewhat beyond that of the general theory used in Chapter 1 is in the influence of the level of strength of competing responses on the behavior of schizophrenics and normals. In Chapter 1 there was a fair amount of discussion of research that supported the point that, because schizophrenics were more susceptible to interfering response tendencies than normals, the introduction of competing response tendencies would have a more harmful effect on schizophrenics, and the inhibition of competing tendencies would be more beneficial to them. This reasoning is easy to understand when it is put in absolute terms, but of course, realistically, the strength of competing responses is usually changed only in degree, and what a certain level of decrease in strength of competing responses should mean, if no competing tendency is completely eliminated, has not been clear.

In our theory, under the limiting condition that dominant and competing responses are not so disparate in strength that $\% R_D$ reaches 100, then a change in the strength of competing responses, positive or negative, will have a greater effect on schizophrenics' performance than on normals. This is easiest to understand from the statement in the theory that schizophrenics' average arousal is abnormally high. The multiplicative effect of higher arousal should exaggerate changes in the habit strength of competing responses. However, all changes in strength of competing responses in the relevant literature are not necessarily in factors such as habit strength, which should be multiplied by arousal. For example, we (Broen & Storms, 1967) stated that "response strength is assumed to be increasingly inhibited over trials with response-contingent punishment ... [p. 282]." The implication in the use of the term "response strength" as being inhibited instead of habit strength is that inhibitory effects should be subtracted after the multiplicative effects of arousal have been allowed for in a manner similar to the way Spence (1958) handled the effects of inhibition. Thus, punishing competing responses to the same extent in schizophrenics and normals should cause the same increases in $RS_D - RS_C$ in both groups. This seems contrary to the research that has been reviewed that indicates that inhibiting competing responses benefits schizophrenics more than normals. However, it should be noted that such special schizophrenic improvement may be due, at least in part, to the more extensive punishment of errors that results from schizophrenics' initially poorer performance.

In addition, one aspect of our theory that has not been presented yet is that the specific relationship between $\% R_D$ and $RS_D - RS_C$, though monotonic, is not linear. In deriving predictions from our theory, we have used Hull's (1952) computing practices. Because of detailed assumptions, which need not be reviewed here, this means that when $RS_D - RS_C$ is small, increasing the difference by a specific amount will result in a greater increase in $\% R_D$ than if $RS_D - RS_C$ were initially larger. When, as is usual in well-practiced situations, schizophrenics' response hierarchies are more collapsed than normals', this means that $RS_D - RS_C$ is smaller for schizophrenics. Therefore, inhibiting a competing response by the same amount in schizophrenics and normals should be more beneficial to schizophrenics than to normals.

However, in view of the emphasis in the theory on the special debilitating effects of increased arousal for schizophrenics, it would seem that the arousal-inducing effects of punishment conditions would offset the beneficial effects of reduced response competition.

With offsetting effects, the result will depend on which effect is more powerful, and in tasks such as used in the Pascal and Swenson (1952) study, the relative power of the two effects should vary over trials. The negative arousal effects that tend to collapse response hierarchies more in schizophrenics than in normals should be immediate. The inhibition of competing responses through response-contingent punishment is incremental, the effects increasing over trials. Thus, our theory predicts that in studies of this type the effects should be sequential, with schizophrenic performance first worsening relative to normals' performance. Because the beneficial effects of inhibiting competing responses become stronger over trials, an improvement in schizophrenics relative to normals should only occur after a number of trials.

In the Pascal and Swenson study, schizophrenics and normals first were given a number of practice trials and schizophrenics performed worse than normals. Then the white noise was introduced, with the noise continued on each trial until correct responses were made. The initial effect was to make schizophrenic performance worse and to increase the difference between schizophrenics and normals. This is in accord with the theory's prediction that lower ceilings in schizophrenics make arousal more likely to collapse response hierarchies. However, as was mentioned in Chapter 1, as the punishment of incorrect responses continued, the schizophrenics improved to the point that their performance was not significantly different from that of normals. This is the sequence of results expected from the theory.

Another study, that by Karras (1962), is relevant here, although Karras did not include normal subjects. Remember that in the Karras study, an aversive level of white noise was used differently for different groups of schizophrenics. In one group, the aversive noise was left on throughout and so could act only to facilitate competing responses. It was not response contingent and so could not inhibit incorrect responses. This group performed worse than a control (no noise) group, with its performance being worse on the first block of trials and remaining worse on successive trial blocks. In another group of schizophrenics, the aversive level of noise was used as Pascal and Swenson used it, to punish incorrect responses. The data from the first block of trials (seven trials) showed this latter group to be similar to the control group, but then this group improved and performed better than the control group on further trials. Thus, again strong aversive stimulation that would seem to be sufficient to increase arousal worsens schizophrenic performance unless it is used to inhibit competing responses. If the aversive stimulation is used to inhibit competing responses, the weakening effects may come to outweigh the activation effects on competing responses, and the result is improved performance.

The final specific theoretical implication that we will discuss is that a major locus of large differences between the performance of schizophrenics and normals will be in situations where the strength of dominant responses is high and therefore more likely to be restricted by response-strength ceiling. An added qualification is that the strength of competing responses must also be high enough so that competing responses do intrude. If this situation holds, schizophrenics' lower average ceilings will cause $RS_D - RS_C$ to be smaller in schizophrenics, and competing responses will intrude more than in normals.

The theory does not say that ceiling effects are the only cause of schizophrenic deficit. For example, when incorrect responses are weak but still dominant, as may be the case sometimes in responding to generalization stimuli, or at the beginning of new learning, then schizophrenics' higher arousal may exacerbate the dominant incorrect responses that are not strong enough to be restricted by ceiling.

The point here is that when correct responses are dominant, a major locus of schizophrenic deficit should be in situations where these dominant responses are strongest.

The Lang and Luoto (1962) study of paired-associates learning which was described in detail in Chapter 1 provided some evidence that supports this implication from the theory. In this study, remember that Ss first learned to associate words to nonsense syllables. There should be little competition from competing responses to the nonsense syllables in this first task, and thus, in general, correct responses would not have to reach high strength to become dominant. Therefore, ceiling effects should not especially hinder schizophrenic performance. On this first task, the performance of schizophrenics and normals differed hardly at all.

In a second task, new responses were to be learned to the same nonsense syllables. The old, now incorrect, responses should provide significant competition, meaning that before a stimulus-response pair could be learned to criterion, the correct responses would have to reach fairly high strength. In the pairs that required most trials to learn, dominant responses would be most likely to be restricted by ceiling in schizophrenics. The pairs could still be learned to criterion through the action of non-reinforced trials in inhibiting competing responses, but the beneficial effects of reinforcement on strengthening correct responses should be decreased by ceiling effects late in learning, especially for schizophrenics. The specific prediction is then that schizophrenic deficit, in terms of number of trials needed to learn a pair to criterion, should be especially great for those pairs that required most learning trials. Figure 13 shows that this was the case.

There must be caution in interpreting the Lang and Luoto results as indicating especially low response-strength ceilings in schizophrenics in that there was a difference in the pairs that tended to be learned early and late. For one-half the pairs, the old response that was incorrect was, however, associated with the correct response. This mediating effect seemed to aid the learning of these pairs. However, it is difficult to see how a mediating-nonmediating dichotomy would produce this progressively increasing deficit. At least the conditions under which the greatest deficit occurred are compatible with the idea that, over trials, dominant responses become strong enough to be increasingly restricted by the lower ceilings in schizophrenics.

The occurrence of greater schizophrenic reduction in dominant responses in situations where the response strength of the dominant responses is greater has also been found in a number of stimulus generalization studies. As was noted in Chapter 1, these deficits do not always occur, and they would not be expected when competing responses have negligible strength. The deficits have also not been noted when special care has been taken to reduce the stress in the experimental situation (Rodnick & Garmezy, 1957). However, when a schizophrenic decrement in frequency of dominant responses does occur relative to normals in stimulus generaliza-

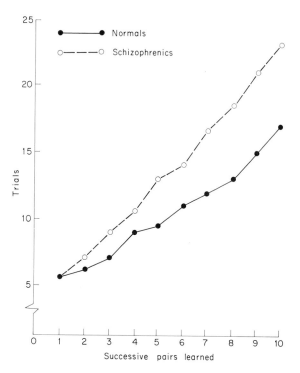

Fig. 13. Mean number of trials required to learn successive pairs from List II. (Adapted from Lang & Luoto, 1962.)

tion studies, it seems to be greatest at training stimuli, where the dominant response should have its highest strength (Dunn, 1954; Garmezy, 1952; Knopf & Fager, 1959). Again, the interpretation of this deficit as due to ceiling effects must be made with caution as alternate explanations are possible. In these particular stimulus generalization studies, lack of attention, tending to randomize the response possibilities, could have played a part in leading to special schizophrenic decrement where the frequency of a particular response was highest in normals.

The point is that greatest schizophrenic deficit relative to normals has often been found where ceiling effects are expected. While specific alternate explanations are possible in some of these studies, the results do seem to be in accord with implications from a theory that has a broader range of specific implications that have also seemed to fit other evidence.

Summary comments

In summary, it seems that the ways in which this theory goes beyond other more basic competing-response theories, such as Cameron's theory, are supported by relevant experiments. Specifically, the nature of response interference in schizophrenics seems to be in accord with the basic statement that schizophrenic deficit can be characterized as a partial collapse of normals' response hierarchies. The error tendencies that are most increased in schizophrenia are response tendencies that are also at significant strength in normals' response hierarchies. Also, the rank order of frequencies of alternate responses stays the same in schizophrenics and normals. In addition to the nature of response interference seeming to be in accord with the theory, the conditions under which the deficit will increase are as implied by the theory. As expected, increased arousal and high-strength dominant and competing responses each seem important in producing a greater equivalence of alternate response tendencies. Also the predictions from the theory that increasing arousal and increasing the strength of competing responses will not only worsen schizophrenics' performance, but will also increase the deficit relative to normals' performance, have received support as has the implication that, given significant competing tendencies, dominant responses will be reduced most in schizophrenics when their strength is highest.

That this theory can be more specific than Cameron's basic form of the same theory is not at all surprising in that it is a more recent modification that has the advantage of being formulated after more research data were available, much of which had been stimulated by Cameron's basic formulation. The same basic similarity with greater specificity regarding relevant variables in the more recent theory is also true of the Bleuler and Chapman-Chapman theories.

If future research continues to indicate that the directions of modification of the basic response-competition formulation that are in our theory are useful, then one area in which it might be helpful to increase specificity is in measurement of response-strength ceiling. The gross statement that schizophrenics' ceilings are, on the average, lower than normal has implications that have received experimental support. However, if level of ceiling is a useful individual-difference variable, then its measurement should be made more precise. Theoretically, this should be feasible; although practically, there is considerable difficulty.

If the habit strengths of dominant and competing responses are no more than moderate, and dominant response probability is tested over a range of arousal, there should be an inverted U-shaped relationship between the probability of the dominant response and arousal. If such relationships can be reliably determined for individuals, level of ceiling could be defined as that level of arousal at which the probability of the dominant response begins to decrease. The problems are in getting equivalent habit strengths in individual subjects, and in developing good inter-individual measures of arousal. However, it is only as theories become specific and such individual measures of relevant variables are developed that major advances can take place. Such measures will not only aid in making individual predictions that should have clinical benefit, e.g., predicting the situations in which a patient could function effectively, but also these measures should help future research. The theory says that schizophrenic behavior may be due to either high arousal or low response-strength ceilings. If these variables can be reliably measured, dividing schizophrenics on these variables in future studies should aid other research. For example, the differences that are here called differences in response-strength ceilings must have a less abstract basis. If this basis were biochemical, then investigations of biochemical differences between schizophrenics and normals might yield clearer results if causal heterogeneity within groups of research subjects were reduced by using measures of ceiling to group subjects.

Before leaving this theory, we should comment on its relationship to the Chapman-Chapman theory. Each of these theories has been fairly well supported by recent evidence, but at first they may appear to contradict each other. The Chapman theory says that schizophrenics overuse dominant meaning responses, and our theory says that dominant and competing responses are closer in strength in schizophrenics than in normals, and therefore competing responses intrude more in schizophrenic performance.

Although these theoretical statements seem to contradict each other, they are really referring to different aspects of performance and are not incompatible. The Chapman-Chapman theory is an account of a two-stage process. In response to a word, a person first generates a sequence of meanings, and the sequence provides information for later responding. Our theory says that the meaning that is most often generated first will be the same for groups of schizophrenics and normals, although its probability will often be less in schizophrenics. An extension of this theory to sequential operations, each response acting as a cue for the next, would imply that behavior sequences would be roughly comparable in schizophrenics and normals especially in the earlier stages of the sequences, though not quite as consistent in schizophrenics. The Chapman-Chapman theory seems to emphasize a different aspect of the process—the length of the sequence that is generated. An implication is that schizophrenics stop generating alternate meanings abnormally early. Thus, their final responses are overinfluenced by the dominant meanings that occurred early in the sequence.

As will be emphasized later, the relative disorganization among competing response tendencies, on which our theory focuses, and the relative restriction in range of information that is used, which Chapman and Chapman emphasize, seem to be two different important processes in schizophrenia. The effects of the two processes seem to overlap in some areas. For example, as we have seen, both the intrusion of non-dominant responses and a focus on partial information would tend to lead to that much-emphasized aspect of schizophrenia — the large number of deviant responses that are, however, associated to task stimuli. In other respects, the two processes have differing influences, and their differences in degree will be seen as a major contributor to the heterogeneity in schizophrenia.

ANXIETY AS A DRIVE THAT RAISES COMPETING RESPONSES OVER THRESHOLD — MEDNICK

Our theory has been discussed as a modification and elaboration of basic response-interferences theories as typified by Cameron. It is that. However, an important idea in the theory — that arousal may have a role in increasing competing responses in schizophrenics — was suggested by Mednick's (1958) very stimulating account of the schizophrenic process. Mednick suggested that emotional arousal, acting as a Hullian drive variable, led to the schizophrenic thought disorder. In Mednick's account, pre-schizophrenic individuals are highly anxiety-prone persons who have abnormally slow recovery rates from anxiety arousal. Mednick also states that many stimuli tend to increase emotional arousal in these persons. Thus, especially when there is some event that is particularly stressful, these individuals would react with high arousal, which decreases slowly, and meeting new anxiety-provoking situations is likely to increase further the anxiety that has not yet had a chance to abate. With slow recovery rates, the anxiety may build to extreme levels.

The schizophrenic thought disorder then results because high anxiety energizes both appropriate and competing responses, pushing many competing responses above evocation threshold. The important point is that remote, low-strength associations, which are below threshold under low drive or arousal, are raised above threshold and can therefore interfere with appropriate associations. Thus, Mednick uses "arousal" and "threshold," instead of our "arousal" and "ceiling," to account for the same type of behavior: the acute schizophrenics' fragmented variation between appropriate and remote associates.

Mednick has also suggested that chronic schizophrenia is different from acute schizophrenia in that chronics learn to channel their thinking along the lines of the remote associations that help them to avoid thinking about anxiety-provoking material. In Mednick's (1958) theory, chronic schizo-

.phrenics seemed, therefore, to be viewed as generally having lower anxiety than acutes, although this lowered anxiety was not seen as constant. "It may be important to note that even the chronic patient is in one sense a very anxious person. He has never had the opportunity to extinguish his prepsychotic fears. They are still excitable; all that is required is that one break through the schizophrenics 'associative curtain' [1958, p. 324]."

Experimental predictions concerning arousal and its effects in chronics would be difficult to make from this formulation, because experimental tasks could be interpreted as interrupting chronics' "associative curtain." However, in a later experimental test of the theory (Higgins & Mednick, 1963), the earlier theory is clearly interpreted as implying reduced arousal in chronic schizophrenics. ". . . early and advanced stages of [schizophrenia] are conceived of as poles on a learning process continuum. This continuum proceeds from a state of heightened arousal (Early Stage) to a state of reduced, eventually subnormal, arousal resulting from the acquisition of anxiety avoidant associative responses (Advanced Stage) [p. 314]."

The Higgins and Mednick (1963) study reasoned that because it had been shown in previous research that high arousal results in greater reminiscence (improvement after rest) in a psychomotor task, early-stage schizophrenics should show more reminiscence than advanced-stage schizophrenics, with normals falling in between. Five massed one-minute trials in which subjects performed inverse-printing, with urging for speed, were followed by two-minute rest and two further one-minute trials. As predicted, increase in responses from before to after the rest was greatest for early-stage schizophrenics; normals were next; and advanced-stage schizophrenics showed least reminiscence. Measuring reminiscence is, of course, a very indirect method of measuring arousal, and, as we will see in a later chapter, the suggestion from this study that chronics have subnormal arousal does not seem in accord with the trend of the evidence in the literature.

Another prediction made by Mednick is that although increased anxiety raises competing responses above threshold, when competing responses are absent, schizophrenics should perform better than normals. For example, in simple conditioning situations, the high anxiety in schizophrenics should increase the strength of the conditioned response. Mednick (1958) cited the results of classical conditioning studies using the knee-jerk response (Pfaffman & Schlosberg, 1936), psychogalvanic response (Mays, 1934; Shipley, 1934), and eyeblink conditioning (Taylor & Spence, 1954; Spence & Taylor, 1953) to support his prediction of enhanced conditioning in schizophrenics. However, most of these studies only show trends in the direction of enhanced conditioning in schizophrenics, not clear differences. Actually, this might have been expected from the theory in that the schizophrenics in these studies are not differentiated on the acute-chronic continuum. Also, in the Taylor-Spence and Spence-Taylor studies, schizophrenics are included in a group with other psychotics.

Lang and Buss (1965) cited a number of other conditioning studies as contrary to Mednick's prediction of superior classical conditioning in schizophrenics. However, the publications they cite as showing either no differences, or inferior schizophrenic conditioning, all used chronic schizophrenics (Howe, 1958; Peters & Murphree, 1954; Pishkin & Hershiser, 1963; O'Connor & Rawnsley, 1959), or did not specify chronicity (Shipley, 1934). Also, in the Shipley study, the trend was as Mednick cites—better conditioning in schizophrenics—contrary to the direction of results Lang and Buss cited. Mednick's hypothesis of lower arousal in chronic schizophrenics certainly does not lead to predictions of better classical conditioning for them, so these studies cannot be considered as contrary evidence. More evidence is needed on classical conditioning in acutes in order to reject or accept Mednick's hypothesis about their superior conditionability.

Actually, there is no reason to make the broad prediction that acute schizophrenics will condition faster than normals. Although only one response is counted by experimenters in classical conditioning studies, other response tendencies, such as competing attentional tendencies, may well be present and be increased by increased arousal. The clearest prediction is the relative prediction that schizophrenic deficit will be greater on complex than on simple tasks. This is because while experimenters will have difficulty in ruling out all interfering responses in "simple" tasks, they can increase the number of competing responses, and this increased response-interference should be exacerbated by increased arousal in schizophrenics. As we have seen, this prediction of greater deficit, relative to normals, when task complexity is increased, has been well verified. Mednick's theory does not come home free here however. Most of the studies showing this differential deficit have used chronic schizophrenics, and if chronics have low, even subnormal, arousal, then chronics should not do relatively better on less complex tasks.

Mednick (1958) also used his theory to predict that schizophrenics would show elevated stimulus-generalization responsivity. Mednick reasoned that this increased generalization would result from higher anxiety that strengthens generalized response tendencies. Among other support for this prediction, Mednick cited the Dunn (1954) and Garmezy (1952) studies where disturbed generalization was found in schizophrenics.

However, there are two difficulties here. First, the subjects used in these experiments were not just acute patients, which is the only group to which the prediction should apply. Second, the logic of the prediction is difficult to apply in another sense. Both of these studies involved choosing which of two alternate responses was to be made each time a stimulus was presented. With a dominant and a competing response to each stimulus, the prediction from Mednick's account is not clear. A "heightened generalization responsiveness" is predicted. Yet, for Mednick, the basic mechanism in schizophrenia is that drive increases the extent to which competing responses are above threshold and therefore intrude on dominant responses. Thus, it would seem that the theory would not imply that there would be any consistent increase in generalized responding in schizophrenics. It would seem to imply that generalized responses should only be increased where there is no response competition, or if there is competition, where the generalized response tendencies are not the dominant responses.

With different predictions having been made from the theory than the theory would at first seem to imply, it is difficult to be sure what is intended and therefore difficult to judge the fit of the theory with evidence.

This difficulty is found even in the most basic use of the theory to account for thinking disorder in schizophrenia. Mednick (1958) stated that, "Predictions from an extension of Hullian theory would suggest that the thinking of individuals with high drive would be disrupted by the intrusion of the remote and irrelevant thought units pushed above the threshold of awareness. The writer suggests that this action of high drive on remote response tendencies is a major root of the disordered thinking of schizophrenics [p. 320]." However, a careful analysis will show that in basic Hullian theory high drive will usually not cause competing responses to interfere more with dominant, appropriate thoughts. More detailed analyses of what should happen in basic Hullian theory when increased drive raises competing responses above threshold can be found in Broen and Storms (1961) and Storms and Broen (1966); however, the basic point can be presented briefly. In normal behavior, appropriate responses must usually be fairly strong, with habit strengths that are dominant over competing tendencies that are below or near threshold strengths. In such situations, the multiplicative action of an increase in drive will increase the response strength of appropriate responses more than the strength of competing associates. Thus, even if competing response tendencies are more frequently above threshold and so could *potentially* occur with greater frequency under higher drive, in actuality the dominant response will be strengthened even more. The dominant response will be raised even further above threshold and $RS_D - RS_C$ will be increased. No decrement in the frequency of appropriate response should be expected when appropriate responses have high and dominant habit strengths, as they must for those behaviors that are important and well practiced in normal behavior. Thus, the specific variables Mednick uses in his theory cannot account for disorganization in these most important behaviors in schizophrenia.

In spite of lack of clarity as to why Mednick's theory should imply some of the predictions that have been made from it, with consequent difficulty in evaluating it in terms of relevant evidence, the impact of the theory has been valuable. Its basic thrust has been in an important direction. Certainly the ideas that (a) an important factor in schizophrenia is increased competition from responses that are normally at low strength, and (b) arousal contributes to this response interference, are in accord with available evidence. Thus, Mednick's theory, which pointed in useful directions and has received much attention, has had considerable heuristic value.

4

NEUROPHYSIOLOGICAL SPECULATIONS ABOUT RESPONSE INTERFERENCE IN SCHIZOPHRENIA

INTERFERING PARALLEL PROCESSES THAT ARE ENERGIZED BY THE RETICULAR ACTIVATING SYSTEM — FISH

Fish's (1961) account of schizophrenia, like the last two theories we have discussed, views arousal as a contributor to response interference in schizophrenia, but his account of the underlying process uses constructs that refer more directly to neurophysiological mechanisms. Fish's theory is a combination and extension of some of the views of Conrad (1958) and Hebb (1949). Fish's neurophysiological description begins with Hebb's statement that "any frequently repeated particular stimulation will lead to a slow development of a 'cell assembly,' a diffuse structure comprising of cells in the cortex and diencephalon (and also perhaps in the basal ganglia of the cerebrum), capable of acting briefly as a closed system, delivering facilitation to other such systems and usually having a specific motor facilitation. A series of such events constitutes a 'phase sequence' — the thought process. Each assembly action may be aroused by a preceding assembly, by a sensory event or — normally — by both. The central facilitation from one of these activities on the next is the prototype of 'attention' ... [Fish, 1961, pp. 832-833, quoting from Hebb, 1949]."

Fish then gives the representation of thinking shown in Figure 14.

"C is the central process consisting of simultaneous active assemblies at three successive moments, while S is the corresponding sensory input. X is an assembly subliminally excited by the central process, Y is an assembly subliminally excited by the sensory input, and Z is an assembly which would become subliminally excited if X were excited [Fish, 1961, p. 833]."

Fish proposed that in schizophrenia there is an overactivity of the reticular activating system (RAS), a relatively non-specific arousal system

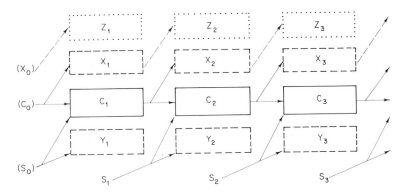

Fig. 14. Diagram of the selective process in thinking (after Hebb). (From Fish, 1961.)

with diffuse cortical projections that provide relatively generalized stimulation and thereby decrease the amount of additional stimulation needed to activate cell assemblies. One of the consequences is that reticular arousal may enhance the effects of external stimuli. For example, brief visual cues are perceived better during reticular stimulation (Magoun, 1958). A result is that the increased reticular stimulation in schizophrenics is likely to increase the activation of the Y assemblies that are normally only subliminally excited by external stimulation. Fish reasons that the activation of these additional assemblies may interfere with the normal central thought process. "This diversion of the central process would initially be sporadic and the central process would be mainly determined in the normal way by the previous cell assembly and the sensory input. However, as the intensity of the reticular overactivity increased, the central process would be diverted and disrupted by the sensory input much more frequently [Fish (1961) p. 834]." Thus, we have the attention disorder of the acute schizophrenic and the enhancement of stimulus effects that is so common clinically, but so hard to explain.

Because of this focus on the reticular activating system, a little more description of this system may be in order. The RAS is structurally and functionally complex, but for descriptive purposes may be divided into two functional systems: the brain-stem reticular formation, and the thalamic reticular system. Stimulation in all sensory modalities provides collateral stimulation to both these divisions, and recent research suggests that the cortical background stimulation provided by these systems does interact with cortical stimulation from specific sensory inputs, and is necessary for conscious recognition of these sensory inputs. A major difference in the two divisions of the RAS is that the thalamic system is more discrete in its cortical action than is the brain-stem system whose cortical projections provide relatively general activation. Thus, the thalamic system seems to be more involved in selective cortical enhancement. However, the descending projections of the brain-stem reticular formation are also fairly discrete and seem able to aid in the organization of attention through differentiated inhibitory control (filtering) of sensory input. In sum, normal arousal of the RAS provides both the general background stimulation needed for increased sensitivity to input and the control that is needed for selective awareness.

From these comments alone it would not seem that increased RAS activation would lead to the disorganization that Fish discusses, though from the importance of the RAS in controlling the organization of awareness, it is not unreasonable to hypothesize that some form of RAS dysfunction may be involved in schizophrenia. However, more relevant to Fish's specific view, it does seem that the balance of generalized excitation and selective filtering may be upset at higher levels of activation. Fish's views receive support from evidence that overactivity of the brain-stem reticular formation may block the thalamic effects, which are more differentiated. On this point, after citing relevant evidence and possible artifacts, Samuels (1959) states, "If the blocking effect is a true one, it would seem to suggest that gross activation or arousal is inimical to the optimal functioning of the regulatory effects mediated by the thalamic reticular system. This overshadowing of the more differentiated functions of the thalamic nuclei by the diffuse arousal response of the brain stem may have its behavioral counterpart in the many failures of discrimination which occur under high emotion and excitement [p. 8]." This brief description of RAS functioning only hints at the complexity of this system [see Samuels (1959) for a more complete review of relevant research]. However, the importance of the RAS in sensory enhancement and selective awareness is clear, and Fish's hypothesis, that RAS overactivity plays a role in the sensory enhancement and disorganized experience in schizophrenia, may well be pointing in an important direction.

The following quotations from early schizophrenics may help to give the feeling of the kinds of experience that seem relevant to Fish's account. "Things are coming in too fast. I loose my grip of it and get lost. I am attending to everything and as a result I really do not attend to anything." And from another early schizophrenic, "Have you ever had wax in your ears for a while and then had them syringed. That's what it's like now, as if I had been deaf before. Everything is noisier and it excites me." And from another. "Colours seem to be brighter now, almost as if they are luminous. When I look around me it's like a luminous painting. I'm not sure if things are solid until I touch them." [All three quotations are from McGhie & Chapman, 1961, pp. 104-105.]

Although there is some quality of wonderment in such descriptions of experience from early schizophrenics, the predominant feeling seems to be one of loss of personal control and of jumbled experience that is strange, aversive, and foreign, especially as the experience is continued. "I can't concentrate. It's diversion of attention that troubles me. I am picking up different conversations. It's like being a transmitter. The sounds are coming through to me but I feel my mind cannot cope with everything. It's difficult to concentrate on any one sound [McGhie & Chapman, 1961, p. 104]."

Following Conrad (1958), Fish suggests that the uncanny, unpleasant nature of the frequent sensory disruptions leads to a delusional mood. The generalized reticular stimulation should also increase the likelihood of firing of the X and Z cell assemblies that are subliminally stimulated by the normal central thought process. So, associated but deviant thoughts will intrude. (This explanation of the effects of arousal—that excessive arousal does not lead to random disturbance, but is more likely to lead to those thoughts that normally receive some, though weak, stimulation—is, of course, very similar to views expressed in the previous chapter.) The broad effect of increased arousal is then that deviant associations will occur in conjunction with changed sensory experience, increasing further the likelihood of delusional misperceptions. Also, the increased independence of cell assemblies from stimulus control (central, internal stimulation plus the stimulation from the RAS provides sufficient excitation) enhances the probability of hallucinations. Fish suggests that because thoughts and perceptions that the person is used to, and recognizes as his own, have been co-determined by external stimuli and central process, these new thoughts and perceptions, which are not a part of this normal process, are perceived as caused by something other than himself. A paranoid attitude results. Paranoid delusions are seen a natural result of the pervasive effects of response interference that are strange and uncontrollable to the early schizophrenic and are, therefore, often perceived as due to external influence.

Chronic schizophrenia, for Fish, is the chronic continuance of the firing of sequences of cell assemblies that are apart from the normal central process. For Fish, several factors may be involved. First, high reticular activity may be chronic, due to such factors as irritative lesions or an adrenal disorder. Also, if high reticular activity is maintained for some time and then subsides, the deviant processes may still continue as a result of changes in cell assemblies and associations between cell assemblies that took place during the period of abnormal activation. Fish bases this notion on Hebb's theory that structural changes occur at synapses that are repeatedly active. In this way, more permanent changes in cortical organization may be caused by temporary disorganization due to reticular effects. For chronics in whom these changes have taken place, general stimulation need not be abnormal, and the divergent pattern of behavior would be more stable, as Mednick also predicts. The major differences here are that, for Fish, chronic schizophrenia may involve either high arousal with continued fragmentation of ongoing behavior, or somewhat lower arousal with stable but deviant behavior patterns, and the stable deviance is the result of neurological alterations, not the learning of defensive habits.

To many persons who have worked with schizophrenics, Fish's explanation of how high arousal leads to a syndrome of sensory enhancement, distractibility, deviant but related associations, a feeling of strangeness — delusional mood, and likelihood of hallucinations, should be quite provocative. Many theories have explained aspects of the acute schizophrenic syndrome, but some parts of the syndrome that are impressive in their frequency, such as sensory enhancement, have been difficult to account for as expected parts of the total picture, determined by the same underlying process that determines other aspects of the syndrome.

GREATER EQUIVALENCE OF SYNAPTIC TRANSMISSION PROBABILITIES — MEEHL

Meehl (1962), in his Presidential Address to the American Psychological Association, posed the following question: "Suppose that you were required to write down a procedure for selecting an individual from the population who would be diagnosed as schizophrenic by a psychiatric staff; you have to wager $1,000 on being right; you may not include in your selection procedure any behavioral fact, such as a symptom or a trait, manifested by the individual. What would you write down? [p. 827]"

Meehl's answer: "So far as I have been able to ascertain, there is only one thing you could write down that would give you a better than even chance of winning such a bet — namely, 'Find an individual X who has a schizophrenic identical twin' [p. 827]."

This, together with evidence concerning neurological defects in schizophrenics, such as the work on vestibular system dysfunction in schizophrenics (e.g., Hoskins, 1946), is used by Meehl to suggest ". . . that schizophrenia, while its content is learned, is fundamentally a neurological disease of genetic origin [p. 837]."

Meehl does not suggest that the neurological defect is the sufficient cause of clinically obvious schizophrenia; rather, he postulates that the neurological defect, while always present in schizophrenics, is most likely to lead to clinical schizophrenia when a child with this defect is reared in an ambivalent and stressful environment.

By themselves, these statements do little to narrow the possibilities for what the inherited neurological defect might be, but, as Meehl suggests, ". . . the plausible alternatives are really somewhat limited. After all, what does a neuron do to another neuron? It excites, or it inhibits [p. 836]."

Also, as has been emphasized throughout our discussion of research on schizophrenia, schizophrenic behavior is often quite similar to normal behavior and this places further limits on the nature of underlying differences between schizophrenics and normals. The most consistent change is a shift in the probabilities of normally dominant and normally competing responses, without a complete loss of any response. Furthermore, these general shifts in response probabilities occur in certain kinds of situations, for example where competing responses are quite strong in normals.

Recognizing this, Meehl (1962) says that, "The schizotypic preservation of relatively normal function in selected domains directs our search toward some minimal deviation in a synaptic control parameter, as opposed to, say, a gross defect in cell distribution or structure, or the kind of biochemical anomaly that yields mental deficiency. Anything which would give rise to defective storage, grossly impaired transmission, or sizeable limitations on functional complexity can pretty well be excluded on present evidence. What we are looking for is a quantitative aberration in synaptic control — a deviation in amount or patterning of excitatory or inhibitory action — capable of yielding cumulative departures from normal control linkages under mixed appetitive-aversive regimes; but slight enough to permit convergence to quasi-normal asymptotes under more consistent schedules . . . [p. 836]."

Those behaviors that are central to the concept of schizophrenia further limit the neurological possibilities, in that a neurological model must be able to account for them as a syndrome. Meehl emphasizes the tendency for deviant-but-associated responses, which, when mild, he calls "cognitive slippage," as one of the fundamental aspects of schizophrenia. He suggests that other fundamental aspects are interpersonal aversiveness, ambivalence, and anhedonia — "a marked, widespread, and refractory defect in pleasure capacity . . . [p. 829]."

Like Fish, Meehl uses a general Hebbian neurological model, but also uses the recent evidence concerning specific limbic positive reinforcement (Olds & Milner, 1954) and aversive (Delgado, Roberts & Miller, 1954) centers, to suggest three possibilities for the schizophrenic's fundamental defect. Briefly, the major assumptions about the neurological model are that, ". . . when a presynaptic cell participates in firing a postsynaptic cell, the former gains an increment in firing control over the latter. Coactivation of anatomically connected cell assemblies or assembly systems therefore increases their stochastic control linkage, and the frequency of discharges by neurons of a system may be taken as an intensity variable influencing the growth rate of intersystem control linkage as well as the momentary activity introduced in other systems [p. 832]." Also, "Most learning in mature organisms involves altering control linkages between systems which themselves have been consolidated by previous learnings [p. 832]," and "Control linkage increments from coactivation depend heavily, if not entirely, upon a period of reverberatory activity facilitating consolidation [p. 832]." Meehl also uses the recent information about specific positive and negative reinforcement centers to assume that, "Feedback from positive limbic centers is facilitative to concurrent perceptual-cognitive or instrumental sequences, whereas negative center feedback exerts an inhibitory influence [p. 832]."

In this section, we will be concerned only with the one of Meehl's hypotheses about neurological defect that is most similar to the theories we have been discussing. These theories have taken the thought disorder—characterized by associative intrusions—as primary, and have explained these intrusions in terms of some factor that causes too-equivalent strength within a family of associates.

In Meehl's neurological hypothesis that takes "cognitive slippage" as primary, the explanation, though in neurological terms, is much the same. In the following statement, note the similarity to our previous discussions of partial collapse of response hierarchies as being the central description of schizophrenic thought disorder. "Suppose that the immediate consequence of whatever biochemical aberration the gene directly controls were a specific alteration in the neurone's membrane stability, such that the distribution of optimal transmission probabilities is more widely dispersed over the synaptic signal space than in normals. That is, presynaptic input signals whose spatio-temporal configuration locates them peripherally in the neurone's signal space yield transmission probabilities which are relatively closer to those at the maximum point, thereby producing a kind of dedifferentiation or flattening of the cell's selectivity. Under suitable parametric assumptions, this synaptic slippage would lead to a corresponding dedifferentiation of competing interassembly controls, because the elements in the less frequently or intensely coactivated control assembly would be accumulating control increments more rapidly than normal [p. 833]."

This description of the basic difficulty is very much like that proposed by Fish (1961), except that Fish specifies generalized stimulation from the reticular activating system as the factor that makes for a general lowering of firing thresholds, thereby enabling a peripheral cell assembly to be fired by another source of stimulation that would normally have only subthreshold intensity.

As with Fish's account, much of the uniqueness of Meehl's hypothesis comes in the way in which the hypothesis is elaborated to account for other important aspects of schizophrenia. For example, in Meehl's account, the relative amounts of positive and aversive feedback from coactivation of the limbic reinforcement centers will also be affected by the lowered selectivity of stimulation. In the past experience of normals as well as schizophrenics, the activation of a particular perceptual-cognitive system may have occurred with coactivation of positive centers on some occasions and negative centers on other occasions. However, in spite of some variation in past contingencies, usually a particular perceptual-cognitive system will have been predominantly associated with one kind of limbic activation. The result will be a differential increase in control increments, and for normals the activation of a particular perceptual-cognitive system will result in fairly clear dominance of one kind of feedback. However, in schizophrenics the dedifferentiation of competing interassembly controls means that the difference in positive versus negative feedback will be attentuated. The result is the abnormal ambivalence often noted in schizophrenics.

There is also an important difference between activities that normally show a relative dominance of positive-center coactivation and those for which aversive center coactivation is dominant. When positive feedback is normally dominant, the reduced selectivity in schizophrenics means that for them there will be a relative increase in the aversive, inhibitory feedback. The increase in aversive feedback will lead to a relative decrease in the reverberatory activity of the sequences that have a dominant positive association. However, in mixed-reinforcement regimes where activity has a dominant aversive feedback, the relative increase in positive feedback in schizophrenics will lead to abnormal continuation and consolidation of the behavior. In neither the positive-dominant or negative-dominant cases is there a reversal of dominance in schizophrenia. However, there is a relative shift toward consolidation of activities that are more inhibited in normals, and a relative inhibition of the activities that are normally positively reinforced together with a decrease in the pleasure gained from these activities. Thus, the abnormal anhedonia in schizophrenics.

An important aspect of what has been said is that the aversive drift will take place in activities that normally have at least some degree of mixed or inconsistent feedback. Thus, the difference in consistency of feedback in logical and physical actions on the one hand, and interpersonal interactions on the other, becomes important. For logical and physical activity, there is relatively great consistency in achieving the desired end when activity is correct. Thus, in schizophrenics, "Cognitive and instrumental linkages based upon sufficiently massive and consistent regimes, such as reaching for a seen pencil, will converge to asymptotes hardly distinguishable from the normal. But systems involving closely competing strengths and automized selection among alternatives, especially when the main basis of acquisition and control is social reward, will exhibit evidences of malfunction [Meehl, 1962, p. 834]." The aversive drift will occur in the more inconsistent social-interaction situations, thus accounting for the fourth important characteristic, aversive feelings about interpersonal situations in schizophrenics.

Of course, when the major interpersonal communications are clear — when positive reinforcements are given unambiguously, then the areas of deficiency can be minimal. On the other hand, when the major sources of socializing feedback (e.g., the mother) mix rewards with belittling, censuring feedback, then the neurological deficiency will result in clinically obvious schizophrenia.

The above implies that, in accord with many clinical reports, inconsistent home backgrounds should be common among schizophrenic patients. However, because such backgrounds would not themselves be a sufficient cause of schizophrenia, they should also be found among normals, though with less consistency. The research evidence on this point, comparing schizophrenics and normals, is not extensive and is somewhat inconsistent. Among the better-controlled studies, Farina (1960) found somewhat more conflict between parents of schizophrenics, primarily parents of poor-premorbid schizophrenics. The research literature on the hypothesis that double-bind (conflicting message) communications should be more frequent in the families of schizophrenics, is sparse and yields little support for this particular hypothesis, possibly due in part to disagreements about what constitutes a double-bind situation [literature reviewed in Schuham (1967)]. Solid, direct evidence regarding familial interactions is of course hard to obtain, and this also contributes to the fact that there is as yet such a paucity of good evidence regarding the possible importance of familial environment in leading to schizophrenia. This one aspect of the formulation should not be overemphasized, however. The essential aspects of the neurological formulation could still encompass the other aspects of schizophrenic behavior that have been mentioned without assuming abnormal inconsistency in schizophrenics' early environments. Under normal environments, which usually have some degree of inconsistency, significant loss of selectivity in the control of competing cell assemblies could still be thought of as influencing behavior in the direction of each of the aspects of schizophrenia that have been discussed in this section.

The reader who has some awareness of the masses of neurological-biochemical hypotheses about schizophrenia may be less than enthusiastic about one more such account. However, there seems to be a major difference between an account of this type and many others that attempt neurological specification. Meehl's account is guided by, and in accord with, the rather consistent trend of behavioral evidence about schizophrenia; being based on the kind of associative interference that is basic in the literature we have looked at thus far. Meehl's hypotheses are further restricted by Meehl's requirement that he must account for a syndrome of other behaviors that, from clinical observations, also seem central in schizophrenia. The majority of other neurological-biochemical accounts usually have what seems at first to have better evidence for the specific aberration they posit. Schizophrenics and normals have, at least in specific samples, been found to differ on a number of substances derived from blood samples, urine analyses, and so forth. However, when the environments of the groups, including diets and incidence of physical illness, are better controlled, these differences have usually not appeared (Kety, 1960). In searching for important neurophysiological aberrations from among the numerous possibilities, many of which are influenced by secondary differences between normals and schizophrenics, an approach like Meehl's, restricting the degrees of freedom by relying on consistent trends in other evidence to indicate general characteristics of what the aberration must be, would seem to be a useful strategy.

Behavioral research would seem able to also provide an additional aid to the physiological search. In addition to narrowing the search to more likely alternatives, measures of individual differences that are based on behavioral research should be used to reduce schizophrenic heterogeneity. This is a guideline that was raised before, but now we can begin to be a little more specific.

Even if there were only one necessary "cause" of schizophrenia, the behaviors of schizophrenics would be expected to vary widely. First, they would vary in severity of those behaviors that are most intimately related, as the degree of the central aberration must vary. Also, we would expect that these central aberrations would lead to other changes, at least avoidance of areas of inability, and other coping behaviors. While the nature of these changes might be quite consistent, reflecting the consistency of the central disturbance, the severity of these secondary changes would not necessarily be linearly related to the severity of the central disturbance. For example, defensive behaviors that are attempts to cope with the aspects of the central disturbance are likely to be learned over time and therefore should depend on an interaction of chronicity and severity of the central disturbance. A third type of change in schizophrenics would simply reflect the disturbed environments they live in once their deviant behavior becomes obvious. For example, the expectancies and reinforcement regimes in psychiatric hospitals are certainly abnormal and must result in behavioral changes that, though a consequence of being schizophrenic, reflect the heterogeneity of specific hospitals. A final important point is that unless we assume a central cause of schizophrenia that is constant over time, we cannot assume that the presence of secondary disturbances reflects the continued presence of primary disturbances.

What is then imperative is that individual-difference measures that reflect different aspects of schizophrenia be developed and used to define samples for neurological-biochemical research. Gross differentiations that may have been useful because they have been somewhat associated with the degree of organization of thinking, such as the paranoid-non-paranoid dimension, or that may, in part, tap the development of coping mechanisms, such as the acute-chronic dimension, should be improved.

We should by now know enough about at least one important dimension—the tendency for thinking to be disturbed by associative intrusions—to be able to define it somewhat better in relevant research. To illustrate, as we have seen, for one of his neurological models Meehl took this "cognitive slippage" as primary and specified something about what the basic type of dysfunction must be. Research guided by his hypothesis should use groups that might differ in this basic factor. In tasks that involve response alternates, more than one of which have more than negligible strength in normals, the degree of fluctuation between dominant and competing responses on repeated trials would provide a measure of susceptibility to associative intrusions. Because the measure should reflect degree of associative intrusions rather than factors such as general inattention to task requirements, a response alternative with negligible strength in normals should probably be available, with a Chapman-type of correction—normally associated minus normally unassociated errors. Because the measure should not be affected by differences in prior training, the test should be based on training in new material, which was prolonged, but with probabilistic reinforcement which, even with this lengthy training, would yield significant competition among the alternate responses. It is likely that using such a measure to classify research subjects would reduce heterogeneity in schizophrenics on at least one dimension that may be related to the type of neurological or biochemical aberration Meehl describes. This is just one possible example of how better behavioral differentiations that are based on the better understanding of the important, consistent differences between normals and schizophrenics, might make for more consistent results in searches for underlying neurophysiological dysfunction.

Some Possible Causes of Changed Synaptic Transmission Probabilities — Stilson and Kopell

Meehl's hypothesis that in schizophrenics ". . . the distribution of optimal transmission probabilities is more widely dispersed over the synaptic signal space than in normals [p. 833]," does not attempt to specify the reason for this lessened selectivity except that it is genetically determined. Stilson and Kopell's research (1964) led them to a neurological account that is similar to Meehl's, but they also suggest possible mechanisms for the change in neurological functioning.

As was described in Chapter 1, research by Stilson and Kopell showed that schizophrenics could recognize simple white geometric shapes on a dark background as easily as non-schizophrenic psychiatric patients and normals. However, when "visual noise" (random white spots) was added, the schizophrenics' recognition was disturbed more than that of the other groups. In other words, when the signal was made more ambiguous the schizophrenic deficit appeared.

Stilson and Kopell accounted for these results and the results of other research by hypothesizing a neurological model where some ". . . schizophrenics have 'neural representations' of patterned inputs that are more diffuse than the corresponding representations in others . . . the 'neural representation' corresponding to a given patterned input (e.g., a Bender design, a word) connects with more and more distinct representations of other patterns. . . . If it is assumed that the diffuseness of all functioning neural representations increases in the presence of visual noise, then this scheme provides an interpretation for the results of this study. With very distinct stimuli, such as ours, the greater diffuseness of the neural representations that may characterize some schizophrenics is insufficient to produce much overlap among the representations in the absence of noise. With visual noise added, however, the greater diffuseness in some schizophrenics, plus an additional increase in diffuseness due to the noise, leads to more overlap among representations and more recognition errors by these patients [p. 218]."

Stilson and Kopell then went on to ask, "By what sort of mechanism might the greater diffuseness of excitability of representations in some patients come about? Here we must resort to still more speculation, but there seem to be three obvious possibilities.

"One guess is that the cortical inhibitory fibers, which Milner [1957] suggests as the basis for limiting the growth of the cell assemblies are less numerous or less effective in some schizophrenics [p. 218]." Along these lines, it should be noted that inhibitory deficiency was also suggested by

Meehl as providing an alternate model to his neurological model for "cognitive slippage" which we discussed.

Stilson and Kopell suggest that, "A second possibility is that there is greater mutual excitability among cortical fibers in some schizophrenics [p. 219]." They then suggest that abnormal cholinergic and/or adrenergic reactivity may be the basis for this "hyperexcitability of cortical neurons (or hypoactive cortical inhibitory fibers) [p. 219]."

"A third possibility is that the density of firing of the nonspecific system . . . into the cortex is greater in some schizophrenics [p. 219]." The resultant greater arousal or tonicity of the cortex from this generalized activation ". . . may increase opportunities for temporal and spatial summation, and thus increase the diffuseness of a neural representation or a thought [p. 219]."

We will not comment further here on the third, arousal, possibility in that, as Stilson and Kopell noted, it is basically the same neurological model that Fish used, which we have discussed already.

THE INTERACTION OF AROUSAL, ACH, AND COLLAPSE OF RESPONSE HIERARCHIES—CARLTON

The second possibility, that abnormal adrenergic or cholinergic activity may be involved in diffuse excitation of cortical representations in schizophrenia, is quite intriguing. There is evidence from animal research (Carlton, 1963) that suggests (a) that adrenaline may be one of the substances involved in mediating cortical arousal, (b) that both arousal-related chemicals and acetylcholine (ACH) are related to a collapse in response hierarchies, but (c) the effects are opposite, at least in situations where arousal is initially at least moderate. In such situations, an *increase* in arousal-related chemicals or a *decrease* in ACH, tends to collapse response hierarchies.

Carlton (1963) suggested that the effects of increased arousal may be thought of as in our model involving a response-strength ceiling, which was discussed in the previous chapter: arousal has a general activating effect on all responses in response hierarchies, and when arousal is initially high, and the strongest response in response hierarchies is restricted at ceiling strength, an increase in arousal can only facilitate the competing responses and will tend to collapse the response hierarchy. Carlton used amphetamine, a drug that is chemically similar to adrenaline, and increases cortical arousal, to test this formulation.

But before we look at some of this research, we should understand Carlton's theory of the action of cholinergic mechanisms. Like increased arousal, decreased ACH is thought to collapse response hierarchies through raising the relative strength of competing responses, but the mechanism is different. Acetylcholine seems to be involved in the inhibition of non-reinforced responses. In general, the responses that are lower in response hierarchies are those that have been reinforced less than the dominant response; the hierarchical ordering is due to differences in reinforcement. Hence, when ACH is reduced, the effects of different reinforcement histories are reduced, and the difference in strength between the dominant and competing responses is reduced.

Carlton's statement that ". . . the effects of attenuated cholinergic activity appear to reduce the normal effects of nonreinforcement. . . . [p. 34]" seems to be meant in a very broad sense. It does not only mean that ACH is required for non-reinforced occurrences of a response to lead to extinction. The cholinergic system also seems to be seen as contributing to the inhibition of responses that rarely occur under normal circumstances, but would occur because of factors such as response generalization if the cholinergic system were not active.

Carlton (1963) reviewed a number of experiments that tend to substantiate his model. We will describe only two of these. One experiment tested the implication that increased arousal and decreased ACH should have similar effects, with both tending to flatten the gradient of strengths of alternate responses. Food-deprived rats learned to do a two-response sequence in order to obtain food. On one wall of the response chamber there were 12 response buttons. An animal had to touch any one of the 12 buttons with its nose and then cross the chamber and press the lever mounted in the opposite wall. Under the normal experimental condition, clear button-response hierarchies were developed. However, when ACH was decreased by injecting an anticholinergic, scopolamine, the result was that, as compared to the effects of saline injections, there was a marked response spread. As is illustrated in Figure 15, alternate responses that were similar to the dominant response became more frequent. The increased response spread was also found when the arousal-related drug, amphetamine, was injected.

Although these effects were similar, the influence of decreased ACH and increased arousal on the effectiveness of non-reinforced occurrences in eliminating a response should be different. Although increased arousal increases the strength of response tendencies, without reduced ACH the inhibitory effects of non-reinforcement during extinction should still occur. However, extinction should be very difficult with reduced ACH. To test this, Carlton trained rats in making a response to avoid shock, then the shock circuit was disconnected and ten 90-minute extinction sessions were given, the sessions being either weekly or bi-weekly. Before each

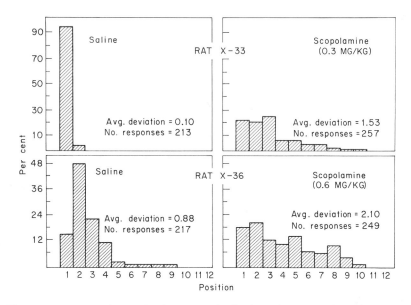

Fig. 15.   Representative relative frequency distributions of responses following saline or scopolamine. (From Carlton, 1963.)

extinction session, one group was given saline injections; in another group, amphetamine was injected; in the third group, ACH was decreased by scopolamine. As would be expected from increased arousal, the amphetamine group gave higher response rates; so, to facilitate comparisons, the extinction data for each session were the percentage of the number of responses that had been given in the first extinction session. By the terminal session, the saline and amphetamine animals did not differ significantly from each other and were giving less than 10% of the number of responses that had been given in the first extinction session. However, the reduced ACH group gave significantly more responses, and at the end these animals were, in fact, responding as much as in the first session. It does seem that the flattening of response hierarchies noted in the first experiment is due to different mechanisms as Carlton suggested; the amphetamine effects due to general response activation of the response tendencies that are present, and the effects of reduced ACH due to a decrease in the inhibitory effects of non-reinforcement.

In the two Carlton studies we have described, the effects of separate arousal and cholinergic changes were compared. Carlton's model also suggests an interaction between the two systems. "... level of activation could be viewed as controlling a tendency for all responses to occur, whereas an inhibitory cholinergic system would act to antagonize this action on non-reinforced responses. The net result of this interaction would be that changes in activation would result in changes in the likelihood of occurrence of only a *few* responses, those that were reinforced [p. 27]." Thus, *with normal levels of ACH,* a moderate increase in arousal (activation) would tend to strengthen appropriate responses, but the parallel activation effect on competing responses would be less. With hierarchies arranged in terms of reinforcement histories, this provides a rough physiological account of the facilatation of dominant responses expected from moderate arousal in normals in a Hullian type of theory, for example our theory (cf. the effects of arousal expected in the left half of Figure 10 in the previous chapter). Normal ACH means that even with fairly high levels of arousal, levels that are more than sufficient to raise dominant responses to ceiling excitation, the inhibition of inappropriate responses tends to maintain clearly ordered response hierarchies.

However, with subnormal ACH, increased arousal will have a relatively greater effect on inappropriate responses, and higher levels of arousal will be more likely to collapse response hierarchies. This suggests a somewhat different interpretation of our hypothesis concerning lower response-strength ceilings in schizophrenics. In terms of physiological models, it may be that response-strength ceiling — the level of practice and stimulation needed to give maximum excitation to a certain cell assembly — is no different for schizophrenics and normals. But other factors that normally inhibit the activation of competing responses may be lower in schizophrenics. The net effect would be that under specific levels of generalized stimulation (arousal), competing cell assemblies would be more likely to fire in schizophrenics; a situation that we account for in terms of lower response-strength ceilings and Meehl, and Stilson and Kopell, describe in terms of abnormal dispersion of optimal transmission probabilities, or diffuseness of cortical representations.

Whether or not lowered cholinergic activity is involved in schizophrenics' collapse of response hierarchies is, of course, quite speculative. It is only one of the types of changes that seem to lead to increased intrusions of competing responses, thus having effects analogous to some of the changes that have been noted in schizophrenia.

5

OVERINCLUSION AND HETEROGENEITY IN SCHIZOPHRENIA

OVERINCLUSIVE THINKING AS A RESULT OF AN INHIBITORY
DEFECT — PAYNE

The suggestion by Stilson and Kopell that overly diffuse neural representations might be caused by less numerous or less effective cortical inhibitory fibers is one form of a line of thinking that has been proposed in many theories about schizophrenia.

Meehl, who in one of his neurological hypotheses also suggested that the primary deficit in schizophrenia-prone individuals is a defect in inhibition, gives a reason that may underlie the commonness of inhibitory-defect hypotheses about schizophrenia. "... [Defective inhibition] is the most direct and uncomplicated neurologizing of the schizophrenic cognitive slippage. Schizoid cognitive slippage is neither an incapacity to link, nor is it an unhealthy overcapacity to link; rather it seems to be a defective *control* over associations which are also accessible to the healthy (as in dreams, wit, psychoanalytic free association, and certain types of creative work) but are normally 'edited out' or 'automatically suppressed' by those superordinate monitoring assembly systems we lump together under the term 'set' [1962, p. 834]."

In terms of the quantity and quality of research to test a theory, the most important recent use of an inhibitory-defect view of schizophrenia is that by Payne and his co-workers. Because of Payne's carefulness in emphasizing the heterogeneity in persons diagnosed as schizophrenics, it should be immediately said that he does not suggest inhibitory defect as basic in more than a subgroup of schizophrenics.

Payne and his co-workers present their theory as an extension of Cameron's views of overequivalence of alternate response tendencies, or, in other words, lack of differentiation between alternate responses, as important in schizophrenic thinking disorder. "It is possible to reformulate Cameron's theory of over-inclusion in a slightly more general way so that a number of predictions follow from it. Concept formulation can be regarded as largely the result of discrimination learning. When a child first hears a word in a certain context, the word is associated with the entire situation (stimulus compound). As the word is heard again and again, only certain aspects of the stimulus compound are reinforced. Gradually the extraneous elements cease to evoke the response (the word), having become 'inhibited' through lack of 'reinforcement.' This 'inhibition' is, in some sense, an active process, as it suppresses a response which was formerly evoked by the stimulus. 'Over-inclusive thinking' may be the result of a disorder of the process whereby 'inhibition' is built up to 'circumscribe' and 'define' the learned response (the word or 'concept'). In short, it could be an extreme degree of 'stimulus generalization.'

"The same theory can be expressed in different terms. All purposeful behavior depends for its success on the fact that some stimuli are 'attended to' and some other stimuli are ignored. It is a well known fact that when concentrating on one task, normal people are quite unaware of most stimuli irrelevant to the task. It is as if some 'filter mechanism' cuts out or inhibits the stimuli, both internal and external, which are irrelevant to the task in hand, to allow the most efficient 'processing' of incoming information. Over-inclusive thinking might be only one aspect of a general breakdown of this 'filter mechanism' [Payne, Matussek, & George, 1959, pp. 630-631]."

Payne *et al.* (1959) tested this formulation using a series of tasks that should measure overly inclusive concepts or a defect in inhibiting or filtering out irrelevant information. Their subjects were schizophrenic inpatients, none of whom were regarded as chronic, and a control group of inpatient neurotics, primarily patients with diagnoses of anxiety state, reactive depression, and obsessional neurosis. The schizophrenics and neurotics did not differ significantly in age or intelligence.

One of the tasks was a modification of the "Handing Over" stage of the Goldstein-Scheerer Object Sorting Test. In this task, subjects were shown a number of objects on a table. One of these objects was selected by the experimenter and the subjects were then asked to hand over to the examiner all the objects that might be grouped with this object. Payne *et al.* hypothesized that if schizophrenics have overinclusive concepts, they should select more objects as belonging together. In other words, if more kinds of stimuli, more aspects of the objects, are attended to, there is greater likelihood that more objects will be included as having something in common. The average number of objects grouped together by the schizophrenics was 11.33, and by the neurotics 5.86. The difference was significant.

A second task involved sorting 12 small objects—four triangles, four circles, and four squares—that varied in weight, thickness, material, and color. This Object Classification Test was constructed so that there should be 10 different ways of grouping the objects, e.g., by shape, size, surface area, and so forth. The subjects first sorted the objects into groups that they thought belonged together and then were told to "sort the objects in as many other ways as you can." Payne *et al.* reported that in a previous study (Payne, 1954), it had been found that normals tended to sort objects by the intended categories, and only rarely sorted the objects in other groupings based on more unusual criteria. Thus, the 10 intended types of groupings of objects can be considered as normal or usual sortings. In the scoring schema, other, unusual sortings are counted separately. These unusual sortings are groupings based on stimulus commonalities usually ignored by normals, such as scratches on the objects or shape of shadows cast by the objects, or stimuli that had already been the basis for a grouping. As predicted, schizophrenics gave significantly more unusual sortings than the neurotics (the respective means were 9.53 and 2.21). The schizophrenics also gave a greater combined total of usual and unusual groupings, although they gave usual kinds of groupings significantly less than the neurotics. Payne *et al.* suggested that this latter difference was due to schizophrenics giving up before the total number of stimuli they attended to could be utilized. This giving up should be greater in schizophrenics than in neurotics because the task is predicted to be lengthier for schizophrenics, in that schizophrenics should attend to a greater variety of kinds of stimuli, which are potential bases for groupings, as the results tended to indicate. Also the relative (schizophrenics compared to normals) effect of this giving up should be primarily reflected in fewer usual sortings in schizophrenics, because it is those sorts on which nonschizophrenics concentrate.

This description of two tasks should be sufficient to illustrate both the way in which Payne *et al.* translated their theory into experiments, and the trend of their results. In all, 13 measures of overinclusion were used in this study, with all results in the direction of greater overinclusion in schizophrenics, although 4 of the 13 differences were not significant.

One notable aspect of the second Payne, Matussek, and George task described above is the focus on defective inhibition as leading to broad stimulus usage in multiple-stimulus situations. Their theoretical orientation, beginning as it did with Cameron's thinking, might equally as well have emphasized inability to inhibit too broad a range of responses to single stimuli. This kind of use of a defective-inhibition account would lead to the same kind of expectation of intrusions of associates as has been emphasized in other theories we have discussed. Thus we note again that a possible cause underlying associative intrusions might also lead to overly broad attention to a variety of external stimuli.

Basically, as was implied by the beginning formulation in Chapter 1, any factor that tends pervasively to collapse response hierarchies—and defective inhibition of competing response tendencies is one example—should lead to a syndrome of associative intrusions to single stimuli and broad unfocused reactions to multiple stimulation. Of course, the prominent aspects of the behavior will differ in different situations, In situations where single stimuli are prominent and where multiple responses are evoked by the stimulus, the increase in competing responses will have the characteristic flavor of intrusions of associates. In multiple-stimulus situations, many of the competing responses are evoked by different stimuli and therefore it is less likely that there will be as strong an associative relationship between the normally dominant responses and the intruding responses. So, although the "flavor" of schizophrenia is often thought to rest primarily in associative intrusions, the inability to organize the less-related response tendencies that are evoked by multiple-stimulation should be a related characteristic. The unifying factor is a partial collapse of response hierarchies, which involves both hierarchies of attention tendencies to alternate stimuli, and hierarchies of response tendencies evoked by a single stimulus.

Although the conceptualization reviewed in the last paragraph is different from that of Payne *et al.* (1959), in that it concentrates on competing responses instead of competing stimuli, the difference may be only a matter of emphasis. The Payne *et al.* formulation, as quoted above, did speak of the need to inhibit incorrect *responses* to stimuli, although the mechanism through which this inhibition came about in normals was that those aspects of *stimulus* compounds that had inconsistent connections to responses became inhibited. Thus, although Payne emphasizes the inhibition or filtering of stimuli, the theory can be understood as suggesting an inhibition of low-probability stimulus-response associations in normals, with the inhibition being defective in schizophrenics. This is very like the main emphasis of our discussion to this point. However, the particular way that Payne *et al.* have stated their theory—in terms of filtering those aspects of stimuli that have not been consistently related to appropriate responding—makes it more likely that tests of the theory will emphasize inappropriate breadth of attention in multiple-stimulus situations, rather than the intrusion of low-probability associates to single stimuli.

Seeing the problem in terms of deficit in inhibiting stimuli instead of responses has another implication in addition to tending to switch the emphasis away from associative intrusions and toward general stimulus distractibility. The theoretical formulation then seems opposed to the Chapmans' proposal that schizophrenics' errors are due to abnormal restriction in the internal (meaning) information that is scanned prior to making a response to a multi-meaning situation. This Chapman formulation seems quite different from Payne's discussion of the deficit in terms of a reduced ability to filter out irrevelant information—internal or external. However, in some respects the conflict between accounts may be only superficial. Consider the Payne *et al.* explanation of the last experiment discussed above. Here schizophrenics used fewer kinds of normally relevant information as a basis for grouping objects, because the unusual information that intruded for them provided so large a pool of information that they did not get to using some of the relevant stimuli. Thus, it is possible that restricted use of relevant information may come from either restricted scanning, as implied by Chapman, or from overly broad attention, which interferes with attention to specific relevant information. However, as will be emphasized later, it is likely that either possibility, by itself, is an incomplete explanation of reduced use of relevant information in schizophrenia.

THE GENERALITY OF OVERINCLUSION

Studies such as the series of experiments by Payne *et al.* (1959) and many of the studies reviewed in Chapter 1 have repeatedly shown that schizophrenics are overinclusive in the sense of responding to an overly broad range of stimuli. However, there are still a number of questions about the importance and distribution of overinclusion. For example, though the Payne *et al.* (1959) experiments indicated that overinclusion was greater in schizophrenic than neurotic populations, this still does not negate the possibility that overinclusion may be a general characteristic of psychosis, or that even if it is specific to schizophrenia, only a large subgroup of schizophrenics are overinclusive.

In a very important study relevant to these questions, Payne and Hewlett (1960) administered 13 different measures that were regarded as relatively pure tests of overinclusive thinking—such as the handing-over and object-sorting tasks described above—to 20 normals, 20 neurotics, 20 psychotic depressives, and 20 schizophrenics. A number of measures of general intelligence, "concreteness" of thinking, and speed of performance were also given to the subjects. On each of the 13 measures of overinclusion, the schizophrenics gave the highest average score, although only six tests of the differences between schizophrenics and the rest of the subjects were significant.

The test battery was then factor analyzed, and three factors were extracted by Thurstone's centroid method. A discriminant-function analysis was used to determine the rotation of the factors so that a single factor would best differentiate the schizophrenics from other subjects. The tests with the eight highest leadings on this factor were all measures of overinclusion. Factor scores on this overinclusion factor significantly discriminated the schizophrenics from the other groups, and there were no significant differences among the neurotics, normals, and psychotic depressives. Thus, overinclusion does seem to be relatively specific to schizophrenia. However, the schizophrenics themselves were quite heterogeneous on this measure. The low end of their range of overinclusion scores matched that of the other groups and only about one-half of the schizophrenics showed abnormally high overinclusion.

The other two factors seemed to measure general intelligence and speed of performance. The intelligence factor did not distinguish the groups (which had been matched on pre-illness intellectual level), but when rotation was done so that a factor would maximally discriminate the total psychotic group (depressives and schizophrenics) from the other groups, the factor that discriminated best was the speed factor. Twenty-five of the 31 loadings greater than .30 on this factor were obtained by measures of speed, with tests of motor speed and tests of speed in complex reasoning both having high loadings. This rotated factor was independent of the general intelligence factor, as was the overinclusion factor, and the overinclusion and speed factors were relatively independent, having a correlation of .38. On speed-factor scores, the depressives were fairly homogeneous, showing rather uniform retardation, but the schizophrenics were again very heterogeneous, with some showing normal speed and others being more retarded than depressives.

One very interesting finding was that those schizophrenics who were abnormally retarded tended not to be overinclusive, but those who were within the normal range of speed tended to be overinclusive. For Payne and Hewlett, these data ". . . suggested that there might be two groups of schizophrenics. One resembles the endogenous depressives, in that it is not abnormally overinclusive. Like depressives, these schizophrenics are abnormally retarded. Indeed they are even slower than a depressive group. . . . The second group of schizophrenics are quite unlike depressives. They suffer from an abnormal degree of overinclusion. While they are slightly retarded, their slowness is merely due to their abnormal overinclusion, which causes them to over-elaborate most tasks and thus take longer to do them. As a group their speed scores are nearly all within the normal range [Payne, 1961, p. 249]."

In the experiments we have discussed thus far in this section, the schizophrenics have been primarily early schizophrenics. If overinclusion is an important aspect of disturbed behavior in many acute schizophrenics and if there is a progressive deterioration in schizophrenia, or if severer disturbance is more likely to be continued without remission, then it is reasonable to hypothesize that a group of chronic schizophrenics would be more overinclusive than a group of acutes. However, when Payne (1962) tested chronic schizophrenics on his Object Classification Test, they not only gave significantly fewer groupings based on usual stumulus classes than did normals, they also did not significantly exceed normals in number of unusual groupings. Payne combined the results of several studies that used his object classification test to yield the compatisons given in Table 8.

Payne (1966) considers his 1962 study to be pilot study in that several factors such as the influence of drugs were not controlled. However, the results of a later and better controlled study by Payne, Friedlander, La-verty, and Hayden (1963), which concentrated on studying the effects of drug status, indicated again that chronic schizophrenics are not abnor-mally overinclusive, whether they are or are not receiving phenothiazines.

The significance of these results is not that phenothiazines do not affect overinclusion. As Payne (1966) points out, the ineffectiveness of a drug in chronic patients ". . . was not so surprising, because presumably their re-sistence to phenothiazine treatment was a major factor in their still being in hospital [p. 86]." The important point is that chronic patients are not overinclusive, at least on Payne's measures. Although they are chroni-cally disturbed, and diagnosed as schizophrenic, the nature of the distur-bance, at least with respect to degree of overinclusion, is different from that of acutes. There are two possible explanations. Either the symptoms changed over time or, of the two classes of acutes, retarded acutes and overinclusive acutes, the retarded stay longer in hospitals. Payne *et al.* (1963) did find that chronic schizophrenics were seriously retarded. Thus, Payne (1966) concludes, "One possible implication is that the pres-ence of overinclusive thinking in an acute patient is a relatively good prog-nostic sign, while an extreme degree of retardation is a bad prognostic sign [p. 87]."

A major difficulty for the statements in the last paragraph is the fact that

TABLE 8[a]
MEAN OBJECT CLASSIFICATION TEST SCORES

Group	Usual sortings	Unusual sortings	Total
Normals	3.96	1.87	5.83
Neurotics	4.21	1.74	5.95
Endogenous depressives	3.15	2.45	5.60
Acute schizophrenics	2.51	8.14	10.65
Chronic schizophrenics	1.62	2.59	4.21

[a] Data from Payne (1962).

many studies have found that chronic schizophrenics are overinclusive—at least overinclusive in the sense of being susceptible to intrusions from an abnormally broad range of associates. As an example, remember Chapman's (1958) study where chronic schizophrenics showed an abnormal tendency to group words on the basis of distracting association. Though this has been called overexclusion because the result is fewer correct placements, it is basically overresponding to intrusive associations. Also, in Chapman's (1961) study of conceptual breadth, chronic schizophrenics had an abnormal tendency to place objects in conceptual classes to which they were related but did not belong. These are just two of the many examples of chronic schizophrenics showing the abnormal equivalence among a family of associates that has also been called overinclusion.

But Payne's data showing that chronic schizophrenics are not overinclusive also seem quite reliable. Obviously, a necessary distinction about different types of overinclusion is not being made.

In each of Payne's studies a broad range of stimuli was available (in terms of the number and stimulus complexity of the objects in a task and/or a subject's range of association to the stimuli), and Payne's measures were intended to tap the range of stimuli that each subject used, for example, the number of ways a subject sorted objects. Payne's results using these tasks then suggest that chronic schizophrenics do not use an abnormally broad range of stimuli. In this specific sense, they are apparently not overinclusive.

Most of the studies that did show overinclusion in chronics (e.g., Chapman, 1961) used one or a few prominent stimuli at a time, and the measure of overinclusion depended on whether correct or inappropriate responses were made to these few stimuli. Thus, in these studies, chronic schizophrenics were overinclusive in the sense that when faced with a particular stimulus (e.g., the name of a vegetable) they were abnormally likely to overinclude that stimulus in an associated category to which it did not belong (e.g., a fruit category). This latter form of overinclusion seems to be an increase in intrusions of non-dominant responses to stimuli, rather than attention to an overly broad range of stimuli, which was the nature of overinclusion in Payne's research.

Consideration of the differences in the two kinds of overinclusion in chronics suggests that, in spite of our earlier discussion of the two kinds of overinclusion as different aspects of the same phenomenon—partial collapse of response hierarchies—the two kinds of overinclusion must be separable. Chronic schizophrenics seem to respond to a single stimulus as if too many of the alternate responses to that stimulus are abnormally equivalent in strength, but they do not seem to respond to an abnormally broad range of different stimuli.

ACCOUNTING FOR THE SEPARATION OF THE TWO KINDS OF OVERINCLUSION

There are two general ways to account for the presence of the one kind of overinclusion, but not the other, in chronic schizophrenics. First, attention to an abnormally broad range of stimuli may, of course, have a different cause than overequivalence of alternate responses to single stimuli, and as Payne suggests, factors underlying stimulus overinclusions may be fairly easily reversible. Thus, schizophrenics whose deficit involves stimulus overinclusion may recover quickly and not tend to become chronically disturbed. This explanation must then assume that abnormal interference among the alternate responses to single stimuli is caused by some second, less reversible factor, in that chronics still exhibit this kind of overinclusion. This kind of explanation could involve a Bleulerian account of the intrusions of deviant associations to single stimuli. The cause may be a loss of associative threads or lack of recognition of aspects of the context that are needed to make correct responses dominant. This loss of the information that is needed to bring a hierarchical order to competing response tendencies is easy to see as part of a syndrome in which there is also attention restricted to a narrow range of stimuli. Thus, whatever causes some aspects of context to become impotent may be fairly irreversible, and this may be the reason that chronics have a syndrome of associated-but-deviant responses together with use of a narrowed range of stimuli.

The second kind of explanation is that a single state, probably involving a partial collapse of response hierarchies, underlies both kinds of overinclusion, but that over time schizophrenics learn methods of coping with distraction from too many stimuli without the underlying process being changed (Broen, 1966). If the factors that cause important deficiencies in behavior remain over a period of time, it seems quite likely that individuals would learn ways of coping with the deficiency, at least to a limited extent. If massive response interference is aversive, and subjective reports from schizophrenics (McGhie & Chapman, 1961) certainly suggest that it usually is, then it may be possible to learn to avoid at least some of the multiple stimulation that is likely to lead to massive response interference.

On entering novel situations, normals usually look around a bit, scanning various stimuli, and then, in spite of the attention tendencies evoked by the various stimuli that have been scanned, normals seem able to set up appropriate attention hierarchies, with dominant focus on stimuli that are important for appropriate performance. This normal pattern of fairly broad scanning is important in order not to miss relevant information. However, if schizophrenics, with their susceptibility to competing response tendencies, scan as broadly as normals, they will not be as able to organize hierarchically the competing attention tendencies evoked by the stimuli they have scanned. Overly broad attention will result. In order to reduce this multiple-stimulus source of response interference, many schizophrenics should be motivated to begin to learn not to scan quite so broadly. A quotation from an early schizophrenic illustrates the beginning recognition of this means of coping with response interference from multiple stimuli. "My concentration is very poor. I jump from one thing to another. If I am talking to someone they need only to cross their legs or scratch their head and I am distracted and forget what I am saying. *I think I could concentrate better with my eyes shut* [McGhie & Chapman, 1961, p. 104. Emphasis added]."

Over time, many schizophrenics should be able to learn quite consistent methods of reducing the sources of competing stimulation. The basic susceptibility to response tendencies evoked by different stimuli may not have changed, but if the schizophrenic has learned methods to reduce the extent of his stimulus input, competing attention responses will not be evoked in as great numbers and he will not show an abnormal range of attention. On Payne's multiple-stimulus measures of overinclusion, these more experienced schizophrenics will tend not to be overinclusive. They will not use an abnormally broad range of stimuli. However, even when scanning operations limit input to few stimuli, in research where the few stimuli that are present do evoke strong competing responses, these schizophrenics still will show abnormal interference from competing responses. Stimulus overinclusion will be reduced in chronics—especially in comparison with acutes—but single stimuli will still often be classified inappropriately. We will explore the possibility of reduced scanning in chronic schizophrenics more in the next chapter, but for now, consider some additional implications of the formulation just described.

Response interference can be reduced either by not observing some stimuli or by segmental scanning—observing different stimuli in carefully time-separated bits, with the separation sufficient to reduce interference from concurrent competing response tendencies. Either method of reducing response interference—tending to ignore some stimuli or slowed pace of scanning—would be likely to retard performance severly in speed tests where quick noticing of relevant stimuli is required.

This means that those schizophrenics who early in their hospitalization have already learned to restrict the extent and speed of their scanning of external and internal information should be more retarded on speed tests. As Payne and Hewlett (1960) found, those early schizophrenics who were the most severely retarded tended not to be abnormally overinclusive in the range of information they used.

On the other hand, in those schizophrenics who still were near normal in their scanning habits, there would be a tendency to note relevant stimuli fairly quickly, though their disorganization of attention hierarchies would mean that relevant attention would at times be disturbed by distractions. Thus, those early schizophrenics who respond to an abnormal range of stimuli should tend to be moderately, though not severely, retarded. As Payne and Hewlett found, extreme overinclusion and severe retardation should tend not to be found in the same schizophrenics.

The important point is that the differences in breadth of cue utilization, which Payne found among early schizophrenics and between early and late schizophrenics, do not necessarily show that there are two distinct types of schizophrenics, which differ on a basic dimension of susceptibility to competing response tendencies. Payne's data can be accounted for by assuming a basic susceptibility to interfering response tendencies together with differences in the extent of a coping mechanism involving reduced and slowed scanning. If changes in normal scanning procedures take time to become habitual, then early (recently hospitalized) schizophrenics, with differences in this learning, should be quite heterogeneous on measures of stimulus overinclusion, as they seem to be. Also, in accord with Payne's data, chronics should tend to be somewhat more homogeneous in showing reduced scanning and retardation.

In general, those recently hospitalized schizophrenics who had been disturbed for a time prior to hospitalization should have had a greater time to learn to begin to narrow their scanning, with resultant retardation and lack of broad stimulus usage early in hospitalization. The more long-term pathology in these patients also implies that for them the basic causes of the schizophrenic disorganization are less reversible and so, as Payne has also suggested, retardation and reduced stimulus overinclusion in recently hospitalized schizophrenics may well be related to poor prognosis. Another possible reason for poor prognosis in those individuals who scan stimuli slowly and incompletely is that even if this change in style of scanning were secondary to experiencing disorganization in complex situations, over time the changed scanning should become a consistent habitual pattern that protects against anticipated disorganization. Thus, even if the cause of the basic response interference were, in fact, ameliorated, the retardation and loss in taking in information would not cease at the same time, but would rather continue to block adequate adjustment to complex and demanding environments.

However, regardless of whether or not retarded and overinclusive schizophrenics are experiencing the results of distinct processes, or are different primarily in degree of a defensive reaction to a common basic process, the main point that should be emphasized here is the heterogeneity in schizophrenia. The research by Payne and his co-workers is compatible with different explanations about underlying processes, but the simple point that there are major differences among schizophrenics is clear. That one locus of differences is in breadth of cue utilization is also clearly suggested. A more thorough discussion of this topic is the focus of the next chapter.

6

DIFFERENCES IN BREADTH OF CUE UTILIZATION

The need for considering the possibility that a major difference among schizophrenics is in the range of cues that are utilized has been apparent since one of the first studies we looked at in Chapter 1. In that study (Ludwig, Wood, & Downs, 1962), Ss were to read a passage while listening to their own voices delayed .2 of a second. As you may remember, this distracting stimulation interfered with normals' performance to some extent and, as expected from considering schizophrenics to be especially susceptible to interference, many schizophrenics were even more distracted than normals. However, another subgroup of schizophrenics was less distracted than normals and we commented at the time that ". . . finding that many schizophrenics were less responsive than normals to the additional source of stimuli means that our formulation is obviously incomplete, at least with regard to some schizophrenics." That the idea of differences in breadth of cue utilization is not a notion that is required only to explain Payne's data is also indicated by our conlusion from other studies discussed in Chapter 1 (e.g., the Chapman & McGhie, 1962, experiments) that ". . . a sub-sample of schizophrenics may confine their observation to certain classes of cues and therefore may be helped especially by relevant and irrelevant stimuli being from easily discriminable classes . . ."

In the last chapter, some more explicit ideas about the schizophrenics who do and do not respond to a wide range of cues began to emerge. We will begin this chapter with a more detailed statement of one of the possible theories about differences in range of cue utilization that was discussed briefly in the last chapter. This more detailed statement is needed in order to generate more specific predictions that can be compared to clinical descriptions of schizophrenia and to the results of experiments we have not discussed as yet.

As we discuss this particular theory in detail, it must be kept in mind that other accounts, some of which will be discussed later, are also very tenable. The theory we will discuss first arrives at predictions about cue utilization from consideration of the interaction between range of scanning and ability to focus on relevant stimuli once scanning has been done. Thus in this theory, the range of stimuli that are scanned is not directly related to range of cues that affect performance and will not be indicated directly by the data in most of the studies we look at. It is for this reason that this chapter is titled "Differences in Breadth of Cue Utilization" rather than "Differences in Range of Scanning." Differences in breadth of cues that are used in a task have a closer relationship to the data; these differences have been demonstrated quite clearly, and are important differences in schizophrenics, regardless of the validity of any particular theory about them.

However, we will emphasize one type of theory, the same type of theory that has been emphasized to this point, primarily because it is a way of thinking about schizophrenia that has held up rather well when examined in the light of a wide variety of experimental data. The basic principle is simply that basic schizophrenic disturbance does not affect the content or rank order of alternate habitual response probabilities, though the probabilities of alternate responses become more nearly equal. Let us examine this principle in the context of what happens when human beings meet complex environments.

A Distinction between Scanning and the Organization of Response Tendencies That Are Evoked by the Multiple Stimuli That Have Been Scanned

The major addition to the emphases in our previous discussion of this principle concerns the obvious point that behavior in a particular situation is not determined simply by the stimuli present in that situation. One example of what human beings bring to situations is that they enter complex situations with stimulus-search habits, which allow them some control over their stimulus input. Because of this, our basic formulation is obviously incomplete when we move from discussing tasks where subjects repeatedly respond to single stimuli to studies where several kinds of stimuli are present, some relevant and some irrelevant, and several different kinds of stimuli must be observed prior to responding in order for a response to be appropriate. The following statements about multiple-stimulus scanning will provide a basis for discussing this more complex kind of situation in a manner that is fairly straightforward and compatible with our discussion of simpler situations.

1. On meeting a complex situation, human beings do not "take-in" at once all stimuli that are present in the environment. Different kinds of stimuli must be taken-in in sequence.

2. Scanning or stimulus-search habits determine where the stimulus-search will begin and affect the pace and the extent of the stimulus input.

3. The scanning of stimuli is organized according to such factors as position and sensory modality. As an example of input sequencing according to position, a person may enter a room, look ahead, then look to one side, and so forth.

4. In complex situations, extensive normally paced scanning will tend to cause an increase in the number of concurrent response tendencies because of the greater number of stimuli that have been scanned.

In other words, persons often scan broadly in order to gain the information needed to respond appropriately, but the broad and complex input that results increases the number of alternate response tendencies, including competing attention tendencies as well as other kinds of response tendencies.

5. In normals, certain of these response tendencies will be clearly dominant. For example, there will be a clear organization of attention, with dominant attention to those of the stimuli that have been scanned that have been most important in past experience with similar situations. The same is true of other kinds of responses. In normals, the complex response hierarchy that results from broad scanning will tend to have appropriate responses clearly dominant.

6. According to our basic principle, the result will be different in schizophrenics. Normally non-dominant responses will intrude with greater frequency. This will affect both scanning priorities and the organization of attention among the stimuli in the input. Concerning scanning, there should be some reduction in the consistency of scanning priorities, though the scanning operations that are dominant should tend to be the same for schizophrenics and normals. In addition, even though a schizophrenic initially scans a situation to the same extent as a normal and thus has the same extent of stimulus input, the result will be that after the initial scanning the schizophrenic then attends to and responds in other ways to more of the stimulus elements in the situation than the normal. Also, because this response breadth involves nearer equalization of the probabilities of alternate response tendencies, the "broader attention" will be relatively disorganized, with somewhat greater randomization among the competing attention tendencies.

The picture that is being drawn is based on a partial collapse of response hierarchies, together with some statements about general charac-

teristics of normal behavior in multiple-stimulus situations. Thus, it is a
"pure schizophrenia" picture, not one that includes the secondary
changes that should result from the basic alterations in behavior. Thus,
what we have said should characterize the very initial, acute stages of
schizophrenia, but not necessarily later schizophrenia.

ATTENTION IN ACUTE SCHIZOPHRENICS

The abnormally broad number of stimuli attended to in a fairly disorganized fashion, with attention to unimportant stimuli subtracting from
attention to more important stimuli, does seem characteristic of many
acute schizophrenics, not only from research such as Payne's, but also
from clinical literature and schizophrenics' subjective reports. As one
early schizophrenic said, "During the last while back I have noticed that
noises all seem to be louder to me than they were before. It's as if someone turned up the volume ... I notice it most with background noises —
you know what I mean, noises that are always around but you don't
notice them. Now they seem to be just as loud and sometimes louder than
the main noises that are going on ... It's a bit alarming at times because it
makes it difficult to keep your mind on something when there's so much
going on that you can't help listening to [McGhie & Chapman, 1961, p.
105]." Another quotation on attention from an early schizophrenic gives a
similar picture: "The colours of things seem much clearer and yet there is
something missing. The things I look at seem to be flatter as if you were
just looking at a surface. Maybe it's because I notice so much more about
things and find myself looking at them for a longer time. Not only the
colour of things fascinates me but all sorts of little things like markings
in the surface, pick up my attention to [sic] [p. 105]."

While the increased attention to unimportant stimuli is what was expected, the emphasis on a change in intensity of these stimuli (e.g., noises
louder and colors brighter) seems harder to understand within this formulation, and yet it is fairly common in reports from early schizophrenics.
Earlier, it was noted that Fish's account explains such phenomena as due
to increased stimulability from high arousal. While arousal may play a
role, it is also possible that any factor that disorganizes attention — leads
to reduced focus of attention — will affect the apparent intensity of stimuli.
The reader may experience this if he stops reading for a moment and lets
his attention wander; lets his attention wander to the sounds that are present. These sounds will then be subjectively much louder than while he
was reading; in fact, the changes in loudness can be quite impressive. I am
writing this in my office at the University early in the morning. I like to
write at this time because it is so quiet; at least that is the way it always

seemed to me until I started writing this section. But now when I pause and do not focus my attention any more, it is amazing how noisy it is. The ventilating system, my watch, occasional street noises, and the birds, are surprisingly loud.

There is some evidence that potentials evoked in the nervous system by unimportant stimuli may actually be greater when attention is not focused on other stimuli. In reviewing literature on selective attention, Egeth (1967) states that, "It is well-documented that the central nervous system exerts centrifugal control over peripheral receptors and that attentional processes are important to that control (e.g., Hernández-Peón, 1961). In one frequently cited study (Hernández-Peón, Scherrer, & Jouvet, 1956), a chronic electrode located in a cat's cochlear nucleus registered an evoked potential when a click was sounded. However, when a bottled mouse was put into the cat's cage, the cat showed many behavioral signs of alertness but the electrode failed to detect any sign of activity when the click was sounded. In further experiments, other investigators have demonstrated that sensory neurons in several modalities are attenuated, if not completely blocked, in the presence of arousing stimuli [p. 50]." Egeth cautions that the evidence does not constitute convincing proof, in part because of the need for research with human subjects, but the hypothesis that unfocused attention can raise the actual level of nervous system "noise" from trivial stimulation, is quite tenable.

As we have seen, the basic collapse of response hierarchies implies a number of changes in the way that multiple-stimulus situations are experienced: like other sequenced behaviors, scanning will, at times, depart from the usual behavior sequence; sequential organization will be disturbed by interference from competing responses. In addition, the lack of attention that is organized and focused on important classes of stimuli will mean that incidental stimuli are experienced as more intense. Taken together, these are rather important changes in the way the world is experienced. Some of the changes may be interesting, such as the increased intensity in some stimuli; however, the distractibility, the inability to control the sequencing of behavior, the confusing, disorganized, more intense, noise environment must, in the main, be aversive, even at times terrfying.

HABITUAL DEFENSES

If acute response interference does have these aversive effects on the way complex environments are perceived, then those behaviors that reduce the confusion should be likely to become habitual over time. Changes in scanning behaviors were briefly mentioned in the last chapter, but several kinds of changes would be motivated, and should be mentioned together to see the clinical picture that is implied.

First, one way to reduce distraction and the intensity of peripheral stimulation would be to involve oneself in simple response chains where the cue feedback from the preceding behaviors was (a) strong enough to dominate the uncontrollable and often complex stimulation from outside oneself, and (b) was unambiguous — did not lead to the competing responses that would be evoked by a complex pattern of prior responses. Certain strongly maintained or strongly repetitive actions would be of this type. They would help to maintain the situation with a single, strong, clearly dominant response tendency wherein the schizophrenic's subjective environment does not slip into a state of intense disorganization.

Another way to reduce the likelihood of strong response competition would be simply to avoid stiuations where multiple concurrent stimuli will evoke competing responses, and also to avoid those single stimuli that evoke complex response hierarchies. Thus, over time, the schizophrenic may learn to face a blank wall, keep his head down, and to avoid social situations with their great likelihood of evoking competing responses.

As was suggested in the last chapter, schizophrenics will also not be likely to move around with much speed because this increases the number of stimuli encountered in a short period of time, and therefore the likelihood of multiple concurrent response tendencies. As an early schizophrenic reported, "I don't like moving fast. I feel there would be a breakup if I went too quick. I can only stand that a short time and then I have to stop. If I carried on I wouldn't be aware of things as they really are. I would just be aware of the sound and the noise and the movements. Everything would be a jumbled mass. I have found that I can stop this happening by going completely still and motionless. When I do that, things are easier to take in [McGhie & Chapman, 1961, p. 106]." Another schizophrenic reported much the same: "When I move quickly it's a strain on me. Things go too quick for my mind. They get blurred and it's like being blind. It's as if you were seeing a picture one moment and another picture the next. I just stop and watch my feet. Everything is alright if I stop, but if I start moving again I lose control [*ibid.*]."

Both these quotations were from fairly early schizophrenics who were already beginning to realize that behaviors that expose them to multiple and changing stimuli result in disorganization. Like the schizophrenic who was quoted near the end of the last chapter, they are beginning to learn that behavioral styles that restrict observation — keeping eyes shut, going completely still and motionless, stopping and watching feet — result in less confusion. The same restriction in motility as a defense against disorganization has also been emphasized by Freeman, who quotes a remark from a catatonic patient that was reported by Sechahaye (1956). "... 'I did not want to move, because if I did everything changed around me and upset me horribly so I remained still to hold on to a sense of permanence' [Freeman, 1960, p. 932]."

The particular methods that different schizophrenics learn to use in attempting to cope with their inability to remain organized while scanning a broad range of stimuli would be expected to be quite varied. Different schizophrenics will learn to emphasize different techniques of avoiding complex stimulation. Some will usually orient themselves to simple, unchanging stimuli, such as floors or walls; others will use repetitive behaviors to maintain focus of attention on stimulation that is not complex. Others, whose basic response disorganization may be less severe, should be able to observe their environment, being careful only to avoid the more complex situations that are likely when one is socializing or moving too fast.

The idea of cause and effect presented here is different from that which is often given in discussions of schizophrenia. Here, withdrawal is seen as a byproduct of the basic pathological disorganization, instead of the converse that has been proposed by others, for example Cameron, who felt that asocialization was primary. The most usual general formulation is that withdrawal is primary in schizophrenia, and that the earliest stages involve cessation of observation — reality testing — which is motivated by a need to avoid stressful ideation. Freeman (1960) briefly summarized the two ways of thinking about cause and effect as follows: "This theory, initially proposed by Freud [1950], of a break with reality as the initial phase in a psychotic illness was challenged by Federn ... His extensive clinical experience with schizophrenic patients led him to propose that the break with reality was a secondary reaction. He believed that the first manifestations in the disease were due to perceptual distortions which then led to the break with reality. These perceptual abnormalities could often be traced to a psychic conflict. Federn's theory has two important implications. First, it suggests that the defect in schizophrenia is to be found in an ego which reacts anomalously to psychic or physical stress. Second, it raises the possibility that the psychotic symptoms are not necessarily linked with an unconscious conflict nor is the aim of the symptoms the provision of a defense against the conscious recognition of the conflict [pp. 933-934]."

Freeman seems to accept the view that withdrawal is secondary to some more basic pathology that involves general reduction in ability to control stimulation, because in his own clinical observations he has also noted that withdrawal seems causally tied to overstimulation in general, and not necessarily to conflict-linked stimulation. In describing a catatonic schizophrenic, Freeman reported, "It was noted that sudden changes in visual perception, brought about by sudden alterations in his visual field, always led to catatonic rigidity. This form of catatonic manifestation appeared not only in response to changes in visual perception but also as a result of an unexpected noise or to a rapid alteration in sounds already heard [1960, p. 932]."

Freeman's summary statement on the psychopathology of schizophrenia clearly parallels the lines of our discussion: "Some of the clinical observations which I have cited suggest that there is a strong reaction against the disintegration of the ego. It would appear as if the patient is attempting to recover his capacity for stabilized thinking, motility and perception by insulating himself against stimulation arising from the environment. This would account for the reluctance and resentment which many patients show when invited to undertake activities or make human contacts. It is as if they feel themselves to be in a state of overstimulation and their desire is to reduce this to manageable proportions [p. 935]."

Of course, as anyone who has spent much time on schizophrenic wards realizes, withdrawal is rarely very complete. The retreat from overstimulation is a matter of degree. Most schizophrenics do attempt to scan their environment to some degree. The major implications in what has been said are only that scanning will usually be less extensive in more experienced schizophrenics than in acutes or normals, and if and when scanning is continued the pace of shifting to scanning new stimuli will be slowed. Chronic schizophrenics should begin to scan, but should have learned to stop their scanning before taking in the amount of information they have realized they may not be able to organize adequately.

Consider the following example (again from Freeman): "The next observations are taken from ... those patients whose illness has continued for many years without remission ... The first example is brief. The patient was a young catatonic man of about 28 who had been ill for several years. He was rather negativistic but would reply when spoken to. He was undergoing psychotherapy and at the beginning of the treatment he was asked if he knew the season of the year. It was in fact a winter's day with snow on the ground but the sun shining brilliantly. The patient looked out of the window and without hesitation answered summer. I do not think this was a nonsensical or evasive answer. Can we not infer that his response had been determined by his awareness of the sunshine and that this percept had overshadowed any other facet of the observed situation [p. 931]."

The above is an example of how reduced scanning results in incomplete information. Only parts of the necessary total stimulus pattern are present and therefore responding is deviant. The reduced scanning and resulting behavior seem to be fairly similar to that described by Bleuler (1950) in his account of schizophrenia. "Concepts lose their completeness, seem to dispense with one or more of their essential components; indeed, in many cases they are only represented by a few truncated notions. Thus, the process of association often works with mere fragments of ideas and concepts. This results in associations which normal individuals will regard as incorrect, bizarre, and utterly unpredictable [Bleuler, 1950, p. 9]." This description would easily apply to a schizophrenic's reply "summer" in the context of a question about the season with sun and snow outside. The major difference is that in our discussion the loss of some elements of the guiding context is seen as a secondary, learned, reaction to basic response disorganization, whereas for Bleuler the reduction appears to be more basic. However, though our discussion of loss of information views this loss as secondary, it is important to remember that the data are cross-sectional and do not provide information about changes over time and about what is fundamental and what is a reaction to fundamental process. Especially in terms of the heterogeneity in early schizophrenics, it is at least as tenable to view loss of information as basic, at least in some schizophrenics.

LOCUS AND NATURE OF REDUCED CUE UTILIZATION

Let us try to be a little more specific about what the characteristics of reduced cue utilization should be if reduced scanning is learned in the way that we have described it. We have already mentioned that it should be more prevalent in chronic than in early schizophrenics, as is suggested by Payne's research with his Object Classification Test. We will look at more evidence on this point later.

If the initial motivation for learning to restrict scanning, and learning a cautious pace in what limited continuation of sequential scanning operations is done, is to reduce anxiety that results from disorganization, then restricted scanning should be seen most in those schizophrenics who were most disorganized initially. Also, in those schizophrenics who would be most uncomfortable with reduced observation this feeling should offset the reinforcement from reduced disorganization. There is some evidence suggesting that paranoid schizophrenics may be less disorganized than other schizophrenics (Lester, 1960), and also paranoids should be less comfortable with reduced vigilance. Thus, reduced cue utilization should be most prominent in non-paranoid chronic schizophrenics.

In addition, the particular stimulus input that is lost will not have the haphazard quality that Bleuler suggests. In our basic formulation of schizophrenia we have said that in simple stimulus situations the same responses will tend to be dominant for normals and schizophrenics. An implication is that on entering situations or beginning a task, the initial scanning response will tend to be the same in schizophrenics and normals. Those additional scanning responses that are likely to increase the complexity of the situation to the point that the schizophrenic becomes disorganized, are therefore the normal secondary, tertiary, scanning responses, and so forth—not the initial scanning response. Thus, chronic schizophrenics should tend to begin scanning with the same observing responses as normals, the reduction being in later scanning.

How broadly should these hypotheses be applied? Although cue utilization is usually discussed in terms of external stimuli, much appropriate behavior requires reviewing or scanning of the several possible meanings of symbols or the scanning or searching for different events stored in memory. Research with normal subjects has revealed consistent individual differences in "... a Scanning principle that is apparent in individual consistencies in the extensiveness with which subjects characteristically sample stimuli," and which is "... relevant to situations in which the subject must attend (a) to stimuli outside himself or (b) to elements of memory schemata within himself [Gardner, 1961, p. 120]." Although Gardner's use of the term "scanning" may not necessarily be the same as ours, as will be discussed later, the attentional consistencies that have been found in normals across different types of information suggest that research on tasks that require both internal and external information may be relevant to our hypotheses.

Using internal information

Reaction-time (RT) tasks are of a kind in which information from previous events affects performance. A subject's readiness to respond to a "go" signal cannot be maintained at top efficiency for long periods of time and so subjects learn to use their prior experience with the task to estimate when the "go" signal will occur.

When the preparatory interval (PI—the interval between "ready" and "go" signals) varies, maximal readiness should be obtained by scanning past PIs held in memory, noting the length of PI when the probability of the "go" signal begins to climb sharply, and beginning to sharpen readiness when that interval has passed since the "ready" signal. Of course, all past trials will not have an equal likelihood of being scanned. We would expect that recent events would be dominant in memory and, if there are any restrictions on scanning, more remote events will be more likely to be ignored. This means that the pattern of readiness preparation should be overdetermined by the length of the immediately preceding preparatory interval (PPI). Thus, in a task where the length of PIs varies, if the PPI has been longer than average, on the present trial the point at which readiness will begin to be high should often be late. Thus reaction time should be an increasing function of length of PPI.

This relationship should hold for both normals and schizophrenics, but to arrive at the main point of our discussion, if memory scanning is more restricted in chronic schizophrenics than in normals, chronic schizophrenics should show a closer relationship between reaction time and length of the dominant PI in memory, the PPI. This is because with their reduced scanning, recent events should compose a larger portion of the remembered events that are scanned. This does not imply that chronic schizophrenics will react faster than normals when the PPI has been short. Reaction-time tasks require at least a dual focus—focus on past PIs and on the source of the "go" signal. If chronic schizophrenics are narrow and slow in scanning, and distractible by irrelevancies in those categories of stimuli they do scan, they will have difficulty with this dual focus. Thus, as a group, chronic schizophrenics should always be slower than normals. Our major point is that when one of the possible relevant sources of information—remembered length of preparatory intervals—is considered, chronics will abnormally restrict their scanning to the more recent information, and the relationship between RT and length of PPI will be greater for them.

The results of two experiments reported by Zahn, Rosenthal, and Shakow (1963) are relevant here. The procedures and apparatus were fairly similar in both experiments, the major difference being that a warning signal was used in the first experiment, but not the second. Also, the subjects in Experiment I had prior experience in RT tasks. The procedures were as follows: When S was ready, he would depress a telegraph key. Then, after a preparatory interval that varied, a tone sounded and the time S took to lift his finger from the key was measured. Each length of PI followed each other PI at least once. There were two groups of Ss: hospitalized normals, and chronic schizophrenics.

We have said that if the time when the S gets maximally prepared for the "go" signal is based on information about past PIs, and if the past PI that is prominent—which is most sure to be scanned—is the preceding PI (the PPI), then the readiness should be overdetermined by the PPI. Figure 16 shows that this is the case for both normals and schizophrenics. Past PIs are not equal in determining readiness. The PPI provides prominent information, in that when it was longer, Ss were less ready to respond after average PIs on the next trial. The slopes of these curves relating PPI to RT were significant for both schizophrenics and normals in both experiments.

That chronic schizophrenics and normals show the same form of relationship between PPI and RT is consistent with the suggestion that both are more likely to scan remembered information about the immediately previous preparatory interval than they are to scan more remote events. Thus, the groups are similar in the information they overuse. It seems reasonable to assume that the information that is overused occurs with above-average consistency in the set of information that is scanned. In other words, the groups are similar in their use of a scanning response that is quite prominent — ranks high in consistency among the alternate scanning responses. Because scanning operations are quite time-limited here, it must be that this rather consistent scanning response is early in the scanning sequence. Thus, the slope of the RT-PPI relationship suggests that PPIs are scanned early, and this early scanning response is made by both groups.

Our main hypothesis was that chronic schizophrenics would not continue their scanning operations as far past these early responses as normals do. Thus, in chronic schizophrenics, the length of the PPI should be a larger part of the available information about length of preparatory intervals, and RT should be more closely related to PPI. This was the case. In both experiments, the RT-PPI slopes were significantly greater for the chronic schizophrenics than for the normals. As Zahn *et al.* conclude,

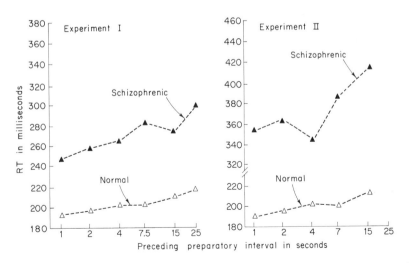

Fig. 16. Reaction time (RT) as a function of preceding preparatory interval (PPI) in normals and schizophrenics. (Adapted from Zahn *et al.*, 1963.)

"Instead of basing their pattern of preparation on their experience with the series of PIs as a whole, then, the patients seem to base it, much more than do normal subjects, on the most recent event in the series [1963, p. 50]."

Zahn et al. discuss their results in a way that is quite similar to the reasoning we have used. "In the present experiment it might be speculated that the patients, being unable to handle the information provided by the series of varied PIs, simplify the task by [basing] their pattern of preparation disproportionately on the information provided by the immediately preceding trial [1963, p. 51]."

In the above experiment it seemed reasonable to assume that more recent events would be dominant in memory, and thus to interpret the overinfluence of PPIs in schizophrenics as due to their tendency to not scan their memory much beyond the information that is dominant in memory. However, recent events are not necessarily always most prominent in memory, and if prominence, rather than recency, is the important thing in determining what information schizophrenics will focus on, then it should be possible to change the information that is used by chronic schizophrenics by arranging conditions where more remote events have been emphasized more than recent events. In such cases, schizophrenics should overly restrict their scanning to the information which, though remote in time, is prominent in memory. One way this could be done is by repeating certain information over and over again. Then the prominence of this information would be such that limited occurrences of later, more recent information would be less likely to be prominent in memory. Remember that in the Zahn et al. 1963 study, PIs were irregular. Thus, there was no regular repetition of information that might overcome the effects of recency in determining the prominence of information.

However, in an earlier RT study (Zahn, Rosenthal, & Shakow, 1961), ten trials with the same length PI were given, followed by trials with a shorter PI. In this study, chronic schizophrenics showed less use of the information provided by the more recent, shorter PIs than did normals. After the series of long PIs, they were less able to switch their "set" to be ready for shorter PIs. Zahn et al. (1961) concluded, "The data indicate, in general, a greater susceptibility to the effects of context of PIs on the part of schizophrenic subjects. More specifically, these subjects show an inability to recover from an inadequate set or response pattern which has been introduced by unfavorable external conditions [p. 168]." However, especially in view of the many other studies showing reduced scanning of information in chronics, it does not seem that this special susceptibility to context should be attributed to broad scanning of context. Rather, this seems to be a case of inability to adapt because of overfocus on more remote information that has become prominent through repetition.

In another study that is relevant to reduced scanning of internal information, Weinstein, Goldstone, and Boardman (1958) compared chronic schizophrenics and normals on a time-estimation task where the influence of recent and remote anchors was compared. If anchor stimuli are not repeated, and are changed as they were in this study, we would expect that chronic schizophrenics would be less influenced by remote anchor stimuli than normals. Thus, chronics' judgments should shift more when anchor stimuli are changed.

Each subject was instructed to report whether the duration of a tone was more or less than one second. Tones of varying length were presented in series of ascending and descending durations, which began with a short tone (short anchor) for half of each group and a long anchor for the other half. For both chronic schizophrenics and normals, the short anchor, as compared to the long anchor, pulled down the point at which subjects judged durations to be more or less than one second, 50% of the time. Thus, in this task, anchor stimuli are determiners of judgments for both chronic schizophrenics and normals.

The most important point for our purposes is the relative effectiveness of these anchor stimuli when they are recent or remote in time. In the last part of the experiment, the subjects who had been given short anchors received a final long anchor, and vice versa. For the normals, their judgments in this last series reflected both the long and the short anchor. There was no effect of recency in that the time-estimation judgments in this final series were not significantly different for those who had the long anchor or short anchor last. However, the judgments made by the chronic schizophrenics in the final series were not as affected by the prior series. Those schizophrenics with short anchors in this final series showed the same kind of downward pull that had been observed when they were tested without opposite prior experience. As Weinstein *et al.* conclude, "When long and short anchors were reversed, the normals demonstrated an anchor interaction, giving judgments which incorporated the past anchor-determined frame of reference; the schizophrenics, however, ignored past experience with anchors, judging solely in terms of the demand value of the new anchor [1958, p. 243]."

The way in which words are used should also reflect the degree to which internal information is scanned. For example, multi-meaning words cannot always be interpreted appropriately unless the different possible meanings are scanned. If a person stops examining the meaning of a multi-meaning word after considering only the dominant meaning, then he will lose much of the meaning of the word. From what we have said, chronic schizophrenics should do just this. They should stop scanning meanings sooner than do normals. Thus, their use of multi-meaning words should be overdetermined by the dominant meaning of a word.

This is, of course, exactly what Chapman, Chapman, and Miller (1964) have said about schizophrenics' use of words. As was discussed in Chapter 2, the Chapman *et al.* research led to the following conclusion: ". . . schizophrenics do not weigh simultaneously the several different aspects of meaning in order to answer appropriately the question at hand, but instead answer by using a more limited number of aspects of the meaning. Moreover, the aspects of meaning which schizophrenics use to excess appear to be those which are more prominent for normal persons [Chapman, Chapman, & Miller, 1964, p. 51]."

Here we are adding two major points: (a) this narrowed observation of alternate meanings should be learned over time, as an attempt to cope with response disorganization and so should be more extreme in chronic than acute schizophrenics, and (b) the narrowed observation is not restricted to scanning the meanings of words, but is, rather, part of narrowing in all aspects of information intake.

Point "a" should be tested by redoing the Chapman research with comparable groups of good premorbid acute schizophrenics, and chronic schizophrenics. At present, we can only note that the schizophrenics in each of the five experiments reported in Chapman *et al.* (1964) and Chapman and Chapman (1965), where the narrowed observation of meaning was observed, were all quite long-term chronic patients.

Point "b," the range of tasks over which reduced observation occurs, will be shown in this chapter, and the differences between acute and chronic schizophrenics in some of these situations will also be shown in the research to be discussed.

But, to return to the effect of reduced scanning on chronic schizophrenics' use of words, the reduced scanning of meanings should lead to words often being used in unusual ways. In the introduction to their important paper, "Interpretation of Words in Schizophrenia," Chapman and Chapman (1965) cited several classic examples of the unusual ways in which schizophrenics use words, especially schizophrenics' word substitutions based on partial overlap of meaning. One instance was in Freud's analysis of the Schreber case where Freud believed that when Schreber wrote of God he really meant to say something about his father.

If the unusual meanings that chronic schizophrenics sometimes seem to intend to convey in the words they use are, at least in part, due to chronic schizophrenics' having observed only parts of meanings, then another prediction follows. Though chronic schizophrenics use words in unusual ways more than normals do, they should be deficient in ability to recognize *specific* unusual meanings of words. Put in another way that directly relates to research that has been done, chronic schizophrenics' deficit in ability to recognize specific unusual definitions of words should be greater than their deficiency in giving definitions of words that are acceptable in standard vocabulary tests.

The reasons are as follows. Willner (1965) has shown that the easy stimulus words on the vocabulary tests from the Wechsler-Bellevue and Wechsler Adult Intelligence Scales tend to be familiar words, often with several alternate meanings, and the more difficult words tend to be unfamiliar, but with fewer alternate meanings. What should be the effect of chronics' collapsed response hierarchies and reduced scanning in such situations? For chronic schizophrenics, occasional momentary dominance of a normally nondominant meaning, together with limited recognition of the range of alternate meanings, should mean that at times the unusualness of their responses or the lack of abstraction in their responses to easy words would be even lower than the fairly low standards that usually exist for scoring easy words. However, on more difficult words, which usually have few alternate meanings, being difficult primarily because of lack of familiarity, chronic schizophrenics should often do surprisingly well in view of their sporadic earlier performance. This kind of scatter has often been noted in schizophrenics. However, the basic point here is not the scatter, but that there should be inconsistency without severe over-all deficit in standard vocabulary tests. At least, the deficit should be relatively less than a deficit in ability to recognize particular unusual meanings because this latter dificit relates more directly to a tendency not to scan non-dominant meanings to the extent that normals do. This latter deficit should be fairly consistent in that it would be a fairly rare occasion on which the particular non-dominant meaning that was relevant would be momentarily dominant for most schizophrenics.

Willner (1965) constructed an Unusual Meanings Vocabulary Test which should tap this special schizophrenic deficit. This test consists of 42 multiple-choice items where the subject is to select one of five choice words that is closest in meaning to a stimulus word. A sample item is *air— pen, tune, sun, lamp, burn.* "Tune" is, of course, the correct choice. The instructions state that, "You will find that in this vocabulary test, the correct answer will almost always be an unusual meaning of the word and not the first meaning that comes to mind [Willner, 1965, p. 406]." Thus, this test requires exactly the continued scanning that should be difficult for the chronic schizophrenic in that it runs contrary to his mechanism for reducing response interference.

Willner used this test to compare the performance of matched pairs of chronic schizophrenics and non-schizophrenic (general medical, psychosomatic, and psychoneurotic) patients. Each pair was exactly matched on WAIS weighted vocabulary score and closely matched on age and education, with the schizophrenics averaging non-significantly higher on these latter two variables. Thus, the subjects are matched on ability to give acceptible, common definitions of words, but, as we have implied, even with such matching, the chronic schizophrenics, with their restricted scanning of meanings, should show greater deficit in recognition of unusual meanings. This was the case. On the Willner Unusual Meanings Vocabulary Test, the chronic Schizophrenics scored significantly lower ($p = <.001$) with a mean of 17.53, as compared to the control group's mean of 22.04.

Thus, in a number of experiments that require the scanning of internal information, chronic schizophrenics seem to have a limited breadth of scanning. In scanning memory (Zahn *et al.*, 1961, 1963), chronic schizophrenics seem to base their readiness in RT tasks abnormally on prominent information—the length of the prior preparatory intervals or the length of regularly repeated PIs. Chronic schizophrenics also appear to focus too much on recent anchor stimuli (Weinstein *et al.*, 1958) and on prominent meanings of words, tending to neglect less prominent meanings (Chapman *et al.*, 1964; Chapman & Chapman, 1965; Willner, 1965).

Using external information

Our intention has been to see if the hypothesis of reduced scanning by chronic schizophrenics is applicable to a very general range of information-monitoring operations. Continuing, we now turn from scanning memory and meaning to the scanning of physical displays in the external environment. Parenthetically, we should note that the distinction between scanning external and internal information is not always as clear as it might at first seem to be. For example, to some extent information that is presented externally may be maintained briefly in short-term memory and reviewed there.

There are a number of ways in which the scanning of information from external sources may be restricted along lawful lines. Sources of stimulation may be organized according to location (e.g., central versus peripheral), color, movement vs. being stationary, or they may be organized by sensory modality. There is little doubt that human beings are able to use scanning selectively with scanning organized according to such stimulus dimensions, and that if motivated, subjects can change the way they scan information. After reviewing a number of experiments on selective attention, Egeth (1967) concluded, "When a multidimensional visual stimulus is available for only a short time, information may be extracted from it, one dimension after another. Furthermore, it is possible to train subjects so they are capable of varying the order of examination of dimensions in accordance with the relative value of the dimensions [p. 55]."

This last point on the possibility of using differential relevance to train subjects to vary what comes first in their scanning suggests an additional strategy for testing our hypothesis about the locus of reduced scanning in chronic schizophrenics. Although Egeth was speaking only of visual stimuli, it would seem that if subjects can learn to vary their priorities of examining stumulus dimensions within a single modality, they should easily be able to vary their priorities in scanning dimensions of information that are as discriminable as visual versus auditory information. Thus, if both visual and auditory information can be relevant in a task, but on recent trials only auditory information has been presented, subjects should be "set" primarily to scan auditory information, with examination of visual information being secondary. Also, if on some trials, visual information has been most valuable, then if subjects do switch the scanning priority in accordance with stimulus value, visual information should come to have priority. These statements may be true only in a relative sense in that there may be modality preferences that override the limited experience within an experiment, but the major point still holds. A modality that has yielded relevant information most recently should tend to be more prominent in scanning operations.

If the sensory modality that has just yielded relevant information has priority in scanning operations on a subsequent trial, and if chronic schizophrenics tend to be more limited than normals in their scanning operations and have an abnormally cautious pace in what limited shifts to scanning additional stimuli that they do make, then chronic schizophrenics should be less responsive than normals to stimulation in a less prominent modality, and should show more relative deficit when relevant information is switched from one modality to another.

An experiment by Sutton, Hakerem, Zubin, and Portnoy (1961) illustrates this phenomenon. Subjects were to lift their finger from a "home" plate as rapidly as possible after any of four stimuli were presented. The stimuli were from two modalities: two different tones and two lights of different colors. After a subject responded to a stimulus, he returned his finger to "home" plate and then after three to five seconds, another stimulus was presented. The experiment was designed so that the stimulus was from the same modality as on the previous trial as often as it was from a different modality. Thus, RT to a changed stimulus modality could be compared to RT to a stimulus in the same modality that had yielded relevant information as the previous trial. As would be expected from more limited scanning of modalities that are less prominent in scanning sequences, in this experiment chronic schizophrenics were slowed relatively more than normals on trials when the modality was shifted. When differences between ipsimodal and cross-modal RTs were plotted for each subject, about one-half of the normals had longer cross-modal RTs, while 87% of the chronic schizophrenics had longer cross-modal RTs. The difference between the distributions was highly significant. These results certainly are in accord with our hypotheses that normals are more constantly and rapidly scanning a broader range of external information than chronic schizophrenics.

A different method of making a specific modality prominent has been used by Kristofferson (1967). In this study, a light and a sound were presented together on each trial, and the subject's task was to release a telegraph key as quickly as possible when one of the two stimuli terminated. Two conditions were used, one where subjects were told which stimulus would terminate first, and one where subjects were not told. Thus, in one condition the relevant modality was made prominent through instruction, and the other condition required broader vigilance. In accord with our discussion, the results were that chronic schizophrenics showed significantly greater differences in reaction times between the two conditions than did normals; the chronics showing most deficit when there was a need for broader vigilance.

The range of external information that a person utilizes effectively can also be assessed by comparing performance in situations where there is little and much relevant information. When the central, prominent information is kept constant in both conditions, with the added information being peripheral, we would expect that chronic schizophrenics' overfocus on the prominent information would mean that they would show less responsiveness to the added relevant information than normals would.

Hamilton (1963) tested cue responsiveness by asking subjects to judge the size of objects under "cueless" and "cue" conditions. These conditions refer to a difference in peripheral cues. Under cueless conditions, size was judged in a darkened enclosure with the objects to be judged being dimly illuminated and the subjects unable to see other cues that are relevant to judging size. In the cue conditions, there was full daylight so other stimuli in the room could be observed. A chin-rest kept the subjects oriented toward the objects to be judged, and instructions to judge an object presumably also acted to keep that object prominent for the subjects. Thus, scanning of the cues that were added in the cue condition would seem to require greater breadth of scanning. Hamilton's "Responsiveness Index" was the change in size judgment from "cueless" to "cue" conditions. The subjects were 20 chronic non-paranoid schizophrenics, 10 chronic paranoid schizophrenics, 10 neurotics, 12 normals, and 4 manic-depressive psychotics. Comparisons of the "Responsiveness Index" for the different groups indicated that ". . . psychotic patients, and non-paranoid schizophrenics particularly, find it difficult to improve a specific perceptual skill when average conditions for its operation become available. To some extent at least, the psychotic patients in this study appeared to operate perceptually under normal conditions as if still restricted by the earlier cueless conditions. They appeared to be less well able than the non-psychotics to modify their judgment of objects when normal field cues had been added to the isolated object stimuli [Hamilton, 1963, p. 37]."

Acute-chronic differences

Except for Payne's research, the experiments we have discussed have shown differences between chronic schizophrenics and non-psychotics, but have not included groups of acute schizophrenics. If, according to our hypothesis, reduced scanning is a learned reaction to the basic response disorganization in schizophrenia, such learned changes in habitual scanning should become greater, or at least more consistent and broadly applied, in chronic schizophrenics. As was mentioned in the last chapter, it may be expected that early in hospitalization some schizophrenics would quickly discover that some forms of reduced scanning would lead to less response confusion, but we would certainly expect that a greater number of chronic schizophrenics would have made this discovery and that, over time, their habits of reduced scanning would have become stronger, with other, more normal, scanning patterns being more inhibited.

Concerning schizophrenics who have been hospitalized fairly recently, a study reported by Sutton and Zubin (1965) does point toward the possibility that a number of these schizophrenics may also have somewhat reduced scanning. In a variant of the multiple-stimulus RT task used by Sutton *et al.* (1961), these schizophrenics showed an abnormal tendency to react more slowly to stimuli that had not been made prominent through use on the previous trial. It should be noted that this abnormal difference in vigilance to different kinds of relevant cues does not contradict the evidence concerning abnormal total breadth of attention (to relevant plus irrelevant cues) in acutes. In the two-factor account of cue utilization we are using, some reduction in scanning would imply less vigilance to certain relevant cues, with a marked inability to focus among the cues that had been scanned still leading to abnormally scattered attention.

A more extreme reduction in scanning in chronics should lead to greater loss of relevant cues, together with the reduction in total cues attended to that was noted by Payne.

If chronic schizophrenics scan less than acutes or normals, this means that in situations where considerable information is required for accurate identification, chronics will discontinue scanning before they have sufficient information; thus, when a stimulus display is difficult to identify, with more and more information presented over time, chronic schizophrenics should stop scanning sooner than acutes or normals, and because of their reduced information, they will make more errors in identifying the stimulus display. The prediction of more errors by the chronics is important because otherwise their stopping scanning sooner could be attributed to quicker or greater information intake per unit of time rather than to habitually reduced scanning.

Draguns (1963) tested three groups — schizophrenics who had been hospitalized continuously for over a year, schizophrenics within their first month of psychiatric hospitalization, and a group of normals — on recognition of realistic drawings of simple scenes that had been photographically blurred in varying degrees. Nine series of 12 pictures each were used, with each series presented in order from the most to least blurred pictures. Subjects could say what they thought the picture represented at any point in the series and when they did so, the series was discontinued.

The more chronic schizophrenics made their judgments significantly earlier in the series than did normal subjects, with acute schizophrenics having an intermediate position non-significantly different from either other group. That the quicker judgment was made with less information was indicated by significantly more recognition errors in the chronics than in the normals, with acutes again holding an intermediate position.

One finding in Draguns' study seems to contradict our discussion. Within the chronic schizophrenics, length of hospitalization was not significantly related to the point in the series at which observation was stopped. Draguns suggests that this may mean that the important variable underlying the above differences among groups may not be duration of the schizophrenic process but, rather, that the chronic group was the extreme group simply because it was more typically schizophrenic in composition in that its members had exhibited schizophrenic behavior over a substantial period of time. It is certainly possible that chronics' tendency toward reduced scanning is the result of differences that have existed from the beginning of hospitalization, with the narrow scanners simply tending to remain longer in hospitals. Remember that this was the explanation of acute-chronic differences suggested by Payne.

It is also possible that the negligible correlations between hospitalization and the number of stimuli that the subject chose to observe, and between length of hospitalization and identification errors, would have been greater if tested over a broader range of the acute-chronic dimension. If we can assume that the degree to which available information is scanned affects the ability to identify silhouettes of familiar, though complex, scenes of objects (such as an oriental soldier), and affects the ability to judge whether or not two objects are at the same distance from the viewer, then a study by Johannsen, Friedman, and Liccione (1964) is relevant here. Johannsen *et al.* tested these abilities on normals and six groups of schizophrenics with differing lengths of hospitalization varying from less than six months to more than 20 years. Both perceptual abilities decreased with increasing chronicity.

Johannsen *et al.* also found that when incomplete simple alpha-numerical or geometric figures — such as the letter H, number 88, or a checkerboard — are to be identified, this ability is not significantly decreased with greater chronicity, though there is a trend in that direction. It seems likely that the amount of information needed to identify such simple figures is less than the stimulus intake needed for accurate depth perception or identification of a silhouette of an oriental soldier. Thus, it is not surprising that performance in the simpler tasks is not as related to chronicity, in that they do not require broad information intake, which is what is hypothesized to change over time.

Another possible explanation of the relationship between chronicity and reduced range of cue utilization is that reduced input is not related to attempts to reduce basic schizophrenic inability to organize multiple response tendencies, but is, rather, due to a long stay in simplified hospital environments. The latter suggestion was made by Pishkin, Smith, and Leibowitz (1962). They found that in a size-judgment task where each observation was time limited by brief illumination, chronic schizpohrenics required a greater number of observations, but still made more errors than normal controls. In their discussion of these results, they noted that, "In an earlier paper Pishkin, Armstrong-Ressy, Aller, and Comstock (1960) suggested that deterioration of schizophrenics' ability to attend to environmental cues decreases with chronicity. It may well be that attention or the amount of information transmitted in a single illumination of the field, used in this study, is related to duration of illness and not to schizophrenic pathology, per se. It may be safely assumed that the perceptual environment of a long-term schizophrenic patient becomes limited (mean duration of hospitalization for this subject population was 9.7 years), and progressively less demanding on the subject's decision-making capacities such as those required in the present task [Pishkin *et al.*, 1962, pp. 328-329]." Although Pishkin *et al.* talk of a distinction between schizophrenic pathology and length of illness, what they seem to be pointing to is a distinction between schizophrenic pathology and time in the protected, less demanding, simplified and consistent hospital environment.

There is some other evidence that suggests that long-term institutionalization rather than basic schizophrenic processes may lead to some of the changes in attentional styles that are found in long-term schizophrenics.

Silverman, Berg, and Kantor (1965) tested early and long-term prisoners on the Titchner Circles Illusion, which is apparently affected by extensiveness of scanning. In this task, two inner circles are each surrounded by a concentric ring of circles. One of the inner circles has a different size on each trial, and the subject is to judge whether this variable inner circle is smaller, equal to, or larger than the standard inner circle. Silverman *et al.* report earlier evidence indicating that extensive scanning of the peripheral circles tends to increase the tendency to underestimate the relative size of the standard circle. Compared to short-term prisoners, long-term prisoners showed less of this tendency. Thus, the Silverman *et al.* results supported their hypothesis that long-term prisoners would show less scanning, paralleling differences between early and chronic schizophrenics. Unless there is a higher proportion of schizophrenics in long-term prison populations, this evidence implies that exposure "to unpleasurable or to strongly aversive situations with no adequate means of escape being available ... [Silverman *et al.,* 1965]" is a sufficient cause for narrowed scanning, and that reduction in scanning is not unique to schizophrenics.

Of course, this is not surprising. As has been suggested here, reduced scanning in many schizophrenics may be a *secondary,* learned, reaction to their basic aversive response interference, and thus there is no reason to suppose that this reaction is unique to schizophrenics.

The last sentence above suggests that, although a perceptual decrement that increases with time in aversive environments may be found in groups other than schizophrenics, in schizophrenics much of their own aversive environment is self-produced; therefore, for them, length of institutionalization may be less important in the development of coping patterns than the duration of their basic pathology. Relevant to this distinction, Johannsen and O'Connell (1965) reanalyzed the significant Johannsen *et al.* (1964) results and found that perceptual decrement was related to the duration of the basic illness (defined as time since initial hospitalization), and not related to percentage of time spent in the hospital since the initial diagnosis. As Johannsen and O'Connell conclude, "This study suggests that perceptual deficits which increase with advancing chronicity are more likely to be a function of factors involved in the disorder itself rather than of environmental factors [p. 246]."

Of course, the Johannsen and O'Connell results do not mean that in long-term schizophrenics processes related to cue utilization would not be affected by any kind of environment. A good test of this question would require comparing the results of the usual simplified low-expectancy hospital environments with environments specifically arranged to expect and reinforce attentive broad observation.

To return to the Pishkin *et al* (1962) study, one finding does clearly limit one aspect of our previous discussion. Remember that in the Draguns (1963) study, chronic schizophrenics had stopped viewing blurred drawings earlier than normals, even though they did not have sufficient information to identify the object. We had expected this from our hypothesis of limited scanning. However, in the Pishkin *et al.* (1962) study, chronic schizophrenics continued to observe the stimulus objects for more trials than other groups — although they apparently still obtained less relevant information. The important differences may be that there were fewer alternate responses in the Pishkin *et al.* task (*S*s were only to make a judgment of larger, smaller, or same instead of identifying a scene), and the schizophrenics had control of the pacing of the task. Thus, the stimuli would lead to less response confusion, thereby being a stimulus situation that was less disorganizing and less aversive to the schizophrenics. Also, it may well be that chronic schizophrenics find experimenter-paced tasks somewhat more aversive in that they have learned that quick multiple stimulation often leads to greater disorganization, as we saw in some of the quotations from schizophrenics at the beginning of this chapter.

In sum, the research we have discussed does support the hypothesis that chronic schizophrenics have a smaller breadth of scanning than normals or acute schizophrenics. The studies on this topic that we have reviewed in this chapter, and in the course of our discussion of Payne's research in the previous chapter, have been intended to illustrate the trend of the evidence, which seems in accord with this hypothesis, and suggests that there is support for applying the hypothesis quite broadly — to a variety of situations where scanning different kinds of information, both internal and external, is needed for normal performance.

There is one aspect of our general hypothesis about narrowed scanning that we have not discussed because the evidence is less clear. This is the suggestion that where the basic response interference is apparently less and where reduced vigilance would be less comfortable (as for the paranoid), then there will be less reduction in scanning in chronics. The literature contains repeated suggestions that paranoids, even if chronic patients, continue to have the broad attention that is generally more typical of acute schizophrenics, but there is less consistency in the results than there is for the basic reduction of range of cue utilization in chronics.

It should also be emphasized again that although the research indicates reduced range of cue utilization in chronics, this reduction can be explained as we have done, or it can be explained in other ways, such as poorer prognosis in patients who do not have broad attention. As has been noted previously, available studies are cross-sectional in nature, and thus do not provide good evidence to separate hypotheses about secondary learning of coping mechanisms from hypotheses, such as Payne's, that what is basic is initial heterogeneity, with differential prognosis.

For a broader review of relevant literature, the reader is referred to

Venables' (1964) excellent paper. Venables' views about causation differ from those in our discussion here (we will discuss his views later), but his review of the literature leads to kinds of conclusions about breadth of cue utilization that are similar to the conclusions suggested here, although his broader review also leads to some possible conclusions about subcategories that we have not covered. A quotation illustrates this: ". . . chronic schizophrenic patients—and possibly included in this category are process patients—tend to be characterized by a state of restriction of the attentional field . . . Attention is restricted not only to the extent that peripheral sensory items contemporaneously present do not rise into consciousness, but also involved is the nonrecognition of items in memory which form part of the meaningful structure in which the present central item appears. . . . In contrast to the chronic patient, the acute (and possibly the reactive and paranoid) patient is characterized by an inability to restrict the range of his attention so that he is flooded by sensory impressions from all quarters. Items of all kinds have equal importance, and the meaningfulness of the external world tends to be lost for the opposite reason to that which applies to the chronic patient [p. 41]."

It should be noted that although Venables' conclusions are, in the main, similar to the lines of our discussion, there are differences in the underlying thinking. Whereas Venables has been careful to speak only of the degree of restriction of attention where acutes and chronics seem to be opposite, our discussion of range of attention was based on two underlying processes—(a) range of scanning, and (b) ability to focus within what has been scanned—and acutes and chronics have not been viewed as being on opposite sides of normals on either of these dimensions. The acutes' broad attention has been hypothesized to be the result of normal or near normal range of scanning with reduced ability to focus. The chronic's reduced range of attention is seen as the result of sharp reduction in range of scanning. This should reduce the number of relevant cues he observes and can utilize, especially the relevant information that is peripheral. However, because most chronics still are seen as having the basic schizophrenic disorganization of attention hierarchies, chronics' total range of attention (to relevant plus irrelevant cues) will not be as markedly below normal as might be expected from the degree to which his scanning is reduced (for example, refer back to Table 8 in the previous chapter). In other words, in chronics their restriction in scanning decreases stimulus input, leaving some relevant cues outside of the input. However, their attention is abnormally scattered among the fewer relevant and irrelevant stimuli in their restricted input.

Because our discussion does not involve chronics and acutes being on opposite sides of normals on underlying dimensions, there is no implication that normals lie between acutes and chronics on any causal variable. However, as was indicated in the last part of the quotation from Venables, Venables suggests that acutes and chronics lie on opposite sides of normals on a causative dimension, which is sympathetic and cortical activation, and it is this that leads to their opposing abnormalities in restriction of attention. This view must assume either that acutes pass through a stage of normality as they become chronics, or that there are two distinct types of schizophrenia with schizophrenics with restricted attention having poorer prognosis. This latter suggestion especially is, of course, a very tenable view, with some similarity to Payne's hypothesis about acute-chronic differences.

STRESS, AROUSAL, AND RANGE OF CUE UTILIZATION

Even if we were to question Venables' conclusion that acute and chronic schizophrenics are opposite in abnormality on the dimension of physiological activation, his conclusion that activation (arousal) is causally related to restriction of attention should be examined further. Actually, there is a line of evidence discussed in Chapter 3 that, when combined with what has been said in this chapter, would lead to the same conclusion.

As was discussed, a number of theories have suggested that arousal increases the degree to which competing response tendencies become more equal in strength and/or interfere with each other, and there is some experimental evidence supporting these views. At least this is what seems to happen under some conditions, such as at upper levels of arousal. In this chapter, it has been suggested that such response disorganization could be offset in part by reducing the number of competing response tendencies through narrowing the range of scanning of stimuli. Thus, high arousal, through increasing response disorganization, should lead to reduced scanning. This line of thinking is not new. Among others, Callaway and Stone (1960) have suggested that high arousal may lead to greater equivalence of the probability of alternate responses, which individuals may attempt to handle by restricted observation.

Experiments with normal subjects

As made by Callaway and Stone, the suggestion that individuals may react to arousal-induced complexity by narrowing their attention was applied to people in general, not just schizophrenics. Actually, unless we assume that schizophrenics and normals are qualitatively different and that processes we see in schizophrenics are distinctly different processes than in normals, this is what we should expect. Our discussion has been concerned with schizophrenics' attempts to cope with their inability to organize competing responses by reducing their range of scanning. Normal persons also meet situations where response complexity is high for them, at least occasionally, and there is no reason to expect that they should not have learned the same type of reactions. Normals' disorganization, even on these occasions, would probably be less than that of the schizophrenic, and normals' disorganization certainly is not as usual for them, so less extreme narrowing would be learned. Also, normals should learn to discriminate situations where their ability to handle complexity would be overloaded, from situations they could handle. The difference would not be that schizophrenics learn uniquely different ways to handle disorganization; rather, because of their more extreme and more general disorganization, persons who become schizophrenic must learn more extreme reduction in scanning and must learn to apply this reduction to situations where they had formerly been able to use broad scanning.

If we do not view schizophrenics as qualitatively different, it is then useful to look at research on normals to gain information about variables that may underlie restricted utilization of relevant cues in schizophrenics.

One of the earlier papers suggesting that stress would restrict observation is a literature review and a report of new experiments by Callaway and Thompson (1953). Their reasons for expecting a relationship between stress and reduced observation were different from those discussed above. They suggest that, "One can, with some assurance, predict that the perception of an acute threat by a relatively normal animal will evoke a sympathetic discharge. Almost invariably, a system within an organism which is operated on by a second system in turn operates on that second system. ... In most biological systems, feedback is negative in sign; that is to say, if a receiving system drives an output system, some of that output is fed back into the receiving system in such a way that the threshold of the receiving system will be raised [p. 433.]." Hence, perception of threat should operate to restrict perception.

Their method of testing this hypothesis was based on the assumption that a reduction in cues would decrease the apparent size of distant objects. To the extent that cues that indicate distance are reduced, distant objects will be judged to be of a size more in accord with the shrunken retinal image. Thus, if sympathetic arousal decreases the range of cue input, "We should expect increased sympathetic activity to decrease that general awareness of gradients by which we correct our shrunken retinal image of a distant object [Callaway & Thompson, 1953, p. 445]."

Sympathetic activity was increased in normal subjects by immersing subjects' feet in a bucket of ice cubes, and, in a second experiment, by inhalation of amyl nitrite. Compared to control conditions, and in accord with the hypothesis, both methods of increasing sympathetic activity caused distant objects to be judged to be significantly smaller.

Two additional experiments provided further evidence to indicate that the reduction in apparent size was due to reduction in cue usage. In one experiment, the size of distant objects was judged in the presence of maximal cues indicating the distance of the object to be judged. The cues were, for example, continuous desk-edge and wall gradients between the subject and the object, which provided clear distance cues. In this situation, an increase in sympathetic activity significantly reduced the size judgments. In other words, when good distance cues were present, there could be a significant reduction in use of relevant cues and apparent size could be decreased by sympathetic arousal.

In the other experiment, the clear, continuous distance cues were reduced by placing the task situation outdoors, without intervening furniture and walls to provide as clear cues. In this situation, without excellent cues, the effect of cue reduction should be less and, as expected, although increased sympathetic activity tended to reduce the apparent size of the distant object somewhat, the results were not significant.

Although the Callaway and Thompson experiments do suggest that an increase in sympathetic activation tends to decrease cue utilization, their specific explanation of this relationship may not be accurate. Remember that they suggest that the specific cause is perception of threat, leading to sympathetic activity, which acts through an automatic neurological feedback to inhibit receptors. This is somewhat different than the hypothesis that the specific causal chain is that sympathetic and cortical arousal may, in some situations, increase response competition, and it is this response competition that human beings react to by reducing their range of observation. [As we have noted, in a later article, Callaway and Stone (1960) do suggest that arousal may increase response complexity, which is reacted to by narrowing of attention.]

Some accounts of the relationship between stress-arousal conditions and response competition (e.g., Broen & Storms, 1961, 1966) emphasize that unless a situation evokes concurrent competing responses, an increase in arousal will not tend to lead to response disorganization. Thus, if response disorganization is an important causal factor in reduced scanning, there must be a fair degree of response competition in the situation or increased arousal will not restrict scanning. These interactions among response complexity, arousal, and reduced scanning would not necessarily be expected if arousal acts automatically to raise receptor thresholds. The thresholds would be raised regardless of the complexity of the task.

An experiment by Bursill (1958) is possibly relevant here, although it may not be legitimate to generalize from the particular stress conditions Bursill used to other stress conditions, including conditions that have clearly been shown to result in sympathetic cortical activation. Bursill varied thermal stress while subjects were performing two tasks concurrently—a central continuous pursuit-meter task where a pointer to be tracked moved from side to side with irregular speed, and a task requiring the subjects to report which one of six peripherally located lights was lighted when that light came on briefly. The effect of the heat-stress was to decrease the awareness of peripheral stimuli; the same general effect—reduction in awareness of peripheral cues—as was found in the Callaway and Thompson experiments. Bursill found this funneling of the field of awareness toward the central point of vision when he increased stress in two similar experiments. Thus, it is clear that Bursill was using a stressor that decreases the range of cue utilization.

The important point for our purposes is that this funneling of attention under stress occurred only when task complexity was quite high. Basically, the task is quite complex. In addition to observing peripheral and central stimuli, subjects had to vary the timing, amount, and direction of movement of a control lever with their right hand in the pursuit-meter task, while signaling the lighting of different lights by pressing one of six keys with their left hand. The length of the time interval within which alternate movements would be required could be varied, which would vary the response complexity of the task. In the two experiments in which attentional funneling was found, the number of pursuit-meter excursions per minute was high—55. In a third experiment, all conditions were the same as in Experiment I, with one exception—the pursuit-meter excursions per minute were reduced to 35. With this reduction in the number of different perceptual and motor responses required per unit time, there was no significant funneling of attention. Clearly then, the funneling of attention that had been found was not just an automatic reaction to the thermal stress. The stress itself did not inhibit receptor functioning. Only a combination of stress and a task of high perceptual-motor complexity led to reduced attention to relevant peripheral stimuli.

Arousal and narrowed cue utilization in chronic schizophrenia

As we have seen, there is a fair amount of evidence indicating that chronic schizophrenics utilize a narrowed range of relevant cues. There is also some evidence that suggests that, in normals, the range of cue utilization may be decreased when stress, arousal, or anxiety is high—at least when task complexity is also high. These two lines of data are consistent with the possibility that increased arousal is a causal factor in chronic schizophrenics' reduced cue usage. There is other evidence that, although it does not demonstrate cause and effect, does indicate that in chronic schizophrenia there is a relationship between arousal and narrowed utilization of relevant cues.

Weckowicz (1958) studied the relationship between level of autonomic activity and size constancy in chronic schizophrenics. His general hypothesis about chronic schizophrenia was that a major factor underlying the pathology was an increase in activity in such regulating centers as the hypothalamus and reticular formation. From Callaway and Thompson's earlier experiments indicating that, in normals, sympathetic discharge decreases the awareness of environmental cues that aid in correcting for decreased retinal images produced by distant objects, Weckowicz then hypothesized that those chronic schizophrenics with greatest reduction in size constancy would have the highest levels of autonomic activity. In an earlier study (1957), Weckowicz had shown that size constancy was lower in chronic schizophrenics, primarily in hebephrenics, than in normals and non-schizophrenic patients.

Weckowicz (1958) measured autonomic activity by the reactivity of blood pressure following Mecholyl injection, with high *basal* activity indicated by low *reactivity*. As would be expected if high autonomic activity narrows the cues available for correcting the reduced retinal image, low judgments of the size of distant objects were related to high *basal* autonomic activity. Specifically, when the object was 7.5 meters distant, there was a correlation of +.52 between *reactivity* and average size estimation. At 15 meters this correlation was +.42.

The primary way in which Weckowicz's discussion of range of attention in schizophrenia differs from the emphasis here is that he views range of attention in terms of a single process. Thus, like Venables, when restricted cue usage is associated with high sympathetic activation in chronic schizophrenia, Weckowicz suggests that the abnormally broad awareness of the acute schizophrenic is due to the opposite, parasympathetic predominance. This difference in interpretation is emphasized again in order to keep us thinking in terms of alternate interpretations, which are not, as yet, settled by the research evidence.

It must also be kept in mind that the Weckowicz (1958) study only showed a relationship between arousal and reduced use of peripheral cues, not that arousal was the cause of reduced cue utilization in chronic schizophrenics. His results were in line with the results of the studies on normals that involved experimental manipulations, and so we may be inclined to accept interpretations in terms of arousal as a cause of the narrowing in schizophrenics. However, the reverse causation is also possible. If reduced scanning is a defense against overstimulation, then reduced range of cue utilization in chronics could well be related to a general tendency to "withdraw." Venables (1963) found this to be the case, although only in non-paranoids. Thus, those non-paranoid chronics who show the most extreme reductions in scanning may think of experimental situations as a specific threat to their pattern of defense, and their especially high levels of arousal in experiments could be, at least in part, the *result* of a special threat to their habitual patterns of defense. This threat may, in turn, exacerbate the defense, but the causation is not clearly unidirectional.

At this point, a distinction between initial cause and continued causal relationship may be useful. In early schizophrenics, as in normals, an increase in arousal may very likely be one contributor to increased response complexity that, in turn, leads to decreased cue utilization. However, if we hypothesize that the rather pervasive and extreme response interference in acute schizophrenia often necessitates beginning to learn new, more generalized, and relatively constant habits of reduced scanning, we would not expect that for individual chronic schizophrenics experimental decreases or increases in arousal would continue to cause as much decrease or increase in cue utilization. Remember that, according to our discussion, the causal effect of arousal on scanning is not necessarily due to an automatic neurophysiological reaction. Instead the relationship may reflect the increase in response interference that, in some conditions, is caused by increased arousal, and which evokes the habit of reduced scanning, which will return response complexity to manageable levels. As long as the habitual changes in scanning are normally discriminative, being closely tied to changes in situational cues that predict degree of response interference, arousal should be causally related to reduced scanning, at least in those complex situations where arousal would significantly increase response interference. This should be the case with normals, and experiments that vary sympathetic discharge suggest that this causal relationship does hold in normals.

It should be noted that this relationship seems to hold for variations in arousal *within* individuals. This is not to say that, among normals, those individuals with less clear response hierarchies will have reduced scanning when compared to other individuals. Gardner (1961) has shown that the ability to "articulate" a stimulus field — to focus on relevant cues and not attend to irrelevant cues — is independent from range of sampling cues in the stimulus field. Thus, it would appear that individuals differ in their comfort with or willingness to scan stimuli that may interfere with appropriate focus. However, the research on changes in range of cue utilization with increased arousal can be interpreted as suggesting that if arousal increases response interference above the level that a particular individual is used to, then the range of scanning is reduced. The reduced scanning may be either a reaction to increased response interference or a reaction to situational cues that in the past have been associated with high probability that response interference will be increased.

However, in the early stages of schizophrenia, there should be little payoff for continuing to attempt to use the old discriminations to guide scanning changes. Especially in those patients where there is rather extreme and pervasive response interference, the old discriminations, which signal where scanning can be normally broad without leading to high interference, will no longer work. Also, the increased response interference makes minor discriminations more difficult. Thus, it may be that unless the factors that cause the abnormal response interference return quickly to normal levels, the patients' reduced scanning becomes abnormally general, being fairly extreme across all but quite simple situations. To the extent that reduced scanning in chronics is "on" except for situations that are less complex than those usually used in research on range of cue utilization, then the causal relationships observed between arousal and range of cue utilization when arousal is varied experimentally in normals might not be as strong in chronic schizophrenics.

It should be noted that there is some experimental evidence that can be interpreted as suggesting that range of scanning is at least not completely invariant and unrelated to stress in chronic schizophrenics. Autokinetic movement seems to be increased when scanning is reduced (Silverman, 1964a), and Silverman has reported an experiment by Hahn in which, in chronic non-paranoid schizophrenics, autokinetic movement was decreased by success experiences and increased by failure. Thus, in chronic non-paranoid schizophrenics, scanning habits do not appear to have become completely invariant and unrelated to the success-failure continuum, which Silverman interprets as an anxiety continuum. However, even if variation in arousal (and variation in response interference) continues to be related to variation in scanning in chronic schizophrenics, it is still quite possible that the modal level of reduced scanning is more general and extreme in chronics, not simply because of higher arousal, and/or continued greater response interference in all chronics, but because the cues that predicted the need for reduced scanning had become more widespread as a result of the experience of relatively pervasive response interference in early schizophrenia.

Because the above discussion has included some rather complex speculations, it may be useful to review briefly the firmer trends in the evidence we have discussed, before we proceed further. As we have seen, there are fairly substantial indications in available research that many chronic schizophrenics use an abnormally narrow range of relevant cues. For chronics as a group, this narrowing is fairly general across types of information, being found for both external and internal cues. There is also some lawfulness to this narrowing in that prominent cues, more recent experience, dominant meanings, centrally located or more intense stimulation, and repeated cues, tend to be overly focused on to the relative neglect of less prominent information. This restricted cue usage is, however, not as apparent in very acute schizophrenics; in fact, there are indications that acute schizophrenics may attend to a broad range of stimulation.

We have discussed this area of research primarily in terms of two lines of theory. One relates range of cue utilization to level of arousal, and postulates parasympathetic predominance as the cause of broad attention in acute schizophrenia, and sympathetic dominance as leading to narrowed cue utilization in chronic schizophrenia. The other is a two-factor theory that views range of attention as a joint product of (a) range of scanning, which controls the range of stimulus input, and (b) organization of attention within the stimulus input, with acutes and chronics both deficient in ability to organize attention, and chronics having more restricted scanning. This restricted scanning means that chronics' stimulus input is especially likely not to include those relevant stimuli that are usually scanned later in scanning sequences. In this theory, high arousal does not directly cause reduced scanning. High arousal is one of the factors that may cause attention hierarchies to collapse. When, as in acute schizophrenia, this collapse is more extreme than can be handled by a person's normal habits of reduced scanning in complex situations, then the result is overly broad attention. The reduction in scanning from early to late schizophrenia is seen as due to the pervasive response interference in early schizophrenia, with the chronic schizophrenic having learned more extreme and more pervasive reductions in scanning through his attempts to guard against extreme response interference.

7

OTHER ACCOUNTS OF ALTERED CUE UTILIZATION IN SCHIZOPHRENIA

SILVERMAN'S ACCOUNT OF DEVIANT ATTENTION IN SCHIZOPHRENIA

The theory of cue utilization in schizophrenia that we have emphasized overlaps the theory proposed by Silverman (1964a) in some important aspects. Our emphasis on range of scanning, and ability to organize attention selectively, as important and separable variables is similar to Silverman's emphasis on somewhat comparable dimensions as important in accounting for heterogeneity in schizophrenia. However, as we shall see, there are also a number of important differences between the theories.

One of the main emphases in Silverman's theory is the continuity of an individual's attentional style from normality through early schizophrenia; the changes are exacerbations of long-term response dispositions. Silverman also emphasizes the heterogeneity of attention styles in schizophrenia, stressing the confusion in the research literature that results if subjects are not grouped in terms of distinctions such as process-reactive, paranoid-non-paranoid, and acute-chronic, all of which are associated with differences in attention dispositions.

With Silverman's emphasis on enduring individual differences in attention dispositions, the heterogeneity in early schizophrenics' attention is seen as reflecting differences found in normal individuals. Thus Silverman concentrates on those attention differences that have emerged from the considerable recent emphasis on attention deployment in normals, especially the research by Gardner and his co-workers.

Gardner (1961) summarized earlier research as suggesting "... that at least two of the control principles apparent in subjects' performances in laboratory and clinical tests may have particular relevance to attention and attention deployment in adaptive behavior. The first of these controls is a Field Articulation principle that is apparent in responses to situations in which subjects are confronted with perceived incongruity in the form of compelling cues relevant and irrelevant to the adaptive requirement ... The second control is a Scanning principle that is apparent in individual consistencies in the extensiveness with which subjects characteristically sample stimuli [p. 120]."

In his 1961 study, Gardner was primarily interested in accounting for differences in responses to illusion-producing figures in terms of differences in the control principles. To do this, he factor analyzed measures of illusion effects together with tests that, from earlier research, seemed to be highly influenced by differences in the two attention-deployment principles. Our primary interest is in these "marker" variables, which did show the clearest differential loadings on the resultant factors, and should help us to understand the nature of these factors. The loadings for these variables on the first two factors are given in Table 9.

The factors are orthogonal and, from the very high loadings on the perceptual tasks, they appear to represent independent dimensions of perceptual responses. Factor I is best defined by tests that require attending to certain cues and ignoring others, such as finding simple figures in complex contexts (Embedded Figures Test) and being guided by gravity cues, and attending to the direction of a rod, while not responding to the tilting of a frame around the rod (Rod and Frame Test). Thus, in Gardner's words, "This is clearly the predicted Field Articulation Factor ... It seems to represent the capacity to achieve differential responses to relevant vs. irrelevant cues ... Low factor scores can be conceived of as representing facility in concentration in the face of compelling distractions [1961, p. 124]."

The interpretation of Factor II is not as clear. The rationale behind the use of the Size Estimation tasks is that the extent to which a visual field is scanned will be a determiner of the apparent size of an object in that field. Specifically, it seems that centering attention on a near (hand-held in this

TABLE 9[a]

ROTATED (ORTHOGONAL) FACTOR LOADINGS: QUARTIMAX SOLUTION

Measure	Factor	
	I	II
1. Embedded Figures: mean log time	.9424	−.1006
2. Rod and Frame: average error, body erect	.6374	−.1108
3. Size Estimation A: constant error	.2384	−.7180
4. Size Estimation B: constant error	.0708	−.8220

[a] Part of a table from Gardner (1961).

case) object will cause its size to be overestimated, while extensive variation in attention around the visual field will reduce overestimation errors
and possibly cause underestimation. The relationship between variable
attention and reduced overestimation of size has been shown in a study by
Gardner and Long (1962a) where eye movements were recorded during
size estimation tasks. In this study, the relationship occurred only on a
task where objects tended to be overestimated. Thus, it seems that more
widespread attention may tend to oppose and correct error tendencies
(although extensive varying of the focus of attention may also lead to
some underestimation). The relationship between variability in attention,
at least as measured by number of horizontal visual excursions off and on
the standard, and overestimation of size in the task that had been used by
Gardner (1961) was not high ($-.32$). However, the relationship was sta-
tistically significant (and was replicated), thus lending some support to the
interpretation of Factor II as a factor related to extensiveness of scanning. In another study, Gardner and Long (1962b) found the highest relationship between apparent magnitude and number of centrations when the
disc to be judged stood out from a relatively weak background, and thus
might be expected to be enhanced in apparent size. Here, number of centrations and apparent magnitude correlated $-.49$.

The rationale relating scanning to size-estimation errors may be a little
confusing in that it seems to be just opposite to our earlier discussion
where centering attention on specific objects seemed to cause them to be
underestimated. One important difference is apparently whether the object to be judged is near or distant. The rationale discussed previously was
that the retinal size of a *distant* object must be corrected by using peripheral cues or else it would be judged as too small. In the Gardner and
the Gardner and Long studies, the object to be judged is near. It then
seems that it might be possible to extend the rationale of the other studies
and say that near objects that are hand-held or observed against relatively
weak backgrounds may often tend to be overestimated, and this overestimation can be counteracted by attention that is varied on and off the object to be judged. As Gardner and Long (1962a) suggest, "The essential
difference between the performances of extensive and limited scanners in
these procedures seems to lie in the amount of information sampled before commitment to a response [p. 139]." However, it should be noted
that the gathering of any particular information may not be what is required. Many repeated shifts of attention between the object to be judged
and other stimuli may tend to reduce the enhancement effects that come
from focusing just on the object, regardless of the nature of the shifts in
attention. It is true that ability to concentrate on certain cues and ignore
illusion-producing cues (field articulation ability) may also contribute to
reduction in apparent magnitude in some situations. However, we are

dealing with a dimension independent from field articulation, which seems to affect size estimation in the expected direction only when prominent other stimuli that are present do not themselves contribute to illusion-producing effects that enhance the apparent magnitude of the object. Hence, it may be that in the situations where number of shifts in attention is related to size estimation, what is important is the simple variability in attention on and off the object, rather than any particular relevancy or information-gathering aspect of the shifts.

This relationship between shifts in attention and the estimated size of near objects brings up an important point concerning what such size estimations mean. The emphasis in our discussion until now has been that degree of variation in attention is a joint function of range of scanning, and response interference among the attention tendencies to the stimuli that are scanned. Thus, it may well be that size estimation of near objects is more related to what we have called the joint product of these two factors — range of attention or cue utilization — than to what we have called degree of scanning by itself. It is true that Gardner (1961) found that degree of field articulation, which has similarity to freedom from response interference, was relatively uncorrelated with the particular size-estimation tasks he used. However, this may be due to another emphasis in our discussion, that low ability to articulate a field may, in general, be reacted to by reduced scanning. Thus, *on the average*, the joint product — range of attention — would tend to be independent of degree of field articulation. Gardner's second factor may then reflect individual variations in the adjustment of scanning to field articulation. In other words, it may reflect range of attention.

Parenthetically, it should be noted that these considerations do not imply that eye movements are an especially good measure of breadth of attention, or that eye movements will always be inversely related to size estimation. We have suggested that variable eye fixations tend to imply variability in attention. However, the reverse implication does not hold with equal force. Attention can certainly vary without variation in eye fixations, as is most obvious when internal events are some of the stimuli to which attention is sporadically shifted. A person's eyes can be fixated without "seeing" or attending to what is in his visual field. Thus, when shifts in attention on and off objects to be judged are a factor in judging their size, such shifts will not always be adequately reflected in eye movements.

The main point is that, as we discuss Silverman's theory — which emphasizes Gardner's dimensions and relies in part on research using size estimation to measure scanning — we should remember that size estimation tasks may measure something closer to what we have called breadth

of attention, a dimension that we have seen as affected by response interference as well as by range of scanning. In most cases, this will not cause
major confusion in the interpretation of differences between different
groups of schizophrenics in that, given an average degree of deficiency in
response interference, broader scanning will cause broader attention.

Silverman suggests that although individuals are quite consistent in
tending to be low or high on Gardner's two dimensions, the extent to
which individuals differ from the average varies in some conditions. For
example, a pilot study reported by Zahn (1959) showed that schizophrenics with poor-premorbid adjustment tended, in general, to overestimate the size of pictures, and, in addition, this tendency was greater
for pictures that had earlier been associated with punishment than for
pictures associated with reward. There was a slight opposite tendency
for good-premorbid subjects, and the differential effects of the reward
versus punishment conditions was significantly different for the two
groups of subjects.

Based on these data and on the relationship between size estimation
and scanning, Silverman (1964a) suggests that ". . . individuals who ordi-
narily evidence minimal scanning, react to unpleasant stimuli by further
reducing their scanning responsiveness and thus enhancing the perceived
magnitude of stimuli. Underestimating-extensive scanners appear to scan
to an even greater degree when confronted with unpleasant stimuli
[p. 361]."

Thus, in that the individual differences in attention dispositions appear
to be made more extreme by aversive situations, Silverman suggests that
the attention dispositions may come to serve a defensive function. For
example, "The extensive scanner has learned that his most effective
means of escaping or avoiding anxiety is to be hyperalert to the presence of
cues which often precede or co-occur with noxious events [p. 369]."
"Thus, it is suggested that early in the development of a schizophrenic
disorder, as isolations, repressions, and denials become less and less
effective, the individual begins to rely on the most basic forms of adient-
abient adjustive mechanisms. These mechanisms include formerly 'con-
flict-free' attention response dispositions [p. 368]." "Under conditions of
severe psychological stress, the characteristic mode of attention responsiveness utilized by the preschizophrenic is exaggerated and takes on a
singularly defensive function. That is either via what Bleuler referred to
as 'enslavement by optical impressions' or by 'completely ignoring the
outer world,' the schizophrenic gains extraordinary control over his perceptions [p. 369]." The way in which these processes work is seen as
quite different for different schizophrenics. For non-paranoid schizophrenics ". . . what appears to be involved are: (a) an anchoring of atten-

tion on dominant objects in the stimulus field (minimal scanning) and/or
(b) global and unarticulated attentiveness to sensory inputs. Such fixedly
motivated attending operates selectively to minimize or 'gate out' much of
the perceptual and conceptual input from other sources [p. 371]."

Silverman emphasizes that complete withdrawal from external stimuli
would bring about a chaotic, highly aversive state. For example, he cites
experiments where spatial orientation can only be maintained by
"*re*afferent stimulation." This is why, for non-paranoid schizophrenics,
their defense against anxiety-producing experience is not to avoid stimulation completely, but rather to rob it of meaning, either through very narrow scanning or through broader but unarticulated observation.

On the other hand, paranoid schizophrenics are hypothesized to be
very broad scanners who defend against aversive stimulation by reinterpretation of events and relationships. This, of course, means that there
must be a relatively high degree of field articulation — ability to select out
those aspects of a stimulus field that will be in accord with an interpretation, while ignoring other aspects.

This differentiation between paranoids and non-paranoids is consistent
with Venables' (1964) conclusion that non-paranoids are heterogeneous
in breadth of attention, and with Venables' suggestion that paranoids may
be more consistently broad in attentiveness. It is also in accord with
much of our discussion in the previous chapter; although, as we will
mention later, Silverman makes a number of other distinctions we have
not touched on as yet. However, Silverman's emphasis on the paranoid-
non-paranoid distinction and his use of the Gardner *et al.* research,
which suggests specific marker variables for dimensions of attention, has
led to research that provides additional tests of the hypothesized
differences.

Following the Gardner emphasis on size judgments as a measure of
scanning, Silverman (1964b) tested paranoid and non-paranoid schizophrenics (mean hospitalization 4.61 and 3.94 years, respectively) in
judging the size of hand-held discs. One analysis of the results is presented in Table 10. The differences between groups on both under- and
overestimation are highly significant.

Insofar as the evidence we have discussed has suggested that extensive
scanning (or broader attention) is a contributor to reduction in apparent
magnitude in such tasks, the results suggest that paranoid schizophrenics
scan more broadly (or have broader attention) than do non-paranoids.
However, it should be noted that in the same study, these two groups did
not differ in susceptibility to the Tichner Circles Illusion, which has also
been used as a measure of scanning (Silverman, Berg, & Kantor, 1965).

Silverman's emphasis on greater field articulation in paranoids than in

TABLE 10[a]
NUMBER OF SIZE OVERESTIMATIONS AND UNDERESTIMATIONS
FOR DIAGNOSTIC GROUPS

Group	Underestimation responses		Overestimation responses	
	M	SD	M	SD
Non-paranoid Schizophrenics	2.65	2.89	9.15	2.96
Paranoid Schizophrenics	7.06	4.51	4.75	4.45

[a] From Silverman (1964b).

other schizophrenics has received some indirect support. Remember that in the Gardner (1961) factor analysis, the Embedded Figures Test appeared as a good marker variable for the field-articulation dimension of attention. Silverman (1964a) cited a study by J. N. Taylor (1956) where schizophrenics who were rated as primarily delusional were compared with schizophrenics who were primarily hallucinatory on the Embedded Figures Test. Silverman reported that the results were consistent with the hypothesis that delusional subjects were more field independent (could articulate the field better).

THE PROCESS-REACTIVE DISTINCTION

Silverman also emphasized the process-reactive distinction as related to dimensions of attention, with process and reactive patients also differing in the way they change over the course of long-term hospitalization.

Primarily on the basis of the Zahn (1959) pilot study and a study by Harris (1957) that indicated that moderately early schizophrenics with poor-premorbid histories overestimate size and good-premorbids tend to underestimate size, Silverman suggests that process (poor-premorbid) schizophrenics are minimal scanners and reactives are extensive scanners. This overlaps our earlier discussion suggesting that those early schizophrenics who attend to a narrow range of cues were likely to have poor-premorbid histories and poor prognosis. In both these studies, the patients had a mean hospitalization time of less than three years, and therefore Silverman confines these conclusions to early schizophrenia.

In a more recent study using schizophrenics hospitalized less than three years, Davis, Cromwell, and Held (1967) used a variant of Harris' task and found again that poor-premorbid schizophrenics judged sizes to be larger than did good-premorbid schizophrenics.

In another recent study, again using subjects hospitalized less than three years, Neale and Cromwell (1968) found that good-premorbid paranoid schizophrenics underestimated size relative to the judgments of normals and poor-premorbid non-paranoid schizophrenics. The latter group tended to show the greatest overestimation of size. This study used methodology that overlaps in some respects the methodology in the above three studies, but more conditions were used, and it may be useful to comment on the effect of different conditions.

In one condition a slide with a fixation point on it was shown on a screen; subjects were asked to focus on that spot; and then a slide showing the figure that was to be judged was shown on the screen for ten seconds. No other prominent stimuli were present. Then six comparison stimuli were shown at once and subjects picked one to indicate their estimation of the size of the standard. In this condition, which should maximize time focused on the standard relative to the variable attention that is expected when the subject is picking one of six comparison sizes, the standard objects were judged to have greater size than in a second condition. In this second condition, the procedures were the same except that the standard was presented for only 100 milliseconds. With such brief presentation time, judging of apparent size would depend more on examination in memory, and the object in memory should be less prominent relative to other internal and external cues. Thus, attention might be expected to vary more, leading to reduced size estimation, as was found. Thus, a condition that might be expected to increase range of attention changed size estimation in a direction comparable to the difference in size estimation from poor-premorbid non-paranoids to good-premorbid paranoids.

Neale and Cromwell suggested an interpretation for these results that has some overlap with an interpretation in terms of range of attention. Using Pribram's stimulus redundancy construct (personal communication to them), they noted that "According to this construct, size-estimation level increases as a function of the redundancy level of the field in which it is being presented. Redundancy may be achieved by either temporal or spatial repetition of homogeneous or unchanging stimulation . . . The poor premorbid nonparanoid schizophrenic may be hypothesized to have a high redundancy level. The good premorbid paranoid schizophrenic may be hypothesized to have a low redundancy level. Differences in scanning behavior may be hypothesized as one, but not the only, mechanism for maintaining these levels [1968, p. 48]." This last comment about scanning seemed to refer specifically to eye movements. Differences in eye movements off and on an object could not be necessary in order for differences in size estimation between groups of schizophrenics to occur, in that these differences occurred in both conditions described above, and the 100 millisecond condition would presumably rule out the effect of eye movements. Of course, under a broader definition of attention, variablility of attention can still occur, and presumably affect performance, when an object that is held in memory is being judged.

Two additional aspects of the Neale-Cromwell study should be noted. First, though there were differences in mean scores, an analysis of frequency of most accurate choice ("hits") from among the comparison stimuli that were available did not show significant differences between the groups. Neale and Cromwell suggested that this meant that ". . . an interpretation of the size-estimation errors of subgroups of schizophrenics in terms of 'perceptual efficiency' is not tenable . . .[p. 47]." However, the analysis of "hits" is hard to interpret in that the six comparison stimuli did not include a stimulus that was exactly the same size as the object to be judged. Thus it seems possible that potentially more accurate judgments of normals may have been forced toward the slight overestimations or underestimations that were common in schizophrenics, and were counted as size-estimation "hits." An unreliability in the direction of choice when being forced away from accurate choice would tend to leave the normals' mean score unchanged, tending only to equalize the groups on a count of number of nearly accurate choices. Also, as a more general point, it should be remembered that abnormal attention processes need not always be reflected in decreased accuracy. For example, the illusion-producing effects of some situations may be offset by a counteracting deviant attention process.

Finally, it is important to note that the Neale-Cromwell study included a condition where blank flashes were presented for 10 milliseconds. The groups did not differ from each other in this condition, which would seem to rule out an interpretation in terms of a simple size-preference response bias.

Taken together the results of the last four studies that have been cited seem to be in accord with the hypothesis that early good-premorbid schizophrenics have abnormally broad scanning (Silverman's interpretation) or abnormally broad attention (our interpretation), and early poor-premorbid schizophrenics tend to have narrower scanning and attention. However, one negative result should be mentioned. Sutton and Zubin (1965) did not find differences between early schizophrenics divided on an overlapping dichotomy—a process-reactive division—in a task that would seem to measure breadth of vigilance. This task was a reaction-time task similar to the Sutton *et al.* (1961) task described in the previous chapter, where cross-modal reaction times were compared to reactions to stimuli in the modality that had been used on the previous trial. However, though this negative result suggests a need for caution in the interpretation, as of now the majority of the results are consistent with the hypothesis that early poor-premorbid schizophrenics are less broadly attentive to their environments than are early good-premorbid patients.

Zahn (1959) also reported the results of a size-estimation task on more-chronic patients. In this study, the average time since first psychiatric hospitalization was 6 years for the good-premorbid subjects and 8.09 years for the poor-premorbids. One aspect of this study that should be noted is that in contrast to the slight overestimation tendency for normals in the Harris (1957), Davis *et al.* (1967), and Neale and Cromwell (1968) studies, normals had a slight underestimation tendency. Also, though the stimuli in all these studies were quite similar, Zahn associated reward or punishment with his stimuli. Because of these differences it is difficult to know if the measures obtained in Zahn's situation should be interpreted in the same way. While this study will be discussed within the same rationale as the other size-estimation studies, this question should be kept in mind. The results showed greater relative size estimation in the good-premorbid chronics (on stimuli associated with punishment). The relatively greater size estimation in this group is a reversal of the results from studies using less-chronic subjects.

To account for these results, Silverman suggests that over the course of long-term hospitalization there is a trend toward reversal in style of attention. Those schizophrenics who had been extensive scanners (good premorbids or reactives) reduce the extent of their scanning. Process-chronic patients who had at first been narrow scanners become broader in their scanning, but their scanning is reorganized so as to be less responsive to ideational input.

"The developmental and motivational bases for this mechanism are conceived to be: (a) initially, an acute psychological state of self-initiated sensory deprivation, ... (b) a consequent reduction of sufficient sensory inputs in an organism who requires such inputs in order to exist, and (c) the gradual modification of self-initiated sensory-deprivation 'strategy' in terms of the processing of sensory input but the simultaneous non-processing of ideational input [Silverman, 1964a, p. 375]."

Silverman's suggestions concerning differences between chronic process and reactive schizophrenics and his ideas concerning a defensive ideational-gating mechanism came in part from a study by DeVault (1955). DeVault measured physiological reactions of chronic schizophrenics to pictures denoting hostility, dependency, sex, and to a neutral picture, and also measured reactions to a loud bell preceded by a verbal warning. The galvanic skin response (GSR) and heart-rate reactions of the reactives were like that of the normals, except for a lower response to the verbal warning. This can be interpreted as normal responsivity to the stimuli that are scanned, with a possible tendency toward narrowed breadth of scanning (fewer stimuli have an effect). Of course the intensity and centrality of each of these stimuli would not provide the best opportunity for narrowed scanning to be observed.

The most surprising findings in the DeVault study were that in the chronic-process schizophrenics, "The mean heart rate changes of this group were all negative and significantly different from the changes of the normals and reactives [DeVault, 1955, abstract p. 3]." In the process group, the GSR changes were also reduced but were in the same direction as normals' reactions.

DeVault interpreted these results in terms of a study by Darrow (1929) where, DeVault reports, sensory and ideational stimuli were shown to produce different physiological responses, with sensory stimuli more likely to excite peripheral responses, and ideational stimuli being more effective in increasing heart activity. Thus, DeVault suggested that the negative heart rate changes in the process group mean that ". . . there is perhaps less tendency to react with ideation, or possibly a higher threshold for fright or anxiety in the process group [p. 51]."

In accord with this interpretation, Silverman suggests that some reduction in breadth of information usage would be observed in all chronic schizophrenics, but in process patients the selectivity would be more in terms of the filtering out of ideational stimuli, thus chronic-process schizophrenics may not show minimal scanning in the sense of reduced registering of physical stimulation.

Actually there is not much additional evidence concerning differences between chronic process and reactive schizophrenics in their scanning. As we have seen, there is quite a bit of evidence indicating that, with the possible exception of paranoids, chronic schizophrenics are responsive to a narrower range of information than normals and acutes. The Silverman hypothesis indicates a need for research concerning individual consistencies in this reduced cue utilization. We have interpreted the reduced information as due to a general reduction in scanning, which can be seen in scanning of physical displays, remembered information, and meaning hierarchies. While it seems to be the case that chronic schizophrenics tend to react to less information from each of these sources, it is not necessarily true that the *same* chronics who have the most narrowed scanning of physical displays will tend to have the greatest restriction in scanning of alternate meanings. The general tendency for reduced information usage by chronics may instead be due to narrowed external observation in one subgroup, with another group having broader external observation together with reduced ideational reactions or with reduced scanning of the meanings evoked by the stimuli they observe. Both ways of reacting would reduce the complexity of the environment, and this reduction may still be the motivation behind both attentional styles.

Although in an earlier discussion we commented briefly on the relationship of cue utilization to premorbid factors and prognosis, now that we have Silverman's more extensive thoughts on the process-reactive distinction it may be useful to relate this distinction in somewhat greater detail to the lines of our earlier discussion.

A decrease in ability to organize attention may be gradual or relatively sudden. If ability to organize alternate response tendencies is basic in schizophrenia, this gradualness or suddenness of change in response organization can be measured by the gradualness or suddenness of onset of schizophrenic behavior, and should be reflected in the process-reactive distinction, and the conceptually overlapping good-premorbid poor-premorbid distinction. Another aspect of this distinction is that good-premorbid histories tend to be related to faster recovery (Farina, Garmezy, & Barry, 1963). Together this implies that in good-premorbid reactives there is a fairly sharp increase in response interference, which is not likely to be very long-lasting.

The acute-reactive schizophrenic should be most like the acute schizophrenics we discussed earlier. His normal, habitual restrictions in scanning that are evoked by cues that have been associated with increases in environmental complexity are now inadequate in coping with the more extreme and more general response interference he experiences. To the extent that the concept of field articulation is similar to the concept of collapsed attention hierarchies, this can be restated — the acute reactive patient scans too broadly in view of his reduced field articulation. The result is the overly broad attention — the distractibility — that has been noted in many acutes.

Because it takes time to learn further restrictions in scanning habits, and because the basic response interference is not long-lasting in many of these patients, their prognosis is moderately good. They not only recover from the response interference, but also the response interference does not usually last long enough for abnormal scanning styles to become habitual. Among these reactive patients, only a limited group should become chronic. If the factors causing the increased response interference continue somewhat longer than usual, or the abnormal reduction in scanning becomes habitual quickly, then the patient will not be normal even with a return to normal field articulation. Even with a return to near-normal levels of response interference, he will continue for some time to lose needed information and thus exhibit deviant behavior because of his habitual, but unnecessary, reduction in scanning. Only if the hospital environment motivates and reinforces broader scanning, which would no longer be disorganizing, would he return to normal behavior. These considerations are consistent with Silverman's description of reactive schizophrenics as relatively broad scanners in their acute stage, and narrow scanners as chronics.

Silverman also reports an unpublished study by Bryant (1961), which found that chronic good-premorbid (reactive) patients showed near-normal field articulation as indicated by analytic, field-independent performance on the rod-and-frame test. Because of the possibility that the good-premorbid, reactive schizophrenics who become chronic are disturbed more by habitual defensive reactions than by a basic susceptibility to competing responses, which is in remission, the Dokecki, Polidoro, and Cromwell (1965) study on stability and commonality of verbal associations is quite interesting. In that collapsed response hierarchies should be reflected not only in attention, but also in sporadic intrusions of non-dominant associations, the Cromwell *et al.* results, showing normal stability and commonality of associations to words in chronic good-premorbids, are in line with the near-normal field articulation found in these patients. Also in line with these suggestions, another study (Ries & Johnson, 1967) has shown that in reactive patients, but not in process patients, word-association commonality improves with length of hospitalization. In process patients, commonality tends to be reduced over time.

In some contrast to the reactive patient, the more long-term involvement or insidious onset of schizophrenia prior to hospitalization in the poor-premorbid patient should mean that it is more likely that at the time of hospitalization he has already begun to adjust his scanning to the increased response interference. His reaction to the more extreme disturbance leading to his hospitalization should be an exacerbation of these tendencies. The poorer prognosis in these patients would be implied by two factors: early learning of debilitating habitual attention styles; and continued abnormal response interference which would not allow the relearning of normal scanning.

Though there is some overlap, which has been noted in the above paragraphs, our interpretation of the more chronic phases of schizophrenia differs from Silverman's. Aside from DeVault's results, which will be reinterpreted in the next chapter, remember that Silverman's interpretation of shifts in scanning in more-chronic patients rests primarily on Zahn's (1959) results in a size-estimation task. As has been noted, it seems quite possible that this type of size estimation is a function of the breadth of attention, a joint function of scanning and response interference, rather than scanning alone.

If this is the case, consider the progression in good-premorbid schizophrenics whom we have viewed as near-normal scanners with marked response interference in early schizophrenia; those patients who become chronics shifting to become narrow scanners over time; and with later remission of response interference. Early in schizophrenia, their range of attention should be broad, with consequent low size estimation in the type of task discussed in this chapter. Later, with narrow scanning and reduced response interference, their breadth of attention should be low, with a consequent tendency toward relative overestimation, as in the results Silverman emphasized.

In poor-premorbid schizophrenics, there seems to be no remission of response interference over time. In fact, the Ries and Johnson (1967) results can be interpreted as suggesting that, in these patients, response interference is progressively worse. These patients are seen as having marked restriction in scanning fairly early in hospitalization, which, because it is used rather pervasively in anticipation of complexity, is usually sufficient to cause some restriction in range of attention, even given these patients' abnormal response interference — hence, their relative overestimation of the size of near objects. Given progressively worse response interference in these patients, the reaction of narrowing of scanning may also be progressive. The result may be no major changes in breadth of attention over time, or if response interference progresses somewhat more than restriction in scanning, the result would be some increase in breadth of attention. Either situation would account for the kind of shift in size estimation relative to good-premorbids that Silverman has emphasized. This account is proposed here because it seems to encompass a broad range of evidence, including that emphasized by Silverman, and it does not require non-monotonic shifts in the underlying factors for any patient from the early stage onward.

These last paragraphs have not described Silverman's theory, but have integrated much of what he says in hypotheses that also are consistent with the major points in our earlier discussion. These last paragraphs have also been consistent with one of Silverman's major emphases: the heterogeneity in schizophrenia and the need to emphasize differences among schizophrenics in theories and research designs. There is not yet sufficient evidence concerning subgroups of schizophrenics to provide a firm basis for the details of Silverman's theory or the kind of speculative discussion we have just engaged in. Regarding differences among schizophrenics, the trend of the evidence only gives fairly firm support to the broader differences we have emphasized. That is, although there is heterogeneity in early schizophrenia, more early schizophrenics respond to an abnormally broad range of cues than is the case for chronic schizophrenics. Silverman's theory emphasizes the need to know more than these gross statements. Specifically, we need to know more than can be learned from cross-sectional research. We need to learn about individual differences in possible exacerbations of basic observational habits from normality through early schizophrenia, and we also need longitudinal studies of the continuing modifications in observational habits as a schizophrenic process continues.

USING THE BROADBENT MODEL

It seems likely that in the future a fair amount of thinking about information usage in schizophrenia will use concepts and models that differ in some respects from those that we have emphasized. This is primarily because, as behavioral processes in which schizophrenics show deficit are identified, there should be increasing use of the extensive research on these processes as they work in normals, with the different theories about these processes in normals used in conjunction with specific hypotheses about schizophrenic deficit. One relevant model is the model of attention processes proposed by Broadbent (1958), which, as Broadbent has illustrated in his excellent book, is based on a great amount of research on attention in normals. In a limited way, Broadbent's model has already been applied to schizophrenia (Payne, 1966; Yates, 1966). For the remainder of this chapter we will concentrate on applying Broadbent's model of normal attention to schizophrenia, both to show how a different conceptual framework can encompass some of the major trends in the research we have discussed, and because discussion of Broadbent's concepts provides a convenient way of integrating a number of other theories of attention in schizophrenia that should be mentioned.

In Broadbent's model, "A nervous system acts to some extent as a single communication channel, so that it is meaningful to regard it as having a limited capacity [1958, p. 297]." This capacity is defined in terms of the amount of information contained in the sensory events being processed. Sensory events do not enter this channel directly; rather, after being registered by sensory receptors, they are held in a short-term store, where they decay rapidly if not selected by a selective filter to enter the limited-capacity information-processing channel. "The selection is not completely random, and the probability of a particular class of events being selected is increased by certain properties of the events [e.g., intensity] and states of the organism [drives] [1958, p. 297]."

Once signals have been selected from short-term store, the conditional probabilities concerning sequences of signals that have been experienced are held in a separate long-term (relatively slowly decaying) store. These conditional probabilities have two functions. They are used to predict redundancy in series of signals and thereby reduce the information load in a series of signals, enabling more other signals to be selected to enter the information-processing channel. Also, when an organism is motivated in a certain direction, it enables behavior to " ... vary in such a way that it receives that ordered series of stimuli which, from a count of past conditional probabilities, has the highest probability of terminating in the primary reinforcement for that drive [p. 298]." Thus, the store of conditional probabilities of past events not only enables more signals to be processed, but also seems to act on the filter to aid the selection of relevant classes of signals from short-term store. It also seems to enable the person to orient himself so as to be more likely to have relevant information register at the senses and enter the short-term store.

There are other principles in Broadbent's model, such as an ability to recycle information from the information-processing channel to short-term store, but the above principles are the major ones. The information flow is illustrated in Figure 17.

Payne was one of the first to apply one of Broadbent's concepts to schizophrenia. Regarding earlier theorizing with his co-workers (Payne, Matussek, & George, 1959), he said, "They speculated that overinclusion could be regarded as being the result of an abnormal amount of stimulus generalization, to use a learning theory concept. Put in terms of a rather different approach to cognitive theory, and using a concept which Broadbent has found experimentally useful, they suggested that overinclusive thinking might be regarded as due to a defect in some hypothetical central

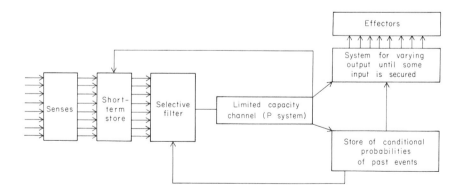

Fig. 17.   Broadbent's tentative information-flow diagram. (From Broadbent, 1958.)

'filter' mechanism, the function of which is to screen out irrelevant data, both internal (in the form of irrelevant thoughts and associations) and external (in the form of irrelevant stimuli), to allow for the most efficient processing of incoming information [1966, p. 79]."

If we use the details of Broadbent's model, this emphasis on reduced relevancy suggests a disorder in the way the conditional probabilities in the long-term store are able to control the filter, and so the disorder could be in the long-term store, the filter, or transmission to the filter. Payne's other emphasis on good prognosis in those early schizophrenics who are overinclusive must mean that although the filter is not as responsive to the guiding information in the long-term store, possibly because the information or its transmission is somehow jumbled, the information itself is not lost from long-term store. If the information about past contingencies in the world were seriously and lastingly disturbed, it would seem that the prognosis for readjustment to that world would be poor.

Other theories have suggested a variable factor that might cause this kind of short-term change in the use of knowledge about past contingencies. Callaway and Stone (1960), whose thinking was mentioned briefly in the previous chapter, reinterpreted Callaway's earlier research on arousal and attention in terms of Broadbent's model, and suggested that increased arousal might be such a factor, leading to "reduced probabilistic coding (i.e., increased overall uncertainty with regard to the stimulus ensemble under consideration) [p. 395]." They suggest that because in Broadbent's model this loss increases the information load, a person would attempt to handle this increase in information load by reducing the size of the stimulus ensemble under consideration.

Callaway and Stone summarize the result they expect from increased arousal in the Broadbent model as, "A reduced ensemble of possible stimuli all considered more nearly equally probable than previously would imply a reduced ensemble of response possibilities all more nearly equally ready for expression than previously [pp. 395-396]."

As we have interpreted Broadbent's model, the reduced probabilistic coding should also mean a loss in information about relevancy, and so the stimulus ensemble let through the filter cannot be as structured in terms of relevance; cannot be as determined by past contingencies, as is normal. [Feigenberg (in press) has also viewed schizophrenia as involving a loss of past information about environmental contingencies, which results in inappropriate attention-orienting responses.]

Thus, taking the Callaway and Stone suggestions, together with the partial loss of relevancy as a guide to filtering, increased arousal may lead to a state of partially reduced observation with partial loss of relevant information, and disorganized, fluctuating, distraction by irrelevant stimuli. To the extent that the equalization of attention to competing stimulation is severe enough to more than offset the reduction in stimulus ensemble, the result should be the overinclusion of the irrelevant that Payne stresses in the early overinclusive schizophrenics. As we have suggested previously, to the extent that the coping mechanism of narrowing attention is only as extensive as learned in normal premorbid experience, the severer disorganization in early schizophrenia should lead to responding to more total stimuli, although fewer relevant stimuli than in the normal state. When we consider that the stresses leading to increased arousal may well be short-term, the prognosis in such a condition should be fairly good. Such individuals should become chronically disturbed only if the high arousal were maintained, or maintained at least for a sufficient time for the disorganization in the filtering process to change significantly the probabilities held in long-term store, and/or if the learning of abnormally extreme narrowing to cope with the abnormal information overload becomes habitual. With these added considerations, Callaway and Stone's use of Broadbent's model can lead to an interpretation of one kind of early schizophrenia that is very much like our earlier discussion of reactive schizophrenia.

A theory of deficit in early schizophrenia proposed by McGhie and Chapman (1961) is less elaborate, but is similar in its concentration on filter defect, distractibility, and arousal as a causal factor. They suggest that "The earliest reported symptoms of a schizophrenic illness indicate that a primary disorder is that of a decrease in the selective and inhibitory functions of attention [1961, p. 114]," which they also suggest may be the result of lack of appropriate inhibition of the reticular activating system.

SUGGESTIONS FROM THE YATES AND CROMWELL-DOKECKI THEORIES

Yates (1966) has proposed the following theory of schizophrenia, which seems quite different from the McGhie-Chapman theory, but which Yates views as an elaboration of the McGhie-Chapman theory. "Broadbent's filter theory postulates that there is a limit to the amount of information which can be processed per unit of time. While the primary processing channel is thus occupied, other information must be held in the short-term memory system. In terms of this formulation, it is here argued that the basic defect in schizophrenia is as follows: first, the rate at which information is processed by schizophrenics is abnormally slow. But, if this is so, an inevitable corollary follows. Since the short-term memory system, by definition, can hold information for only a short time, the amount of stored information lost per unit time will be much greater than in normals. Hence, only a fragmentary part of the relevant stimulation will be successfully processed. From this, it follows inevitably that, over long periods of time, thought disorder or other bizarreness of behavior must appear [Yates, 1966, p. 128]."

That this type of formulation can account for a considerable body of research on schizophrenic behavior has been shown by Cromwell and Dokecki (in press), who have proposed a similar formulation. Their theory proposes that "... *an important dysfunction in schizophrenia is the inability to disattend from stimuli.*" They illustrated what they meant as follows: "When you, as a normally functioning individual, read this sentence and approach the end of it, you have attended to, 'processed,' and disattended from the first part of the sentence and are fully ready to receive the last part of it. In other words the disattention mechanism operates very quickly and allows a readiness to receive and even anticipate new stimuli. By contrast, the schizophrenic is often not able to do this." (The quotations are from pages 66 and 67 in the prepublication copy.)

Along somewhat similar lines, Williams (1966) concluded from a series of experiments, in which schizophrenics were asked to complete verbal passages that varied in length and verbal constraints, and their performance was compared with that of normal controls with and without pressure to make a fast response, that, "The performance of schizophrenic patients was in some ways similar to that of controls under time-pressure; both groups tended to associate to the first words of the sequences presented rather than following the given verbal constraints. It is suggested that the difference between schizophrenic and normal behavior in the completing of verbal passages is mainly due to the speed with which incoming auditory stimuli are dealt with [p. 161]."

Obviously, the Cromwell-Dokecki and Williams type of slow-processing formulations, like Yates' similar theory, are able to account for many of the findings on limited cue usage in many schizophrenics, and schizophrenics' distraction by, or overuse of, the cues in a situation that they scan first.

One possible difficulty in the way Yates uses his formulation lies in Yates' assertion in speaking of his theory that, "This theory is very similar to that proposed by Chapman & McGhie, except that they stress the importance of irrelevant stimulation which is not screened out. This part of the theory seems unnecessary, however. It is here argued that the basic difficulty is an inability to process relevant information which is being presented at too fast a rate to be efficiently handled, caused by the abnormally slow rate of processing [Yates, 1966, p. 128]."

In spite of Yates' assertion that an inability to screen out irrelevant information seems unnecessary in accounting for schizophrenic deficit, it does not seem that his theory of the deficit can account for all of the type of evidence on which the Payne, and the McGhie and Chapman theories were based. The excessively *broad* attention that McGhie and Chapman (1961) found in subjective reports from early schizophrenics, and Payne *et al.* (1959) found in their research, does not seem to be explainable in terms of slow-processing that leads to a loss of cues that are in short-term store. Some kind of account of broad and more indiscriminate intake of information seems needed, and the filter-defect theories provide one such account.

However, the apparent inability of Yates' theory to account for the overinclusion data in Payne's sense of the term does not mean that Yates' account may not be useful. It may just have been applied too broadly. Remember that on Payne's measures of overinclusion, only about one-half of early schizophrenics were overinclusive and the other half were retarded on a number of speed-measures. "There was also a significant tendency for those schizophrenics who were overinclusive not to be re-tarded, and for those who were retarded not to be overinclusive. The two types of thought disorder tended not to co-exist in the same schizophrenic patient [Payne, 1966, p. 82]."

While Yates' theory of slowness in processing information in the lim-ited-capacity channel may not account for overinclusion, it would seem applicable to general retardation. Let us assume for the moment that when Yates' account is applied to early schizophrenics it is relevant only to the subgroup of early schizophrenics that Payne calls retarded and, again following Payne, hypothesize a poorer prognosis in these patients. In other words, slowness in processing is a long-lasting abnormality. Then the main implications seem in accord with some of the major emphases in the literature.

Using Broadbent's model, once a slowness in processing information begins, there will be a reduction in available information because of the decay of information in short-term storage, as Yates suggests. Cues that are not prominent and therefore are not selected early from short-term storage will have an abnormally high probability of being lost. At least this will be true of the common life situations, where relevant information is only displayed for a limited time. A secondary result is that with parts of sequences of information missing, there will be a slow, progressive decay in the information about consistencies in the environment that are held in the long-term store (which information, although not permanent, is quite long-lasting). With the gradual loss of predictability about signal contin-gencies, the information load in a sequence of signals is increased, and because the capacity of the processing channel is in terms of information, the reduced capacity to attend to and utilize available cues will be pro-gressive.

The gradual loss of stored knowledge about environmental consistencies will have another effect. Insofar as these stored contingencies help in the selection of classes of information that are relevant to the task at hand, the partial decay of this information will mean that there is a greater likelihood that physical properties of stimuli, instead of relevancy, will become relatively more important in guiding the operation of the filter. When physical prominence becomes increasingly important relative to relevance in these slow-processing individuals, unless they are in situations where relevance is highly correlated with stimulus properties such as intensity, their reduction in relevant information will be exacerbated because they will be progressively more likely to select a higher proportion of irrelevant signals to take up what little information-processing capacity they have.

Thus, Yates' theory of schizophrenic deficit, together with study of what this deficit should mean in Broadbent's model, describes a type of individual whose disturbance seems much like that of Payne's group of early schizophrenics that was retarded, did not use an abnormal number of cues, and was thought to have poor prognosis. The progressive disturbance in individuals who have "narrow scanning" early in their disorder, with a gradual change toward relatively greater proportion of attention given to irrelevant stimuli, and with physical characteristics determining attention rather than the meaning given by conditional probabilities in long-term store, also has similarities to Silverman's account of the course of schizophrenia in poor-premorbid or process schizophrenics. There are, of course, differences. One important difference is that, in contrast to Silverman's theory, the relative increase in attention to irrelevant stimuli, which should occur when relevant stimuli are not prominent and total stimulation is greater than can be handled by the very limited-processing system, is not defensively motivated. The flood of stimulation relative to the limited capacity of the processing system may still be experienced as aversive. As in our interpretation of the chronic stages of process schizophrenia, when stimulation is more than minimally complex there may be continued motivation for reduction in stimulation, which is progressive because of progressively limited ability to handle complex stimulation. An important additional emphasis in the material considered in the last few pages is the reminder that, while in some schizophrenics narrowed attention may result from attempts to cope with information overload on a normal-capacity system, in others, reduced information-processing capacity may be primary.

8

PHYSIOLOGICAL AROUSAL IN SCHIZOPHRENIA

As we have seen, recent research and theory emphasize two major kinds of behavioral changes in schizophrenia: (a) increased response interference — a trend toward disorganized variation among competing responses; and (b) relatively disorganized attention with breadth varying in different individuals from broad to narrow.

Several different theories have suggested that increases in variables such as anxiety, tension, and physiological arousal are causally related to both kinds of changes, and research has tended to support this view. For example, the series of experiments by Storms, myself, and our colleagues (Broen *et al.,* 1961, 1963, 1964; Storms *et al.,* 1967), and the experiments reviewed by Carlton (1963), indicate that in situations where both dominant and competing responses are evoked, increased muscular tension, stressful levels of noise, time-stress, and "activating" drugs tend to increase the variability among alternate responses. "Activating" conditions, such as arousal-producing drugs and the "cold pressor" situation, also appear to cause changes in breadth of cue utilization, with the evidence suggesting that the direction of change is narrowed attention. We have discussed some of the work of Callaway and his co-workers that is in accord with the summary statements by Callaway and Stone (1960) that "Some drugs make people less responsive to things occurring at the periphery of attention (Callaway and Thompson, 1953; Callaway and Dembo, 1958; Callaway, 1959). Drugs that have this psychological effect are also capable of increasing electroencephalographic arousal. Atropine, which can block or decrease electroencephalographic arousal has the opposite effect (Callaway and Band, 1958) [p. 373]." There is a much broader literature on this topic than we have discussed, but the additional evidence, much of which has been reviewed in a stimulating paper by Easterbrook (1959), supports the conclusion that ". . . the number of cues uti-

186

lized in any situation tends to become smaller with increase in emotion [Easterbrook, 1959, p. 197]."

It is, of course, true that some evidence that stress or arousing condition may be able to lead to two types of disturbances that seem important in schizophrenia does not mean that such conditions are *the* cause of these changes in schizophrenia. Some of the reasons why such a statement would go too far have been mentioned previously, but it may be good to remind ourselves of them at this point. First, there is no reason to assume that response interference and narrowed cue utilization (which may be a direct result of increased stress or secondary to the increased response complexity under stress) have only one cause. For example, among other factors, near equivalency of alternate response tendencies can be due to varied reinforcement during training; a reduction in factors that mediate the inhibition of non-reinforced responses; or increased tension, and each of these factors seem to interact with each other (Broen *et al.,* 1961; Carlton, 1963). Second, even though arousal-producing conditions, such as high stress, may play a part in the initial appearance of response interference and narrowed cue utilization, if the reward-punishment mileau in which schizophrenics live does not expect appropriate responding, including appropriate stimulus-search habits, then less-appropriate responding and deficient cue utilization may persist after the initial cause has been ameliorated.

In spite of the strong likelihood of multiple determination of the behavior differences observed between schizophrenics and normals, if physiological arousal is *an* important determinant, then, *on the average,* physiological arousal should be higher in schizophrenics than in normals. Examining physiological arousal in schizophrenics should also be useful in thinking about alternate hypotheses regarding the course of schizophrenia. For example, Venables (1964) and Hoffer and Osmond (1955) have suggested that there is decreased sympathetic arousal early in schizophrenia with above-normal sympathetic activity occurring later, while Mednick (1958; Higgins & Mednick, 1963) suggests the opposite — high arousal in acutes, with reduced arousal in chronics.

Another reason for looking at the literature on arousal in schizophrenia is that increased physiological arousal may cause changes that we have not discussed as yet. For example, it has been hypothesized that continued or repeated high arousal may enhance the probability that protective inhibitory mechanisms will be triggered, and we should examine the literature on such allied charges.

However, before we begin to look at research on arousal in schizophrenia, we must be clearer about what is meant by talking about an arousal dimension, how it can be measured, and some problems and ambiguities in dealing with "arousal."

USING THE CONCEPT OF AN AROUSAL DIMENSION

The basic reason why clarification is needed is that, until now, we have implied that many different conditions mean the same thing. For example, when the increased muscular tension induced by squeezing a hand dynamometer was shown to collapse response hierarchies more in schizophrenics than in normals (Broen & Storms, 1964), this experiment was cited as indicating that increased arousal leads to increased response interference in schizophrenics. Also, when putting a bare foot in a bucket of ice cubes ("cold pressor") led to reduced utilization of peripheral cues (Callaway & Thompson, 1953), the experiment was also cited as relevant to the effect of physiological arousal. In addition, both induced muscular tension and the cold pressor situation have been thought of as changing behavior in the same directions as psychological stress.

The reason that these different conditions have been talked of in the same way is that they are fairly similar in their effects on a number of physiological measures, and the commonality of effects is on measures that usually increase when persons are alerted, activated, or aroused.

In order to show how stress influences a number of physiological measures, we turn to a study by Schnore (1959). Schnore used two kinds of tasks—visual pursuit tracking, and arithmetic—with each kind of task being given under low stress and high stress. For example, in the tracking task, the low stress trials were given as if they were not a part of the experiment, and the high-stress trials were given under the threat that a shock at twice the level of a sample shock would be given if performance was not improved. In the arithmetic task, stress was varied by varying task difficulty with the subject heckled if he gave a wrong answer or responded slowly.

The physiological effects of these two different stress conditions can be seen in Table 11. The scores are differences between pre-test and test T-scores, which were used to make the different measures comparable (these difference scores were also corrected for differences in pre-period scores because the pre-period and change scores were correlated).

Table 11 indicates that larger physiological changes from pre-period scores tend to be associated with the high-stress conditions, and that, in general, the two different ways of increasing stress lead to comparable physiological changes. In a separate analysis, Schnore also found that the physiological changes that most consistently appeared under increased

TABLE 11[a]
COMPARISON OF MEAN DISPLACEMENT IN PHYSIOLOGICAL ACTIVITY
ASSOCIATED WITH DIFFERENT EXPERIMENTAL CONDITIONS

Variable	Condition				χ_{r^2}	p[b]
	Low-stress tracking	Low-stress arithmetic	High-stress tracking	High-stress arithmetic		
Heart rate	− 0.2	0.0	+ 4.6	+ 8.2	49.3	.001
Blood pressure (systolic)	+ 3.1	+ 8.5	+ 8.7	+13.1	33.0	.001
Palmar conductance	− 1.9	+ 2.8	+ .07	+ 4.0	55.2	.001
Respiration rate	+ 2.8	+ 2.8	+ 4.6	+ 4.3	27.2	.001
Skin temperature	0.0	+ 0.01	− 0.02	+ 0.01	−	N.S.
Right forearm EMG	+27.2	+29.4	+34.1	+38.9	43.32	.001
Left forearm EMG	+ 2.4	+ 1.9	+ 4.3	+ 3.0	24.7	.001
Neck EMG	+ 0.4	+ 0.2	+ 0.2	− 0.3	3.2	N.S.

[a] Adapted from Schnore (1959).
[b] One-tailed test.

stress were increased heart-rate, systolic blood pressure, respiration-rate, and right forearm electromyogram (EMG).

From the nature of Schnore's conditions, we certainly would expect that his subjects would be more alert, activated, aroused in the high-stress conditions, and from his results we see that (a) increased activation of a number of physiological systems occurs together under such conditions, and (b) different kinds of high-stress conditions are associated with similar physiological changes — at least in such physiological indicants as heart-rate, systolic blood pressure, muscular tension, and respiration-rate.

The generality of increases in these physiological measures under a different form of stressor is shown in the results of a study (Goldberg, 1966) where a variant of the cold pressor situation was used as a stressor. As Schnore had found under two different kinds of increased stress, Goldberg found that sudden immersion of a foot in cold water leads to increased heart-rate, respiration-rate, skin conductance, and systolic blood pressure.

A study by Pinneo (1961), which we have referred to earlier, shows that increases in such physiological measures also reflect other ways of increasing tension, and also indicates the continuity of these changes throughout a range of increased tension. Pinneo increased tension by asking subjects to squeeze a hand dynamometer at different levels while they were engaged in an auditory tracking task. Figure 18 shows the resulting differences in the physiological measures that had also been used by Schnore.

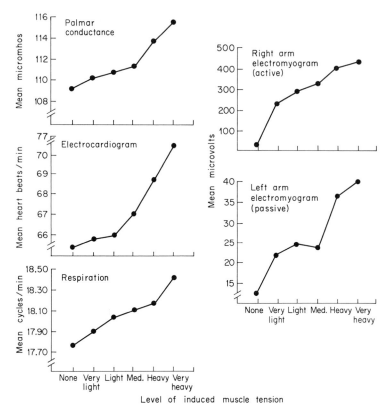

Fig. 18. Peripheral measures of autonomic activity and measures of muscle tension as a function of induced muscle tension. (Adapted from Pinneo, 1961.)

From these studies it becomes fairly clear that a variety of conditions that are apparently similar only in that they would be labeled as stress conditions, have some commonality of effect that is reflected in fairly general increases in the various physiological measures we have listed. Because the conditions that cause these changes would be expected to be tension increasers, or arousers, and the effects (e.g., increased heart-rate and respiration-rate) are indicants of a more activated organism, these general physiological effects have usually been said to reflect general activation or arousal level. Thus, we should be able to use such physiological measures to gain evidence about differences in arousal between normals and schizophrenics and between different groups of schizophrenics.

However, there is a major argument against speaking of a general dimension of activation or arousal that is measured by such peripheral physiological variables. The correlations between the different physiological measures have often been found to be low, both for resting (base) levels, and for the degree of change from low-stress to high-stress conditions for different individuals (Lacey & Van Lehn, 1952).

On the other hand, it has been found that within individuals the changes in these variables are fairly reliable, both when the same stressor is repeated (Lacey & Van Lehn, 1952) and when reactions to different stressors are studied (Schnore, 1959). Also, regarding interindividual consistencies, in the studies we discussed, most subjects showed the same direction of physiological change when stress was increased, though the amount of change varied from person to person. Thus, in spite of low interindividual correlations for these physiological measures, these measures still seem to reflect changes in stressed or aroused states.

As Schnore (1959) puts it, "That an S may be high relative to others in one physiological function and low (again relative to others) in another physiological function is what we should expect from findings of idiosyncratic patterns of physiological activity. . . .

"But there is a point that, curiously enough, appears to have been overlooked by some writers. Despite his idiosyncratic pattern, an individual placed in an arousing situation will, according to the results of the present study, probably show a general increase in most physiological functions [pp. 125-126]."

Thus, it may be, as Malmo (1959) has suggested, that activation (arousal) ". . . is a quantifiable dimension and the evidence indicates that physiological measures show a sufficiently high intraindividual concordance for quantifying this dimension [p. 385]."

However, the idiosyncratic patterning of individuals' levels on different physiological measures indicates that there are problems in using physiological measures to assess differences in a general arousal state between individuals. We certainly cannot take one measure, say heart-rate, and assume that because one person has a higher heart-rate than another, this difference is a good measure of a relatively general arousal state. The reverse order may be found on other variables. Levels on physiological measures are obviously not determined by a single factor that has general effects. Among other determinants, these levels are influenced by anatomical and physiological differences between persons, and type of orientation or "set" toward a situation, in addition to variations in factors that seem to influence more diffuse activation. Lacey's (1967) comment is a good one here. "What interpretation can be given to the dual facts that (a) in general, a large number of physiological processes are simultaneously thrown into action, probably by separate but intimately related pathways, by stimuli generally conceded to be arousing, activating, or stressful, but (b) these processes show, at best, only moderate intercorrelations. I propose that activation or arousal processes do *not* reflect just the intensive dimension of behavior . . . [p. 25]."

Because the activation of physiological processes can reflect many factors, which are often relatively specific in their effects, any physiological evidence that is used to suggest differences in a fairly general energizing dimension or activated state, which is what many theories of schizophrenia that have used the term arousal have meant, must at least include demonstration that there are general physiological differences in the same direction on several of the variables that have been shown to react together to changes in highly motivating, energizing, stressing conditions. Schnore (1959) has suggested that, "although any one physiological measure appears to be an unreliable criterion of the general arousal level, by using a number of measures in combination, it seems highly probable that one can reliably differentiate among individuals [p. 126]."

It has also been suggested that using average data to compare groups, as we shall be doing, provides an additional protection against incorrectly attributing physiological differences to differences in a general arousal level. Zahn (1964) discussed this point as follows when he described a study showing higher average physiological levels for schizophrenics than for normals on a single physiological measure—s' in conductance. He states, "In interpreting this as a difference in arousal level, it should be noted that it is supposed that individuals vary on this measure for a variety of purely anatomical and physiological reasons having nothing to do with the level of arousal. The same is true with most absolute psychophysiological measures. However, since we have no good reason to suppose that the two groups were not sampled randomly with respect to these variables, we may reasonably attribute the difference to a difference in arousal [p. 159]."

While group data may provide some protection against incorrect conclusions about a general arousal difference between groups, it must be remembered that schizophrenics and normals are not necessarily equated on other factors that affect levels on specific physiological measures. For example, attentional styles, which, as we will discuss later, affect specific physiological variables, causing different patterns of physiological responses (Lacey, 1967), can not safely be said to be comparable in schizophrenics and normals. Thus, consistently higher levels over a range of physiological variables are clearly the preferred data from which to suggest elevation on a dimension of relatively diffuse activation even if group data are used, and as we now turn to research results we must remember that confidence in conclusions about general arousal levels must still depend on the range of variables studied.

AROUSAL LEVELS IN SCHIZOPHRENICS

Studies of general physiological activation in schizophrenia have been numerous, reflecting the importance many investigators have attached to this dimension, but the results have seemed quite inconsistent. Only in the past few years have there been studies that, by dividing schizophrenics into subgroups, and by using different classifications of measures, have seemed to begin to bring some order to the findings.

The apparent heterogeneity of results is most obvious when a broad range of studies from different laboratories and time periods is studied. Within single research groups there has often been a fair degree of consistency that probably reflects the commonality of techniques in a single group of researchers, in spite of differences in the variables that are studied.

The rather consistent view of a few decades ago was expressed by Angyal, Freeman, and Hoskins (1940), who reported on the work of the research group at Worcester State Hospital. "It is generally recognized that in spite of the great variety of clinical pictures in the schizophrenic group of disorders, one symptom is common to all of them. This is the schizophrenic withdrawal. . . . However, the life of the schizophrenic person runs at low ebb not only psychologically but also physiologically [pp. 621-622]." They then presented the results of a number of physiological studies done in the Worcester laboratories, each of which measured physiological reactivity to stimulation, most stimulus conditions being fairly stressful.

Angyal *et al.* (1940) summarized the results from their laboratories as follows: ". . . we may say that in schizophrenia a rather general reduction of physiologic responsiveness is present. The reaction to metabolic stimulants, such as thyroid and dinitrophenol, was definitely diminished. The reaction to epinephrine administered intravenously as well as to the blocking of heat loss through the lungs was definitely less in schizophrenic than in normal persons, including reduction of autonomic responsiveness. The nystagmic response to rotation and caloric stimulation was greatly diminished. The change in cutaneous resistence in response to a preparatory stimulus was far below the normal [p. 624]." Angyal *et al.* did note that other findings showed some inconsistency, but the clear emphasis was on the reduction of physiological functioning in schizophrenics.

Quite a different picture has resulted from some studies that emphasize autonomic levels under resting (basal) conditions rather than comparisons of *reactions* to stress stimuli. A study by Gunderson (1953) provides an example. Gunderson had predicted that his sample of schizophrenics (males, mean length of hospitalization 24.8 months, all at least 24 hours drug-free) would deviate from normals in the direction of dominance in function of the parasympathetic branch of the autonomic nervous system. Without considering the question of whether individual autonomic deviations are consistent enough to justify a concept of general parasympathetic versus sympathetic deviation from a normative base line, what his prediction meant was that, on the average, schizophrenics were expected to be lower than normals on the measures we have described as indicants of arousal. Gunderson used a number of measures that we have discussed as varying with arousing conditions: systolic blood pressure, heart-rate, respiration-rate, and the somewhat less-discriminating palmar conductance (Schnore, 1959), as well as a number of other measures of sympathetic vs. parasympathetic dominance. His work was carefully done, with his measures corrected for such relevant factors as time of day and room temperature.

Comparisons of the schizophrenics' basal physiological levels with results from a sample of normals tested earlier on the same measures indicated "a striking reversal of expected deviations [p. 61]." Of the measures Gunderson used that we have discussed as measures of arousal, only skin conductance failed to be significantly higher in the schizophrenics.

The schizophrenics' basal levels were also compared with results from an earlier sample of psychoneurotic cases and a sample of ulcer patients. For the comparison with the psychoneurotic group, who had been judged to deviate from normals in a direction of sympathetic dominance, the results showed "clearly a tendency for the schizophrenic group to deviate even more markedly in a sympathetic [high arousal] direction on all of these same functions [p. 65]." The deviations for each of the measures we discussed were significant except again for conductance. The same direction of deviance emerged again when the schizophrenics were compared with the ulcer patients who had been chosen because they were assumed to be individuals in fairly pronounced stress situations.

Thus far, it seems that schizophrenics are highly aroused physiologically in a standard physiological basal-measurement situation, but are hyporeactive to additional stimulation. However, there are differences in samples and experimental situations between the Worcester and Gunderson studies and so this conclusion must be very tentative until we look at studies where base levels and reactivity were measured in the same study.

Research by Reynolds (1962) is relevant here. Reynolds compared normals and chronic schizophrenics (each schizophrenic with total hospitalization > three years), divided into process and reactive groups on the basis of Becker's revision of the Elgin Prognostic Scale, on both base levels and reactivity. For each subject, muscle tension, systolic and diastolic blood pressure, heart-rate, and respiration-rate were measured during the final stage of each of four rest periods and immediately after three stress periods that intervened between the rest periods. The three stress conditions were mild exercise (leg raising), cold pressor (hand in ice and water), and a period of verbal criticism while doing mental arithmetic. These stress periods are indicated as S_1, S_2, and S_3, respectively, in Figure 19, which shows the results.

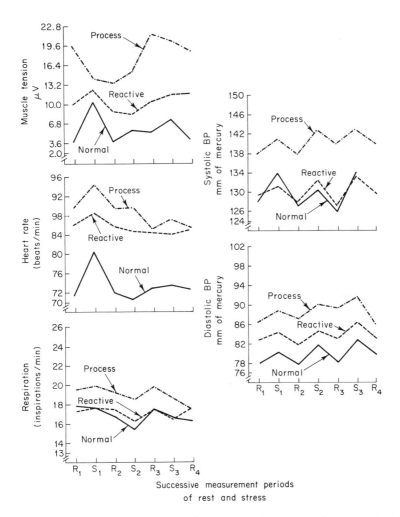

Fig. 19. Mean physiological measures during successive periods of rest and stress for normals, and reactive and process schizophrenics. (Adapted from Reynolds, 1962.)

From Figure 19, it seems quite clear that chronic schizophrenics, especially the process patients (those with poor premorbid histories, insidious onset of schizophrenia, and apparently poor prognosis), tend to be abnormally high on the arousal measures, both during periods of relaxation and following stressors.

Straight reactivity measures showed different results, however. When the score in the prior rest period was subtracted from the level under stress for each of the measures and stress periods, there were few significant differences between groups. When significant differences did occur, it was the normals who showed the greatest change in response to stimulation. The significant differences that were found were that schizophrenic patients showed reduced reactivity in muscular tension, heart-rate, and systolic blood pressure in response to one stressor (S_1), and reduced reactivity in systolic blood pressure in response to another stressor (S_3). The one significant difference between process and reactive schizophrenics was in reaction to the stress condition (S_3) where normals showed the most increase in systolic blood pressure. Here, process patients showed significantly less increase in systolic blood pressure than reactive patients.

However, when the effect of homeostatic mechanisms is considered, it seems very possible that reactivity for groups that differ in base level may not be a fair basis for comparison. To the extent that there are physiological regulatory mechanisms that operate to attenuate deviations from normal levels, these compensatory pressures may be stronger when base levels are higher. If so, it may be that change scores should be corrected for the influence of base level. Reynolds did find negative correlations between base and change scores, although these correlations were low and most were not significant. Reynolds felt that the apparent small influence of base level differences on reactivity may have accounted for the few reactivity differences that were found. He then matched subsamples for base level scores and found no significant differences between these groups in change scores from rest to stimulation.

The clearest finding that emerges from the Reynolds and Gunderson studies is that schizophrenics are abnormally aroused on a number of physiological measures. Discussing the question of whether such findings are due to peripheral or central factors, Reynolds (1962) says, "The pervasiveness of the higher levels of functioning over so many different measures is unusual. Among normal subjects it is not uncommon to find one or two somatic measures elevated above the expected value. Usually these deviations can be accounted for on the basis of peripheral changes, e.g., hypertension due to arteriosclerosis. With schizophrenic somatic levels, however, it is hard to believe that such a widespread deviation could be due to peripheral changes or anomalies, and the data would lend themselves more readily to an interpretation that some disturbance in a central neurological or chemical mediator influences the somatic balance toward the sympathetic side [p. 89]."

The results of Reynold's study also make it clear that resting levels of arousal and reactivity are quite different. Normal or lower than normal physiological changes in response to environmental changes seem to accompany high arousal, at least in chronic schizophrenics, and should, in fact, be expected when the effects of limiting or homeostatic mechanisms are considered in the context of a high base system.

This pattern of results found by Reynolds — high base arousal with normal or subnormal increase to increased stress — was also found by Williams (1953) in a group of schizophrenics that was somewhat younger than Reynolds' group (age 20 − 35, as compared to an average in the late 30's), and with less hospitalization (1 − 3 years, compared to 3 years' minimum). Like Reynolds, Williams interspersed rest and stress periods. Williams' stressors were viewing a film of a fight to the death between a mongoose and a snake, a word-association procedure emphasizing a search for personal problems, and a mental arithmetic task with failure feedback. His physiological measures were respiration-rate, pulse-rate, and galvanic skin response. Williams' results comparing the schizophrenics with a control group of normals, and combining rest periods together, and stress periods together, are given in Table 12.

At rest, the schizophrenics were significantly higher on all measures with the least clear differentiation being in the galvanic skin response, which from prior results we would not expect to provide quite as marked differentiation regarding stressed or diffusely energized states.

As for changes under increased stress, Williams' data suggest more

TABLE 12[a]
PHYSIOLOGICAL MEASURES AT REST AND INCREASE UNDER STRESS

Measure	Mean at rest		Mean increase under stress[b]	
	Controls	Schizophrenics	Controls	Schizophrenics
Respiration-rate (per minute)	14.49	18.16	1.73	.06
Pulse-rate (per minute)	79.84	89.11	7.42	1.93
Galvanic skin response (micromhos)	147.03	159.41	18.23	15.18

[a] Adapted from Williams (1953).
[b] Not corrected for differences in base level.

strongly than Reynolds' data that schizophrenics' higher base level is associated with little change under increased stress. The normals, with a lower base, seemed to have more room to react with increased arousal under stress. The end result was that the difference in arousal between schizophrenics and normals was reduced under high-stress conditions, and under such stress the only significant difference was that respiration rate was still somewhat higher for schizophrenics.

These studies seem to bring some order to what could be diverse findings if they are not considered together. Schizophrenics may be considered either to be abnormally high in arousal, or to have normal arousal levels, depending on whether the stress in the experimental situation is low or high. When stress is low, their arousal seems to be abnormally high. When the stress is higher, their arousal is more like that of normals. In great part, this seems to be because schizophrenics' reactivity, at least in response to some stressors that have strong effects on normals, is reduced. Thus, with less fluctuation in response to stimulation, schizophrenics may show quite different relationships to normals, depending on the level of stress or stimulation in the measurement situation.

This hypothesis has been investigated more directly by Zahn (1964) and his co-workers. Chronic schizophrenics and normals were tested in five separate sessions where the "demand" on the subjects varied. In the first condition, a mild tone was presented repetitively and no behavior was required of the subject. The second condition was the same except the subject was asked to press a telegraph key each time the tone was presented. The key-press instructions stated that speed and pressure were not important. The tasks in the last three sessions were reaction-time tasks where the key was to be depressed in response to a "ready" signal, and then released as quickly as possible following a tone.

The base-line data on skin conductance and data on non-specific GSRs suggested that normals' arousal tended to vary with the "demand" of the situation, both between and within sessions. Thus, at the beginning of situations, normals' arousal was high and decreased during the session as the task became more routine. Also, normals' arousal levels increased from the first through the third session in accordance with differences in "demand" between situations, then trended downward again with repeated experience in reaction-time tasks.

In contrast, in schizophrenics these measures were higher in general and varied less over conditions. Thus, on the first reaction-time task, where "demand" was highest, there was least difference between the two groups.

Zahn (1964) also reported data from a study with acute or early schizophrenic patients (specific hospitalization time was not reported). These data tended to show the same base-level patterns as for the chronic-normal comparison, except that the differences were less marked. In all sessions except the highest demand situation (the first RT condition), the acutes tended to have somewhat higher base arousal than normals, with similar trends for skin conductance, heart-rate, and finger pulse volume.

Such results suggest again that schizophrenics' arousal levels are nearer to the point at which significant homeostatic feedback is evoked. However, before turning to further discussion of this point, we should first summarize our discussion of comparisons of arousal levels between schizophrenics and normals. The most consistent result is that when stress is minimal, chronic schizophrenics, especially "process" patients, seem hyperaroused on a number of physiological measures. There are less data on changes in base arousal in low-stress situations from early to late schizophrenia, but within the range of hospitalization in the subject groups we have looked at thus far, the schizophrenics have all shown higher base levels under low situational demand: from Zahn's "acute or early" schizophrenics, Gunderson's group with average two-year hospitalization, Williams' one- to three-year group, to Zahn's chronic subjects, and Reynolds' subjects who had all been hospitalized for at least three years. However, the differences did seem less marked in Zahn's early schizophrenics, and the conclusion of high base arousal is most clearly applicable to chronic patients. The major variability in results seems to come when schizophrenics and normals are compared on reactivity to stimulation or are compared on their continuing levels in situations that are relatively stressful. Here, in these more stressful situations, the expected high arousal in normals, contrasted with schizophrenics' relative lack of change from less-stressful situations, means that normals' arousal may reach or exceed that of schizophrenics.

This, of course, must lead to variability in results if the stress level of situations varies. Zahn's summary of prior research is an especially good one on this point. After commenting that part of the hyperarousal of schizophrenics may be due to the strangeness of the experimental situation, he comments, "Still we are faced with the problem of explaining differences in results between our studies and previous ones which have generally found chronic schizophrenics to be less highly aroused and less responsive than normal subjects. There are various factors that could be mentioned, especially in view of the great variability of schizophrenic subjects, and differences in the way patients were sampled. However, we think there is a more important difference. In virtually all of the studies in the literature, the stimuli have been stronger or more meaningful than in our study [1964, p. 160]."

This pattern of results would, of course, be expected from the operation of homeostatic inhibitory feedback mechanisms, which should tend to be stronger in persons who have higher general arousal under low-stress conditions (schizophrenics), and which should be exacerbated when these persons are placed under more extreme stress.

The studies that have been discussed have been selected to illustrate the major trends in the literature. The intent has been to clarify, but of course this means that the heterogeneity in findings may not have been sufficiently emphasized. This heterogeneity has been most notable in data on skin-conductance, which, as we saw from the beginning in Schnore's (1959) research, was not as markedly related to stress conditions as is the case with other measures. However, it should be emphasized that the major points that have been made are supported by the major trends in the broader literature. After extensive review of the recent literature, Lang and Buss (1965) said, "In summary, the habitual level of somatic activity in schizophrenics appears to have the following characteristics. Skin resistance levels are generally similar to those of normals, although two samples were clearly higher and at least one was lower than that of control subjects. During experiments, the cardiovascular systems of schizophrenics tend to be at a higher activation level than those of normal controls. However the relationship between cardiac functioning and such dimensions as process-reactive or chronic-acute is not yet clear. All reports indicate higher than normal muscle tension in schizophrenics, the highest levels being associated with chronicity and the process label [p. 90]."

Later, after a review of reactivity studies, Lang and Buss (1965) noted that, "The hypothesis that schizophrenics suffer from an underactive arousal mechanism would seem to receive support from the studies demonstrating psychomotor and physiological hyporeactivity in chronic patients. However, Malmo (1958) argues cogently that activation is measured more directly in studies of basal physiological level than in research on responsivity. Thus, studies showing high resting somatic activity in schizophrenia would indicate that schizophrenics are generally hyperaroused rather than the opposite. Furthermore, their reduced responsivity is not inconsistent with this view. Malmo (1958), Lacey (1956), and Wilder (1950) have all presented evidence that responsivity progressively decreases when plotted on an abscissa of increasing activation (defined by base activity level) [p. 97]."

DECREASED AROUSAL WHEN STRESS IS INCREASED

If, as seems likely, some inhibitory process limits reactivity in highly aroused systems, it is quite possible that the increasing inhibition under higher arousal may not only limit activation, but at some point may even begin to produce a net arousal-reducing effect.

This idea has been most emphasized in the Pavlovian concept of transmarginal or protective inhibition. [See Gray (1964) for a thorough discussion of this idea and related research.] An important notion in Pavlovian thinking is that when nerve cells are subjected to especially intense stimulation, they become less reactive or cease reacting. This property is seen as protecting against damage that may result from excessive stimulation. In line with its protective role, the level of stimulation necessary to produce the transmarginal inhibition is said to be lower in individuals with weaker, more excitable nervous systems, among whom are schizophrenics (Pavlov, 1941).

In Pavlovian theory, the basis for schizophrenic pathology is then excessive nervous-system inhibition, which should cause lowered reactivity to stimulation and lowered ability to form and maintain stimulus-response associations, which is what has been found repeatedly in Russian research [reviewed in Lynn (1963)], and is not necessarily inconsistent with much of the research we have discussed. However, Russian research has also suggested that in schizophrenics, subnormal base levels of cortical and autonomic activation are most prominent, in contrast to the trend of the evidence in western research, which has emphasized higher basal autonomic activation.

However, though Russian theory and research emphasize the predominance of low cortical activation in schizophrenia, the effects of protective inhibition are not assumed to be uniform. This is because, as is fairly well established, cortical cells normally control each other and control subcortical physiological systems through two kinds of processes, inhibitory as well as excitatory (Milner, 1957; Gellhorn, 1953). Therefore, the net effects of transmarginal inhibition will be either excitatory or inhibitory, depending on which kind of control is inhibited.

In Pavlovian theory, the initial effects of transmarginal inhibition are in decreasing normal cortical inhibitory control — the control that is needed for appropriate discriminative functioning. Thus, in some schizophrenics, the major effects of protective inhibition are in producing a loss of appropriate discrimination; increasing the reactions to stimuli that are normally inhibited; and producing a net increase physiological activation, especially at subcortical levels. Russian researchers have found this picture primarily in acute and paranoid schizophrenics (Lynn, 1963).

This same principle has been used by Lovibond to account for schizophrenics' loose associations as measured by Lovibond's Object Sorting Test. "In these terms high scores on the Sorting Test result from a weak attention response, or a failure to inhibit irrelevant linkages as a concomitant of low level of cortical excitability [Lovibond, 1963, p. 101]."

This idea that inhibitory processes can decrease the suppression of normally inhibited response tendencies should not be strange to the reader. As Pavlov (1941) points out, a somewhat similar picture occurs in the beginning stages of intoxication from the depressant, alcohol. It is when protective inhibition is more extreme that reactivity to stimulation should be decreased, as in the majority of less acute and non-paranoid schizophrenics.

In some ways then, the Pavlovian idea of protective inhibition as an important factor in schizophrenia, and the results of the research stimulated by this idea, parallel the differences in attentional processes in different groups of schizophrenics that have been emphasized in our earlier discussion; are in accord with other results indicating lowered physiological reactivity in many schizophrenics; and are certainly in accord with the idea of possible paradoxical physiological reactions to quite high levels of stress. The major difference is in the Russian emphasis on lower basal physiological levels in most schizophrenics, which is the opposite of the trend in the findings we have discussed. Of course, if we are dealing with non-monotonic relationships, as may be the case in the relationship of stimulus intensity to physiological responses, then differences in findings are not surprising in view of differences in experimental situations.

In some contrast to the conceptual language in the details of Pavlovian discussions of protective or transmarginal inhibition, Gray (1964) has attempted to discuss the processes that are involved in terms of physiological processes that have been more generally emphasized in discussions of physiological arousal, principally involving " ... the generalized activation properties possessed in particular by the brain-stem reticular formation [p. 302]." In his discussion of generalized arousal, Gray has also been concerned with the thalamic reticular system, which, in contrast to the brain-stem reticular system, seems more general in its descending effects that in cephalic effects.

Gray's interpretation of transmarginal inhibition is as follows: "The hypothesis we shall adopt, then, is that transmarginal inhibition is the result of the operation of a reticulo-cortico-reticular negative feedback loop of the kind described by Dell and his collaborators; stimulation of the reticular formation increases the level of cortical activation; this increase in turn leads to an increase in the inhibitory effect of the cortex on the reticular formation, with a consequent decrease in the organism's general responsiveness to stimulation; this decrease in responsiveness may eventually become so great that signs of drowsiness and sleep occur. Now, according to Dell *et al.* (1961), 'the greater the activity of the cortex, the greater is this dampening effect on the reticular formation.' It follows, therefore, that the appearance of transmarginal inhibition depends on the degree of reticular activation of the cortex—the greater the degree to which the reticular system activates the cortex, the sooner will transmarginal inhibition arise. The degree to which the reticular system activates the cortex will, in its turn, be greater, the more intense, prolonged, or frequently repeated is the stimulation to which the organism is exposed. Furthermore, since, by our definition, weak individuals are those in whom, for any given intensity of stimulation, bombardment of the cortex from the reticular system is greatest, we should expect them to be the most susceptible to transmarginal inhibition . . . [pp. 324-325]."

As has been mentioned, in Pavlovian theory the comments about weak or excitable nervous systems apply to schizophrenics. Therefore, from Gray's interpretation, we should expect, as Zahn (1964) found, that in low-stress situations, schizophrenics' physiological arousal would be abnormally high, with arousal levels decreasing relative to normals' levels as the stress in the situation is intensified.

As will be discussed, other inhibitory processes than that initiated by activity of the reticular formation have also been suggested as important in schizophrenia. It is the general principle that inhibitory mechanisms are stimulated at high levels of arousal in different physiological systems, and may come to dominate active systems, that is important.

If homeostatic controls limit the activation of many physiological systems, consider where strong inhibitory feedback should be likely to occur, and where such feedback might be likely to be sufficient to lead to a decrease in arousal in response to added stimulation. First, greater inhibitory feedback should be most likely in systems that are initially highly aroused, and in persons where these systems tend to be more highly aroused under minimal stimulation. In such persons and systems, additional stimulation of the systems that are already highly aroused is most likely to cause stimulation to go beyond the point at which homeostatic feedback begins to deactivate the system involved. In the results we have discussed, in very low-demand situations cardiovascular arousal has tended, with fair consistency, to be abnormally elevated in schizophrenics, and there is some evidence suggesting that this elevation may be greatest in process patients. Thus, we might expect that as the amount, intensity, and stressfulness of stimulation is increased above that in low-demand situations, strong inhibitory feedback in response to stimulation is likely to be observed in cardiovascular measures in process schizophrenics.

In line with these thoughts, remember that in the DeVault (1955) study, which was referred to in an earlier chapter, process schizophrenics showed *negative* reactivity in heart-rate, but not in GSR amplitude. The process patients showed decelerated heart-rate in response to each of different pictures depicting sex, dependency, and hostility. Normals and reactive schizophrenics responded significantly differently than the process patients; both normals and reactives responding with accelerated heart-rates.

It should also be noted that even in DeVault's basic "pre-stimulation" experimental situation, the process patients' heart-rates were not significantly elevated. This, together with the negative reactivity to further stimulation, can be interpreted as suggesting that, in the process patients, strong inhibitory feedback may have been at work even under the relatively lower stress of the basic experimental situation. But if this interpretation is correct, why should DeVault's process subjects have shown this attenuation of heart-rate that apparently began at lower levels of stimulation and stress than has been observed in other studies?

One special characteristic of DeVault's subjects is their chronicity. DeVault's schizophrenics were very long-term patients, each having been hospitalized at least six years. Thus, it may be that over time there is a decrease in the stimulus level that will produce maximal cardiovascular arousal. In the middle ranges of chronicity, schizophrenics, especially process patients, respond to basic physiological measurement situations with high cardiovascular arousal, and both process and reactive schizophrenics respond to further stimulation with abnormally restricted increases in cardiovascular functioning (Reynolds, 1962). In very long-term schizophrenia, the process patients, who had shown the highest arousal in other experimental situations, seem now to have attenuated arousal in a basic situation, with negative reactivity to additional stimulation. Thus, it may be that repeated high-arousal responsivity to relatively low or moderate stimulation may eventually sensitize and exacerbate the homeostatic feedback. In other words, under repeated experience with high arousal, a given amount of homeostatic feedback may be stimulated earlier and earlier in the arousal sequence.

That such changes are possible in human beings who have repeated experience with arousal that increases to very high levels is also suggested by the results of normals' reactions to abnormal stress sequences, such as the severe stress in parachute jumping. As the right half of Figure 20 illustrates, in novice parachutists heart-rate increases to the point that would be expected to be maximally stressful—the jump altitude. However, in experienced parachutists (100 or more times through the sequence), heart-rate begins to shown an inhibitory or decelerating change earlier in the sequence. The left half of Figure 20 indicates that the same general kind of change as a function of experience occurs in skin conductance, though the change is less marked, with little change until the latter part of the sequence.

It should be noted that Epstein (1967) has presented longitudinal data on individual subjects that indicates that inverted V-shaped curves relating arousal to level of stress do develop during the course of experience with stress sequences.

Why conductance is not attenuated at as low levels of stress as heart-rate, when both have been repeatedly aroused, is unclear. Possibly it is because through the moderate levels of stress, conductance is increased less, relative to its total range (e.g., see Fig. 20). Thus, under moderate stimulation, inhibitory feedback is less likely to become attached to the early cues in the sequence. Also, of course, there is no need to assume that there is similarity in the nature and intensity of the homeostatic controls affecting heart-rate and skin conductance. The major point regarding differences between heart-rate and skin conductance is that repeated arousal of both systems may lead to heart-rate being attenuated at lower levels of stress and lower levels of arousal, and that this inhibition as a function of repeated arousal is not as marked for skin conductance.

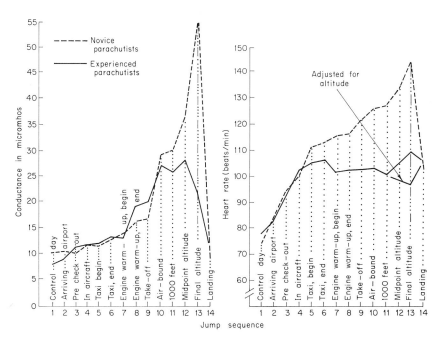

Fig. 20. Skin conductance and heart-rate as a function of experience with a stress sequence. (From Fenz and Epstein, 1967.)

It must, of course, be recognized that parachuting, with its approach motivations, may lead to physiological changes that differ from other changes under repeated experience with physiological activation. However, in spite of the necessary caution in interpretation, it is true that the deviant pattern of physiological arousal observed in DeVault's long-term process subjects—abnormal heart-rate attenuation in response to stress, with GSR reactivity being less attenuated—is quite similar to the pattern observed in parachutists with considerable experience with abnormally high arousal. This similarity would seem to add somewhat to the plausibility of the hypothesis that, in some long-term schizophrenics, chronicity of experience with high arousal may eventually exacerbate the inhibitory pattern stimulated by increased heart-rate.

In this discussion of inhibitory control, we should note that Fenz and Epstein (1967) argue that the inhibitory process shown by their data ". . . must be psychological in origin." Their reasons for this conclusion are that this inhibitory mechanism ". . . cannot be accounted for by a physiological homeostatic central mechanism reacting to a high level of arousal for only the experienced parachutists demonstrated the effect, while it was the novices who reached the highest levels of arousal. Nor, for the same reasons, can it be ascribed to homeostatic control of individual organs. Physiological homeostatic control can, of course, be viewed as a further line of defense [p. 49]."

However, the appearance of an inhibitory pattern at earlier points in a sequence of physiological and external cues after considerable experience with the sequence, does not, in itself, negate the possibility that the inhibitory response system is the same both early and late, with the only change being that it has become conditioned to earlier cues.

Fenz and Epstein suggest that what is learned over the course of experience with stress is, in part, the focusing of awareness by directing the content of thought to important non-stress ideation. While this ability to ignore some cues is in accord with subjective reports from the parachutists, these changes in awareness may be an integral part of a physiological process, and do not necessarily indicate the operation of a separate "purely psychological" process. This is not to say that learning to reduce the range of observation is necessarily just a by-product of the physiological process. In earlier discussion of chronic schizophrenia, we have emphasized the possibility that learning to change observational patterns may serve to reduce schizophrenics' response interference. What we need to consider now is the relationship of these changes in observational style to physiological processes. As we shall see, observational style may be intimately related to physiological inhibitory mechanisms.

HEART RATE CHANGE AS A STIMULUS FOR AND RESPONSE TO PHYSIOLOGICAL INHIBITION

Gellhorn (1953) was one of the first in this country to emphasize that physiological overactivation continued over time might well exacerbate normal homeostatic feedback and lead to the reduced physiological reactivity observed in schizophrenia. In this connection, and with some similarity to Gray's interpretation of transmarginal inhibition, he emphasized the role of the hypothalamus in stimulating both the cortex and autonomic reactions, and emphasized the role of inhibitory feedback to the hypothalamus from the cortex. From a thorough review of literature on homeostatic feedback, and on physiological reactivity in schizophrenia, Gellhorn concluded that in schizophrenia, ". . . there is a deficient reaction in the sympathetic division of the autonomic nervous system at the hypothalamic level, possibly initiated by overactivity and favored by constitutional factors [p. 438]."

Although many specific types of mechanisms are involved in autonomic homeostasis and may well be important in schizophrenia, the research that to some extent underlines cardiovascular functioning leads us to emphasize one specific inhibitory system. This system is stimulated by pressure-sensitive receptors in the carotid sinus and cardio-aortic area.

Our focus on this system is not guided only by available research, which is not extensive enough to be more than suggestive regarding the working of this particular system in schizophrenia. Part of our emphasis is because this system has been the focus of some recent theoretical discussion that points in other directions that seem quite relevant to schizophrenic behavior, and which should be presented for heuristic reasons.

The baroreceptors of the cardio-aortic area, with their location close to the heart, are sensitive detectors of increased heart pressure and rate. Lacey and Lacey (1966) and Lacey (1967) have reviewed considerable evidence that shows rather convincingly that these baroreceptors are normally active, with attenuating effects on both the cortex and on heart-rate, and that further stimulation of the baroreceptors—increased pressure—can produce a decrease in cortical electrical activity, a reduction in the effects of stimulation, an inhibition of motor activity, and decelerated cardiovascular functioning.

This system is especially interesting not only because it meets the requirement of being intimately related to heart-rate, but also because this same system is related to another aspect of chronic schizophrenia we have emphasized—a decrease in registering or responding to environmental information.

The most straight-forward interpretation of the relationships among schizophrenics' heightened arousal, lowered reactivity, and reduced cue utilization in terms of this system is that given by Reynolds (1962). "The results of the present experiment, which show hyporeactivity among schizophrenics in heart-rate and blood pressure, point to a premature or over-vigorous inhibitory effect by the baroreceptors of the carotid sinus reflex. The over-inhibition of autonomic activity would be accompanied by an over-inhibition of cortical electrical activity, and this in turn is presumably a state in which the influence of the external environment is diminished. The heightened level of sympathetic tonus as found among schizophrenics and as produced by drugs [here he refers to the research by Callaway and his colleagues], may influence the baroreceptors to be more sensitively tuned to increases in blood pressure, and in turn produce through them a direct over-inhibiting effect on cortical electrical activity. This lowered cortical activity may mediate the diminution in the influence of the environment . . . [p. 97]."

Although this explanation sounds quite good in itself, there are the problems we have already discussed of the apparently increased over-attention to a broad variety of stimuli in acute schizophrenics. This can be handled, as Venables does, by suggesting abnormally low sympathetic tonus in acute schizophrenics, but as we have seen, there is no good evidence for this.

A possible revision of Reynolds' account is suggested by the reminder by Lacey and Lacey (1966) in speaking of studies relevant to the activation of these baroreceptors, that ". . . it should be clear that although most of the investigations referred to speak of 'levels of sympathetic tonus,' they never revealed the effects of long-enduring and sustained levels of autonomic function. They dealt rather with relatively abrupt changes of level produced by electrical or pharmacological stimulation [as did Callaway's research], or with spontaneous fluctuations of level. The general physiological principle that effective stimulation is more accurately characterized as a change of energy delivered to a receptor, rather than as actual amount of energy, seems applicable here, especially with regard to carotid sinus mechanisms [p. 178]."

Thus, even if the Callaway research is interpreted in terms of physiological inhibition instead of the interpretation that has been emphasized in our discussion, this research, dealing as it did with more abrupt changes in sympathetic level, need not suggest that reaching high levels in early schizophrenia implies the frequency of large change or sensitivity to small change that is sufficient to lead to a notably consistent decrease in reactivity to environmental stimuli. Instead, as we have discussed before, in early schizophrenics an abnormally high level of arousal may tend to equalize varied attention tendencies stimulated by cues that are registered at some level, leading to distractibility in many early schizophrenics. An additional point is that the action of the baroreceptors and their inhibitory action on sensory stimulability cannot be considered in isolation. When stress, with its relatively general arousing properties, is the cause of cardiovascular arousal, then the concurrent activation of other systems involved in stimulability may more than offset the inhibition of these other systems. Under our interpretation of the Callaway research, the result will be overstimulation and information overload, which normals may react to with reduced scanning of information, but the normal habitual reduction in scanning under stress may be insufficient to counteract the extreme overload in early schizophrenia.

The heightened sensitivity of the baroreceptors, which may eventually be sufficient to reduce the abnormal stimulability in schizophrenics, or at least attenuate it when stress is increased, may only come with considerable repeated experience with high activation. In other words, over the course of repeated increases in heart-rate, the baroreceptors may be increasingly conditioned to react to slower or smaller change in heart-rate. Thus, that part of decreased reactivity to the environment that is due to inhibitory action stimulated by the baroreceptors may increase with the repetition of the high cardiovascular arousal to even moderate stimulation that has been observed in schizophrenia.

It is not implied that the physiological mechanisms triggered by a spurt in heart-rate are solely responsible for reduced cue utilization in some chronic schizophrenics. As has been emphasized in our discussion to this point, human beings have considerable voluntary control over the complexity of stimulation they meet, and it would seem unlikely that schizophrenics, with their stimulus or information overload, did not have some other ways to voluntarily isolate themselves. Certainly, physiological processes that attenuate stimulation may be especially sensitive in long-term chronics and may protect them to some degree against highly stressful stimulation, but such physiological triggering of homeostatic feedback is likely to be only part of the protective armor.

Anticipatory Physiological Set

One possibility that would aid schizophrenics in not having to experience as sharp an increase in stimulation that is stressful for them before the physiological protection would occur is if they could "set" themselves physiologically so as to sensitize this homeostatic mechanism. At first it seems unlikely that this is possible, but if it were, it would certainly be a useful part of the chronic schizophrenic's voluntary defensive armamentarium along with other changes in those scanning responses that are under voluntary control. Thus far, we have emphasized the influence of stress and automatic inhibitory mechanisms on physiological measures. However, as was discussed earlier, physiological variations are certainly caused by multiple factors, and here we will explore the possibility of physiological patterns that are *anticipatory* sets, or patterns of readiness, distinct from reactions to stress.

Let us consider two questions together. First, is it possible for human beings to "set" themselves physiologically so as to be better prepared for conditions they expect to experience? Second, if people can do this, what kind of physiological set would we expect in schizophrenics?

We can say what the task of the physiological set should be for schizophrenics. Response interference, with its attention disorganization and information overload, has been emphasized as a basic disturbance in schizophrenia, whether it results from a "filter-defect," collapsed response hierarchies, Pavlovian decrease in internal inhibition, or some other process resulting in an overload of irrelevant stimulation on a limited-processing system. If, as we have assumed, such overloads of interfering, disorganizing stimulation are aversive, then what would be desired is a physiological set that would most aid in inhibiting stimulation, thereby enhancing the probability that the overload on processing capacity would be reduced.

We then face the question of whether or not anticipatory physiological sets that control the range of cue intake are possible. The answer is that it does seem that when normal human beings are faced with tasks in which they are instructed to be open to a range of information, they show one kind of physiological pattern; when they are to concentrate on, organize, and deal with a limited amount of information, they show another physiological pattern.

For example, as a part of a much broader program of studying patterns of autonomic responses to different situations, Lacey (1959) studied heart-rate and skin-conductance reactions to a visual attention situation and to situations requiring "empathic listening," "thinking," and "withstanding pain." In the visual attention situation, subjects were asked to note colors and patterns and were told they were to report them later. In "empathic listening," a recording of the thoughts and feelings of an injured and dying man, acted by an experienced professional actor, was played with subjects told only to listen empathically and attentively. In the thinking situation, an arithmetic problem was given orally and subjects were to solve it mentally and give an answer; the situation was repeated as many times as was possible in two minutes. The pain situation was a cold pressor test. The results are presented in Figure 21.

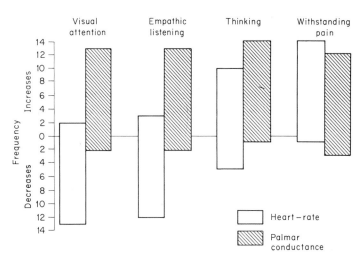

Fig. 21.   Direction of change in heart-rate as a function of type of task. (From Lacey, 1959.)

Different directions of change in heart-rate clearly seem to be associated with differences in need to shut out or receive stimulation. Decreased heart-rate is predominant where external attention is the primary requirement, with increased heart-rate predominating when there is a need to concentrate, to not be distracted, and even more when external stimulation is aversive. This type of result has been found repeatedly. As Lacey (1967) said, "Our research in the past five years has shown with increasing clarity and certainty that the cardiovascular system is particularly and peculiarly responsive to the intention of the subject to note and detect external stimuli [p. 33]."

That change in heart-rate can be an anticipatory preparation to vary openness to stimulation is particularly suggested by heart-rate changes prior to the "go" signal in a reaction-time study reported by Lacey (1967). When regular four-second preparatory intervals were used, there was ". . . a dramatic, highly significant, completely obvious, beat-by-beat deceleration during the preparatory interval [p. 35]" that produced lowest heart-rate at the time the signal to respond came on, with later recovery. The time at which the signal is expected is, of course, the time when the subject most wants to be open to receive this specific relevant environmental signal and be most prepared to react quickly to it, and this desire is associated with an anticipatory decrease in heart-rate.

The reason why preparatory cardiovascular "sets" work is apparently because the cardiovascular changes control the activity of the inhibitory mechanisms stimulated by the cardiovascular baroreceptors, and in this way control the broad effects these mechanisms have on cortical activity and sensori-motor stimulability. It seems fairly clear that when heart-rate changes are not secondary to other changes (e.g., in stress), a decrease in heart-rate exacerbates stimulability, and increased heart-rate inhibits cortical activity and stimulability. Lacey (1959) reported a study showing that when stimuli that subjects had been told not to respond to were presented at the time heart-rate had spontaneously increased, then incorrect responses to these stimuli decreased. Also, Lacey and Coquery [reported in Lacey (1967)] have shown that a spontaneous increase in heart-rate is associated with decreased cortical activation.

In view of our earlier emphasis on decreased heart-rate in the DeVault study as due to the action of an inhibitory system, this emphasis on increased heart-rate as part of a pattern that causes inhibition may seem inconsistent. What must be made clear is that when a change in heart-rate is part of a pattern of preparation, then the changes are not a consequence of the inhibitory system having changed the intensity of its feedback. Rather, in this case the change in heart-rate *controls* the degree of operation of the inhibitory system, with increased heart-rate acting to intensify the inhibition. However, when the operation of the inhibitory system is intensified beyond a point, then the inhibitory feedback is expected to decelerate the activating system itself. This exacerbation of inhibitory feedback to the point where the stimulating system is reduced in activation is how DeVault's data were interpreted.

Another possible area of confusion may occur because our earlier discussion of reactions to stress involved a dimension of fairly general activation wherein arousal of heart-rate should tend to occur in concert with arousal in other systems. This, again, seems at first inconsistent with the suggestion that an increase in heart-rate is inhibitory. Again, the clarifying distinction is embodied in what is cause and what is effect. Stress situations do seem to cause general activation, and in response to stress an increase in heart-rate generally occurs together with arousal of a number of other physiological systems. Cardiovascular activation does in turn stimulate an inhibitory system that tends to attenuate heart-rate as well as having some inhibitory effect on several other systems. As was mentioned briefly before, the research on stress that was reviewed earlier in this chapter indicates that, in the context of general arousal as from stress, the general inhibitory effects are overcome by the excitation, and heart-rate and a number of other measures tend to increase together. At least this is the case under moderate stress and without long-term repeated experience with stress. However, when heart-rate is increased by non-stress factors, such as a specific task "set," the evidence suggests that the general excitation effects are not present to the same degree, leaving the inhibitory action to predominate in the systems that are not specifically stimulated by the "set." Heart-rate itself, because it is activated by the "set," usually shows an increase in spite of inhibitory feedback. However, in systems not specifically activated by the "set," such as the cortex, there is not offsetting excitation. Thus, when heart-rate is increased *apart from or beyond the level of a reaction to stress*, a close relationship between *increased* heart-rate and *decreased* cortical arousal can be observed as Lacey and Coquery have found. This negative relationship shows that, by itself, increased heart-rate is inhibitory, even though the general excitation provided by stress usually arouses heart-rate together with other systems, including the cortex.

To return to the main thread of our discussion, basic schizophrenic deficit seems to involve cue overload; increased heart-rate inhibits cortical activity and stimulability; and an intent or "set" to reduce openness to stimulation can produce increased heart-rate. It then seems quite likely that some schizophrenics would learn to adopt this set. This set should be especially motivated and used most over the longest time by those schizophrenics who seem to use and should continue to require methods of reducing information overload — from the evidence in the last two chapters, primarily chronic nonparanoid and process schizophrenics.

This physiological set for general inhibition of input cannot be "on" constantly as it is a *change* in cardiovascular functioning that is probably the effective stimulus. Thus, other voluntary mechanisms that reduce the range of input would still be motivated and used quite consistently, with the physiological set used when additional environmental complexity begins to occur. This set would be activated more in schizophrenics than in normals because, as has been emphasized, normals are more able to organize their behavior in complex situations. Normals do not need much additional inhibition unless task and stress combine to result in quite high levels of complexity, and such inhibition would not be used more than is necessary because inhibition of stimulability does, of course, increase the likelihood of the loss of relevant information.

Thus, many schizophrenics, especially those most unable to organize responding in the face of multiple stimulation, should learn to use an attentional set that increases cardiovascular functioning, and should adopt such a set under lower levels of stress and environmental complexity than is the case for normals. Standard experimental situations that are not intended to be very stressful might then be expected to be situations where cardiovascular functioning would be fairly consistently among the physiological measures abnormally elevated in schizophrenics. Though Lacey's research shows that skin conductance may also be elevated when the intent is to shut out stimulation, this component of the set would not be elevated, in comparison to normals' levels, with as much consistency. From

Lacey's research, this component is fairly invariant over different attentional sets and therefore should not be as important a differentiator of groups with different kinds of set.

To the extent that certain environmental and internal cues, such as some increase in physiological stress reactions (which may be a partial cause of and/or reaction to information overload) repeatedly signal the need to adopt the set that increases cardiovascular functioning still further, the resulting inhibitory process should become conditioned to cues earlier in the sequence of signals — for example, smaller heart-rate acceleration. In this manner, the cardiovascular-inhibitory system, because of its more frequent use by some schizophrenics, may come over time to be especially sensitized in some schizophrenics.

Reactivity in skin conductance would be less attenuated over time because, as was noted in the Fenz and Epstein (1967) research, repeated arousal of skin conductance does not seem to eventuate in the same degree of attenuation of responsivity.

In sum, in many schizophrenics the use of a set against stimulation that tends to increase cardiovascular functioning may be, along with a tendency toward more diffuse activation, a contributor to the abnormally high cardiovascular arousal that has been noted in schizophrenics in many measurement situations. The repeated use of this set may decrease the activation intensity needed to stimulate the inhibitory pattern that is evoked by cardiovascular activation. This pattern includes inhibition of stimulation as well as homeostatic feedback to the primary activating system. Thus, repeated use and progressive sensitization of this inhibitory system means that when higher and higher levels of stress and environmental complexity are introduced, cardiovascular functioning will be among those processes most likely to show attenuated or eventually even negative reactivity.

While it might be desirable to be able to leave the discussion at this point, with an interpretation that seems to integrate several trends of evidence, an alternate interpretation is possible and should be mentioned.

In a very interesting recent article, Silverman (1967) also suggests that, especially in chronic non-paranoid and process schizophrenics, stimulability is varied by an attention set that alters activation in a feedback loop involving the cardiovascular system and the cortex. However, his interpretation of the set seems to be the opposite of that suggested above. Silverman suggests that the attention set is toward *receptivity* to environmental stimulation. Therefore, in accordance with Lacey's research, the set itself involves cardiac deceleration, which, because it protects against the inhibition stimulated by the baroreceptors, is excitatory and enhances stimulability. Silverman views this as protective because attention to stimulation distracts from aversive cognitive inputs. Because for Silverman this set is most stimulated by overload of stressful information, "Under extreme stress conditions, hyper-responsiveness to sensory inputs becomes pronounced and attention is focused almost solely on sensory attributes; connotative attributes of stimuli are partially or even completely dissociated from their sensory configurations. Objects and people may then appear as unfamiliar, unreal, unintegrated. Especially unpleasant or psychologically threatening connotative inputs may be excluded from awareness [Silverman, 1967, p. 243]."

More evidence than is presently available is needed before specific hypotheses about defensive mechanisms used by schizophrenics are accepted. The emphasis in this chapter has been placed on inhibitory control rather than openness to stimulation, primarily because this interpretation seems more in line with other evidence on reduced range of cue utilization in chronic non-paranoid schizophrenics. Silverman's picture of many non-paranoid process schizophrenics as focusing on sensory attributes, with connotative attributes of stimuli dissociated from their sensory configurations, and objects and people therefore appearing as unfamiliar, unreal, unintegrated, is like many schizophrenics describe their experience. However, though this could occur from broad, distractible sensory awareness, as in acute schizophrenia, the evidence we have reviewed in earlier chapters suggests that lack of meaningful integration of sensory configurations in chronic non-paranoid and process schizophrenics is likely to involve reduced environmental intake — intake that is restricted to incomplete, fragmented items of information about the world.

SUMMARY COMMENTS ON AROUSAL IN SCHIZOPHRENIA

Because the final sections of this chapter have included some fairly speculative discussion, a very brief review that begins by emphasizing conclusions based on firmer evidence may be useful.

The evidence we have discussed indicates that, in situations that are relatively low-stress situations for normals, schizophrenics tend to be abnormally aroused on a number of physiological measures, including muscular tension, measures of cardiovascular functioning, and respiration-rate. The physiological picture during the very earliest stages of schizophrenia is uncertain, but fairly early and moderately chronic patients both tend to show abnormally elevated sympathetic arousal.

Whether these abnormal arousal levels occur to the same degree in familiar ward environments is also uncertain, but they do tend to occur in experimental situations that for normals would seem to be fairly low-demand, low-stress situations.

In view of the evidence we have discussed concerning the effect of tension or arousal-producing conditions in increasing variability between alternate responses, it seems plausible to hypothesize that, at least in some schizophrenics, their high and relatively diffuse somatic tonus may be one of the factors that contributes to abnormal response interference.

With abnormal activation under moderate stress, in many schizophrenics some physiological systems seem to be activated to a level near ceilings imposed by homeostatic feedback, as indicated by relatively attenuated and at times even negative reactivity in response to more extreme stress.

The result of inhibitory feedback is not always simply to control the overactive system. Rather, as Lacey and others have pointed out, inhibitory processes stimulated by the activation of a physiological system can have fairly important effects on other systems. For example, it seems that a spurt in cardiovascular functioning activates an inhibitory process that not only provides homeostatic feedback to the heart, but also tends to counteract the activation of processes involved with sensory receptivity.

In that cardiovascular functioning can apparently be increased by an intent to reduce stimulation, it may be that this inhibitory process is repeatedly activated by those schizophrenics who, because they are often overloaded with stimulation beyond their capacity to organize and selectively utilize, learn methods of reducing their stimulability. Repeated activation may exacerbate and sensitize this inhibitory process, contributing to some chronic schizophrenics' relatively reduced cue intake in complex environments. It is not implied that such physiological processes are the only contributors to loss of cues. Learned alterations in other observational habits, such as learning to move slowly, to face blank walls or floors, and general refusal to continue normally extensive search for cues, may be at least as important.

9

CONCLUDING REMARKS

Although it may not at first seem reasonable to say it, the most accurate summary of what has been learned from research on schizophrenic behavior may be some form of: By now we know a fair amount about schizophrenia, but as a single entity there may be no such thing. It is true that so much of the research points in similar directions that by now a number of statements about schizophrenic behavior can be made with fair certainty. For example, most research on general samples of schizophrenics has indicated that on the average these groups show abnormal response interference and reduced utilization of relevant cues. However, when finer discriminations are made among schizophrenics, it becomes obvious that the extent and patterning of differences from normals is anything but uniform.

This heterogeneity in schizophrenic behavior, which may reflect different remission rates in basic process, possible causal heterogeneity, and differences in secondary reactions, does not make the recognition and clarification of major kinds of behavioral deficit any less important. On the contrary, more relevant, meaningful differentiations into homogeneous behavioral groups, which should do much to aid further research on underlying differences between these groups, should be aided mightily by the clearer understanding of the characteristics of the kinds of different behavioral deficits that seem most prominent in persons who have been called schizophrenics.

It has been emphasized that a characteristic that seems notable in the responding of most groups of unremitted schizophrenics is response interference. Compared to normals, responding is a relatively disorganized mixture of the usual normal responses together with sporadic intrusions of competing responses. In general, when situations are responded to, the most prominent characteristics are (a) behavioral instability with (b) much of the variation being among the varied response tendencies that are also evoked in some strength in normals. The tendency toward randomization among the alternate responses is far from complete. Those responses that have the highest probability in normals also tend to have the highest probability in schizophrenics, and when groups of schizophrenics and normals are compared, the rank orders of the frequencies of different responses in the two groups seem similar. The major difference is that the different responses have more equal probabilities in schizophrenics.

However, as is obvious to those who have interacted to any extent with individual schizophrenics, the emphasis on similarities in response hierarchies between normals and schizophrenics is somewhat overstated in the reports of average data in experiments. The intrusion of idiosyncratic responses, mediated by associations to the experimental stimulus that came from relatively unique past experience with such situations, or are evoked, not by "the stimulus," but by concurrent unrelated preoccupations, clearly seems more frequent in schizophrenics.

This does not contradict the theme of the discussion in that an increase in idiosyncratic responses should be expected if in many schizophrenics there is increased equalization among concurrent response tendencies. The different response tendencies in a situation come from many different sources—alternate responses to task-relevant stimuli, as well as to other internal and external stimuli—and in normals as well as schizophrenics, some of these response tendencies are based on unshared experiences. For both groups, these idiosyncratic tendencies will, in general, be weaker than those that are shared, because they will be based on rarer past contingencies. Thus, they will rarely intrude in normal responding where alternate response tendencies are so hierarchically organized, but will intrude more in schizophrenics' response patterns.

Even so, the relative increase in responses that are not associated to the prominent experimental stimuli will often not be a significant factor in research results. Specific idiosyncratic responses would, by definition, occur with an n of 1. Hence, in group data where the frequencies of specific responses are counted, the specific error responses that intrude with greatest frequency in schizophrenics will be competing tendencies that are shared by members of a culture, schizophrenics as well as normals. It is this kind of associated deviancy, with schizophrenics' errors being exacerbations of those competing tendencies that are also noted in normals, that is most prominent in the literature.

Probably the shortest way to encompass much of the meaning of response interference as intended here is to describe schizophrenics' response hierarchies as partially collapsed. The "partially" in this description indicates the organization in response frequencies that is still there, but this description also indicates schizophrenics' relatively greater randomization among the different types of response tendencies that normals also have; appropriate, incorrect-but-shared, and more idiosyncratic tendencies.

This concept of partially collapsed response hierarchies, or however else the response-interference principle is stated, enables a considerable ability to predict schizophrenic behavior in new experiments. Also, as is often not realized by persons who are not familiar with theory and research on schizophrenia in the last two decades, it is possible to control the amount of schizophrenic deficit. In that many schizophrenics are abnormally susceptible to the introduction of competing response tendencies, the amount of schizophrenic deficit from normal behavior can be varied by varying response complexity. Even the response tendencies that are mediated by internal cues can be controlled to a major extent by increasing the relative prominence of relevant stimuli and by reducing the strength of competing tendencies through response-contingent punishment; at least this seems to be the case in that the use of such procedures has, in many studies, resulted in changing schizophrenic deficit to a level of performance that does not differ from that of normals.

In spite of the utility of a response-interference principle in describing and controlling deficit for many groups of schizophrenics, the initial point — heterogeneity — must not be forgotten. Groups of schizophrenics overlap normals' distributions to a major extent and some groups — paranoids and possibly good-premorbid chronics -- have seemed to have less response-interference than other schizophrenics.

A second variable that seems to be of major importance in schizophrenic behavior is range of cue utilization. Here heterogeneity is, if anything, more obvious, especially in the total range of cues that are responded to — relevant plus irrelevant cues. Some acute schizophrenics seem responsive to a range of cues that is wider than the range of cues normals respond to, while many non-paranoid chronic schizophrenics seem to respond to a reduced range of stimuli.

It seems quite possible that the abnormally broad range of cue utilization that occurs in some schizophrenics is one aspect of abnormal response interference. The attention tendencies and other response tendencies evoked in multiple-stimulus situations are not as organized as in normals, and attention is distractible, tending to fluctuate over a wide range of stimuli. This broad distractibility may lead to some reduction in the utilization of relevant cues in that appropriate focus is not maintained as well as is the case for normals. It also seems possible that response interference contributes to the style of attention within some non-paranoid chronics in that, within their reduced range of attention, response interference may contribute to reduced ability to focus on relevant or usual cues within the limited set. However, a response-interference principle by itself cannot account for the apparent reduction in total range of cue utilization.

Recent theories have used two different kinds of accounts of reduced cue utilization. One suggests that reduced cue utilization is a learned and defensive style of attention; for example, suggesting that reduced scanning of stimuli reduces the confusion from the extensive response interference that occurs when there is wide scanning, and is therefore used even at the cost of reduced information. The second type of theory suggests that reduced cue utilization is the direct result of a basic disturbance in schizophrenia; for example, high arousal and consequent inhibitory feedback, or abnormally slow ability to process information, which results in much information being lost.

Variants of both types of theories overlap considerably in implications about what kinds of information will or will not be lost. In general, if a sequence of scanning responses is stopped abnormally early for defensive reasons, the result is much the same as if only the first information in a processing system can be handled because of the capacity of the system. In both cases, the information that is scanned first will tend to be retained and other information lost. Thus, with information about the variables that determine scanning sequences, considerable predictability about cue utilization in schizophrenia results. The most parsimonious theory of information usage in schizophrenia (Chapman, Chapman, & Miller, 1964), in fact, states only that dominant information will be overweighted in schizophrenics, and has thereby accounted for many of the kinds of errors in judging meanings that are made by chronic schizophrenics.

As we have seen, many theories of schizophrenia overlap in the behavioral phenomena they emphasize, while varying in what is considered to be basic or secondary and in changes that are thought to occur over time. The need for longitudinal observation using measures of the behavioral phenomena that have been emphasized in past research is obvious.

However, the major emphases from past cross-sectional research on (a) abnormal response variability in situations that evoke competing response tendencies, and (b) reduction in range of cue utilization, also suggest that experimental research on cause-and-effect relationships in these two areas of behavior should do much to aid our understanding of the kinds of disturbance we have called schizophrenia.

REFERENCES

Angyal, A., Freeman, H., & Hoskins, R. G. Physiologic aspects of schizophrenic withdrawal. *Archives of Neurology and Psychiatry*, 1940, **44**, 621-626.

Arieti, S. *Interpretation of schizophrenia*. New York: Brunner, 1955.

Atkinson, R. L., & Robinson, N. M. Paired-associate learning by schizophrenic and normal subjects under conditions of personal and impersonal reward and punishment. *Journal of Abnormal and Social Psychology*, 1961, **62**, 322-326.

Berlyne, D. E., Borsa, D. M., Hamacher, J. H., & Koenig, I. D. V. Paired-associate learning and the timing of arousal. *Journal of Experimental Psychology*, 1966, **72**, 1-6.

Blaufarb, H. A demonstration of verbal abstracting ability in chronic schizophrenics under enriched stimulus and instructional conditions. *Journal of Consulting Psychology*, 1962, **26**, 471-475.

Bleuler, E. *Dementia praecox or the group of schizophrenias*. Translated by Joseph Zinkin. New York: International Universities Press, 1950. (originally published, Leipzig: Deuticke, 1911.)

Broadbent, D. E. *Perception and communication*. New York: Pergamon Press, 1958.

Broen, W. E., Jr. Response disorganization and breadth of observation in schizophrenia. *Psychological Review*, 1966, **73**, 579-585.

Broen, W. E., Jr., & Storms, L. H. A reaction potential ceiling and response decrements in complex situations. *Psychological Review*, 1961, **68**, 405-415.

Broen, W. E., Jr., & Storms, L. H. The differential effect of induced muscular tension (drive) on discrimination in schizophrenics and normals. *Journal of Abnormal and Social Psychology*, 1964, **68**, 349-353.

Broen, W. E., Jr., & Storms, L. H. Lawful disorganization; the process underlying a schizophrenic syndrome. *Psychological Review*, 1966, **73**, 265-279.

Broen, W. E., Jr., & Storms, L. H. A theory of response interference in schizophrenia. In B. A. Maher (Ed.), *Progress in experimental personality research*, Vol. IV. New York: Academic Press, 1967, Pp. 269-312.

Broen, W. E., Jr., Storms, L. H., & Goldberg, D. H. Decreased discrimination as a function of increased drive. *Journal of Abnormal and Social Psychology*, 1963, **67**, 266-273.

Broen, W. E., Jr., Storms, L. H., & Schenck, H. U., Jr. Inappropriate behavior as a function of the energizing effect of drive. *Journal of Personality*, 1961, **29**, 489-498.

Bryant, A. R. P. An investigation of process-reactive schizophrenia with relation to perception of visual space. Unpublished doctoral dissertation, University of Utah, 1961.

Bursill, A. E. The restriction of peripheral vision during exposure to hot and humid conditions. *Quarterly Journal of Experimental Psychology*, 1958, **10**, 113-129.

Burstein, A. G. Some verbal aspects of primary process thought in schizophrenia. *Journal of Abnormal and Social Psychology*, 1961, **62**, 155-157.

Buss, A. H., & Lang, P. J. Psychological deficit in schizophrenia: I. Affect, reinforcement, and concept attainment. *Journal of Abnormal Psychology*, 1965, **70**, 2-24.

Callaway, E. The influence of amobarbital (amylobarbitone) and methamphetamine on the focus of attention. *Journal of Mental Science*, 1959, **105**, 382-392.

Callaway, E., & Band, R. I. Some psychopharmacological effects of atropine. *Archives of Neurology and Psychiatry*, 1958, **79**, 91-102.

Callaway, E., & Dembo, D. Narrowed attention: a psychological phenomenon that accompanies a certain physiological change. *Archives of Neurology and Psychiatry*, 1958, **79**, 74-90.

Callaway, E., & Stone, G. Re-evaluating focus of attention. In L. Uhr & J. G. Miller (Eds.), *Drugs and behavior*, New York: Wiley, 1960. Pp. 393-398.

Callaway, E., & Thompson, S. V. Sympathetic activity and perception. *Psychosomatic Medicine*, 1953, **15**, 443-455.

Cameron, N. Reasoning, regression and communication in schizophrenics. *Psychological Monographs*, 1938, **50**, No. 1 (Whole No. 221).

Cameron, N. Deterioration and regression in schizophrenic thinking. *Journal of Abnormal and Social Psychology*, 1939, **34**, 265-270.

Cameron, N. Experimental analysis of schizophrenic thinking. In J. S. Kasanin (Ed.), *Language and thought in schizophrenia*. Berkeley and Los Angeles: University of California Press, 1944. Pp. 50-63.

Carlton, P. L. Cholinergic mechanisms in the control of behavior by the brain. *Psychological Review*, 1963, **70**, 19-39.

Carson, R. C. Intralist similarity and verbal rote learning performance of schizophrenic and cortically damaged patients. *Journal of Abnormal and Social Psychology*, 1958, **57**, 99-106.

Cavanaugh, D. K., Cohen, W., & Lang, P. J. The effect of "social censure" and "social approval" on the psychomotor performance of schizophrenics. *Journal of Abnormal and Social Psychology*, 1960, **60**, 213-218.

Chapman, J., & McGhie, A. A comparative study of disordered attention in schizophrenia. *Journal of Mental Science*, 1962, **108**, 487-500.

Chapman, L. J. Distractibility in the conceptual performance of schizophrenics. *Journal of Abnormal and Social Psychology*, 1956, **53**, 286-291. (a)

Chapman, L. J. The role of type of distractor in the "concrete" conceptual performance of schizophrenics. *Journal of Personality*, 1956, **25**, 130-141. (b)

Chapman, L. J. Intrusion of associative responses into schizophrenic conceptual performance. *Journal of Abnormal and Social Psychology*, 1958, **56**, 374-379.

Chapman, L. J. A reinterpretation of some pathological disturbances in conceptual breadth. *Journal of Abnormal and Social Psychology*, 1961, **62**, 514-519.

Chapman, L. J., & Chapman, J. P. Interpretation of words in schizophrenia. *Journal of Personality and Social Psychology*, 1965, **1**, 135-146.

Chapman, L. J., Chapman, J. P. & Miller, G. A. A theory of verbal behavior in schizophrenia. In B. A. Maher (Ed.), *Progress in experimental personality research*. Vol. 1. New York: Academic Press, 1964. Pp. 49-77.

Chapman, L. J., & Taylor, J. A. Breadth of deviate concepts used by schizophrenics. *Journal of Abnormal and Social Psychology*, 1957, **54**, 118-123.

Cohen, B. D., Senf, Rita, & Huston, P. E. Effect of amobarbital (amytal) and effect on conceptual thinking in schizophrenia, depression, and neurosis. *A.M.A. Archives of Neurology and Psychiatry*, 1954, **71**, 171-180.

Conrad, K. *Die beginnende schizophrenie*. Stuttgart: Thieme, 1958.

Cromwell, R. L., & Dokecki, P. R. Schizophrenic language: a disattention interpretation. In S. Rosenberg and J. H. Koplin (Eds.), *Developments in applied psycholinguistics research*. New Jersey: Macmillan, in press.

Darrow, C. W. Differences in physiological reactions to sensory and ideational stimuli. *Psychological Bulletin*, 1929, **26**, 185-201.

Davis, D., Cromwell, R. L., & Held, J. M. Size estimation in emotionally disturbed children and schizophrenic adults. *Journal of Abnormal Psychology*, 1967, **72**, 395-401.

Davis, R. H., & Harrington, R. W. The effect of stimulus class on the problem-solving behavior of schizophrenics and normals. *Journal of Abnormal and Social Psychology*, 1957, **54**, 126-128.

Delgado, J. M. R., Roberts, W. W., & Miller, N. E. Learning motivated by electrical stimulation of the brain. *American Journal of Physiology*, 1954, **179**, 587-593.

Dell, P., Bonvallet, M., & Hugelin, A. Mechanisms of reticular deactivation. In G. E. W. Wolstenholme and M. O'Connor (Eds.), *The nature of sleep. Ciba Foundation Symposium*. London: Churchill, 1961. Pp. 86-102.

DeVault, S. H. Physiological responsiveness in reactive and process schizophrenia. Unpublished doctoral dissertation, Michigan State University, 1955.

Dokecki, P. R., Polidoro, L. G., & Cromwell, R. L. Commonality and stability of word association responses in good and poor premorbid schizophrenics. *Journal of Abnormal Psychology*, 1965, **70**, 312-316.

Donahoe, J. W., Curtin, M. E., & Lipton, L. Interference effects with schizophrenic subjects in the acquisition and retention of verbal material. *Journal of Abnormal and Social Psychology*, 1961, **62**, 553-558.

Draguns, J. G. Responses to cognitive and perceptual ambiguity in chronic and acute schizophrenics. *Journal of Abnormal and Social Psychology*, 1963, **66**, 24-30.

Dunn, W. L. Visual discrimination of schizophrenic subjects as a function of stimulus meaning. *Journal of Personality*, 1954, **23**, 48-64.

Easterbrook, J. A. The effect of emotion on cue utilization and the organization of behavior. *Psychological Review*, 1959, **66**, 183-200.

Egeth, H. Selective attention. *Psychological Bulletin*, 1967, **67**, 41-57.

Epstein, S. Overinclusive thinking in a schizophrenic and a control group. *Journal of Consulting Psychology*, 1953, **17**, 384-388.

Epstein, S. Toward a unified theory of anxiety. In B. A. Maher (Ed.), *Progress in experimental personality research*. Vol. IV. New York: Academic Press, 1967. Pp. 1-89.

Faibish, G. M. Schizophrenic response to words of multiple meaning. *Journal of Personality*, 1961, **29**, 414-427.

Farina, A. Patterns of role dominance and conflict in parents of schizophrenic patients. *Journal of Abnormal and Social Psychology*, 1960, **61**, 31-38.

Farina, A., Garmezy, N., & Barry, H. Relationship of marital status to incidence and prognosis of schizophrenia. *Journal of Abnormal and Social Psychology*, 1963, **67**, 624-630.

Feigenberg, I. M. Probabilistic prognosis and its significance in normal and pathological subjects. In M. Cole and I. Maltzman (Eds.), *Handbook of contemporary Soviet psychology*. New York: Basic Books, in press.

Fenz, W. D., & Epstein, S. Gradients of physiological arousal in parachutists as a function of an approaching jump. *Psychosomatic Medicine*, 1967, **29**, 33-51.

Fey, Elizabeth T. The performance of young schizophrenics and young normals on the Wisconsin Card Sorting Test. *Journal of Consulting Psychology*, 1951, **15**, 311-319.

Fish, F. A neurophysiological theory of schizophrenia. *Journal of Mental Science*, 1961, **107**, 828-838.

Freeman, T. On the psychopathology of schizophrenia. *Journal of Mental Science*, 1960, **106**, 925-937.

Freud, S. Psycho-analytic notes upon an autobiographical account of a case of paranoia (dementia paranoides) (1911). In *Collected Papers*. Vol. III. London: Hogarth Press, 1950.

Gardner, R. W. Cognitive controls of attention deployment as determinants of visual illusion. *Journal of Abnormal and Social Psychology*, 1961, **62**, 120-127.

Gardner, R. W., & Long, R. I. Control, defense and centration effect: a study of scanning behavior. *British Journal of Psychology*, 1962, **53**, 129-140. (a)

Gardner, R. W., & Long, R. I. Cognitive controls of attention and inhibition: a study of individual consistencies. *British Journal of Psychology*, 1962, **53**, 381-388. (b)

Garmezy, N. Stimulus differentiation by schizophrenic and normal subjects under conditions of reward and punishment. *Journal of Personality*, 1952, **20**, 253-276.

Gellhorn, E. *Physiological foundations of neurology and psychiatry.* Minneapolis: University of Minnesota Press, 1953.

Goldberg, D. H. The physiological effects of multiple stressors. *Behavioral Science*, 1966, **6**, 438-443.

Goodstein, L. D., Guertin, W. H., & Blackburn, H. L. Effects of social motivational variables on choice reaction time in schizophrenics. *Journal of Abnormal and Social Psychology*, 1961, **62**, 24-27.

Gottesman, L. E. Forced-choice word associations in schizophrenia. *Journal of Abnormal and Social Psychology*, 1964, **69**, 673-675.

Gottesman, L. E., & Chapman, L. J. Syllogistic reasoning errors in schizophrenia. *Journal of Consulting Psychology*, 1960, **24**, 250-255.

Gray, J. A. *Pavlov's typology. Recent theoretical and experimental developments from the laboratory of B. M. Teplov.* New York: Macmillan, 1964.

Gunderson, E. K. Autonomic balance in schizophrenia. Unpublished doctoral dissertation, Univer. of California, Los Angeles, 1953.

Hamilton, V. Size constancy and cue responsiveness in psychosis. *British Journal of Psychology*, 1963, **54**, 25-39.

Hamlin, R. M., Haywood, H. C., & Folsom, Angela. Effect of enriched input on schizophrenic abstraction. *Journal of Abnormal Psychology*, 1965, **70**, 390-394.

Harris, J. G. Size estimation of pictures as a function of thematic content for schizophrenic and normal subjects. *Journal of Personality*, 1957, **25**, 651-671.

Hebb, D. O. *The organization of behavior.* New York: Wiley, 1949.

Hernández-Peón, R. Reticular mechanisms of sensory control. In W. A. Rosenblith (Ed.), *Sensory communication.* New York: Wiley, 1961. Pp. 497-520.

Hernández-Peón, R., Scherrer, H., & Jouvet, M. Modification of electric activity in cochlear nucleus during "attention" in unanesthetized cats. *Science*, 1956, **123**, 331-332.

Higgins, J., & Mednick, S. A. Reminiscence and stage of illness in schizophrenia. *Journal of Abnormal and Social Psychology*, 1963, **66**, 314-317.

Hoffer, A., & Osmond, H. Schizophrenia—an autonomic disease. *Journal of Nervous and Mental Disease*, 1955, **122**, 448-452.

Hoskins, R. G. *The biology of schizophrenia.* New York: Norton, 1946.

Howe, E. S. GSR conditioning in anxiety states, normals, and chronic functional schizophrenic subjects. *Journal of Abnormal and Social Psychology*, 1958, **56**, 183-189.

Hull, C. L. *A behavior system.* New Haven: Yale Univer. Press, 1952.

Huston, P. E., Shakow, D., & Riggs, L. A. Studies of motor function in schizophrenia: II. Reaction time. *Journal of General Psychology*, 1937, **16**, 39-82.

Johannsen, W. J., Friedman, S. H., & Liccione, J. V. Visual perception as a function of chronicity in schizophrenia. *British Journal of Psychiatry*, 1964, **110**, 561-570.

Johannsen, W. J., & O'Connell, M. J. Institutionalization and perceptual decrement in chronic schizophrenia. *Perceptual and Motor Skills*, 1965, **21**, 244-246.

Johnson, R. C., Weiss, R. L., & Zelhart, P. F. Similarities and differences between normal and psychotic subjects in responses to verbal stimuli. *Journal of Abnormal and Social Psychology*, 1964, **68**, 221-226.

Karras, A. The effects of reinforcement and arousal on the psychomotor performance of chronic schizophrenics. *Journal of Abnormal and Social Psychology*, 1962, **65**, 104-111.

Kausler, D. H., Lair, C. V., & Matsumoto, R. Interference transfer paradigms and the performance of schizophrenics and controls. *Journal of Abnormal and Social Psychology*, 1964, **69**, 584-587.

Kety, S. S. Recent biochemical theories of schizophrenia. In D. D. Jackson (Ed.), *The etiology of schizophrenia.* New York: Basic Books, 1960. Pp. 120-145.

King, H. E. *Psychomotor aspects of mental disease.* Cambridge, Mass.: Harvard Univer. Press, 1954.

Knopf, I. J., & Fager, R. E. Differences in gradients of stimulus generalization as a function of psychiatric disorder. *Journal of Abnormal and Social Psychology,* 1959, **59,** 73-76.

Kristofferson, M. W. Shifting attention between modalities: a comparison of schizophrenics and normals. *Journal of Abnormal Psychology,* 1967, **72,** 388-394.

Lacey, J. I. The evaluation of autonomic responses: toward a general solution. *Annals of the New York Academy of Sciences,* 1956, **67,** 123-164.

Lacey, J. I. Psychophysiological approaches to the evaluation of psychotherapeutic process and outcome. In E. A. Rubinstein and M. B. Parloff (Eds.), *Research in psychotherapy.* Washington, D. C.: National Publishing Co., 1959. Pp. 160-208.

Lacey, J. I. Somatic response patterning and stress: some revisions of activation theory. In M. H. Appley and R. Trumbull (Eds.), *Psychological stress: Issues in research.* New York: Appleton-Century-Crofts, 1967. Pp. 14-37.

Lacey, J. I., & Lacey B. C. The relationship of resting autonomic activity to motor impulsivity. In *The brain and human behavior.* New York: Hafner Publishing Co., 1966 (facsimile of 1958 edition). Pp. 144-209.

Lacey, J. I., & Van Lehn, R. Differential emphasis in somatic response to stress. *Psychosomatic Medicine,* 1952, **14,** 73-81.

Lang, P. J., & Buss, A. H. Psychological deficit in schizophrenia: II. Interference and activation. *Journal of Abnormal Psychology,* 1965, **70,** 77-106.

Lang, P. J., & Luoto, K. Mediation and associative facilitation in neurotic, psychotic, and normal subjects. *Journal of Abnormal and Social Psychology,* 1962, **64,** 113-120.

Lawson, J. S., McGhie, A., & Chapman, J. Perception of speech in schizophrenia. *British Journal of Psychiatry,* 1964, **110,** 375-380.

Lester, J. R. Production of associative sequences in schizophrenia and chronic brain syndrome. *Journal of Abnormal and Social Psychology,* 1960, **60,** 225-233.

Levin, I. P. Induced muscle tension and response shift in paired-associate learning. Unpublished doctoral dissertation, Univer. of Calif., Los Angeles, 1965.

Lewinsohn, P. M., & Elwood, D. C. The role of contextual constraints in the learning of language samples in schizophrenia. *Journal of Nervous and Mental Diseases,* 1961, **133,** 78-81.

Losen, S. M. The differential effects of censure on the problem-solving behavior of schizophrenic and normal subjects. *Journal of Personality,* 1961, **29,** 258-272.

Lothrop, W. W. A critical review of research on the conceptual thinking of schizophrenics. *Journal of Nervous and Mental Diseases,* 1961, **132,** 118-126.

Lovaas, O. I. Supplementary report: the relationship of induced muscular tension to manifest anxiety in learning. *Journal of Experimental Psychology,* 1960, **59,** 205-206.

Lovibond, S. H. Conceptual thinking, personality and conditioning. *British Journal of Social and Clinical Psychology,* 1963, **2,** 100-111.

Ludwig, A. M., Stilson, D. W., Wood, B. S., & Downs, M. P. Further studies in audition in schizophrenia. *American Journal of Psychiatry,* 1963, **120,** 70-71.

Ludwig, A. M., Wood, B. S., & Downs, M. P. Auditory studies in schizophrenia. *American Journal of Psychiatry,* 1962, **119,** 122-127.

Lynn, R. Russian theory and research on schizophrenia. *Psychological Bulletin,* 1963, **60,** 486-498.

McGhie, A., & Chapman, J. Disorders of attention and perception in early schizophrenia. *British Journal of Medical Psychology*, 1961, **34**, 103-116.

Magoun, H. W. *The waking brain.* Springfield: Thomas, 1958.

Malmo, R. B. Measurement of drive: an unsolved problem in psychology. In M. R. Jones (Ed.), *Nebraska symposium on motivation.* Lincoln, Nebr.: Univer. Nebraska Press, 1958. Pp. 229-265.

Malmo, R. B. Activation: a neuropsychological dimension. *Psychological Review*, 1959, **66**, 367-386.

Mays, M. A. Studies of catatonia. V. Perseverational tendencies in catatonic patients. *Psychiatric Quarterly,* 1934, **8**, 728-735.

Mednick, S. A. Distortions of the gradient of stimulus generalization related to cortical brain damage and schizophrenia. *Journal of Abnormal and Social Psychology*, 1955, **51**, 536-542.

Mednick, S. A. A learning theory approach to research in schizophrenia. *Psychological Bulletin*, 1958, **55**, 316-327.

Meehl, P. E. Schizotaxia, schizotypy, schizophrenia. *American Psychologist*, 1962, **17**, 827-838.

Meyer, D. R. On the interaction of simultaneous responses. *Psychological Bulletin*, 1953, **50**, 204-220.

Meyer, W. J., & Offenbach, S. I. Effectiveness of reward and punishment as a function of task complexity. *Journal of Comparative and Physiological Psychology*, 1962, **55**, 532-534.

Milner, P. The cell assembly: Mark II. *Psychological Review*, 1957, **64**, 242-252.

Moran, L. J. Vocabulary knowledge and usage among normal and schizophrenic subjects. *Psychological Monographs*, 1953, **67**, No. 20 (Whole No. 370).

Moriarty, D., & Kates, S. L. Concept attainment on materials involving social approval and disapproval. *Journal of Abnormal and Social Psychology*, 1962, **65**, 355-364.

Neale, J. M., & Cromwell, R. L. Size estimation in schizophrenics as a function of stimulus-presentation time. *Journal of Abnormal Psychology*, 1968, **73**, 44-48.

Nelson, S., & Caldwell, W. E. Perception of affective stimuli by normal and schizophrenic subjects in a depth perception task. *Journal of General Psychology*, 1962, **67**, 323-335.

O'Connor, N., & Rawnsley, K. Two types of conditioning in psychotics and normals. *Journal of Abnormal and Social Psychology,* 1959, **58**, 157-161.

Olds, J., & Milner, P. Positive reinforcement produced by electrical stimulation of septal area and other regions of rat brain. *Journal of Comparative and Physiological Psychology*, 1954, **47**, 419-427.

Olson, G. W. Failure and the subsequent performance of schizophrenics. *Journal of Abnormal and Social Psychology*, 1958, **57**, 310-314.

Pascal, G. R., & Swensen, C. Learning in mentally ill patients under conditions of unusual motivation. *Journal of Personality*, 1952, **21**, 240-249.

Pavlov, I. P. *Conditioned reflexes and psychiatry.* Trans. and Ed. by W. H. Gant. New York: International Publishers, 1941.

Payne, R. W. An investigation into the possibility of defining "dissociation" as a personality trait by means of objective tests. Unpublished doctoral dissertation, Univer. of London, 1954.

Payne, R. W. Cognitive abnormalities. In H. J. Eysenck (Ed.), *Handbook of abnormal psychology.* New York: Basic Books, 1961. Pp. 193-261.

Payne, R. W. An object classification test as a measure of overinclusive thinking in schizophrenic patients. *British Journal of Social and Clinical Psychology*, 1962, **1**, 213-221.

Payne, R. W. The measurement and significance of overinclusive thinking and retardation in schizophrenic patients. In P. H. Hoch and J. Zubin (Eds.), *Psychopathology of schizophrenia*. New York: Grune & Stratton, 1966. Pp. 77-97.

Payne, R. W., Friedlander, D., Laverty, S. G., & Hayden, P. Overinclusive thought disorder in chronic schizophrenics and its response to "Proketazine." *British Journal of Psychiatry*, 1963, 109, 523-530.

Payne, R. W., & Hewlett, J. H. G. Thought disorder in psychotic patients. In H. J. Eysenck (Ed.), *Experiments in personality*. Vol. II. New York; The Humanities Press, 1960. Pp. 3-104.

Payne, R. W., Matussek, P., & George, E. I. An experimental study of schizophrenic thought disorder. *Journal of Mental Science,* 1959, 105, 627-652.

Peters, H. N., & Murphree, O. D. The conditioned reflex in the chronic schizophrenic. *Journal of Clinical Psychology,* 1954, 10, 126-130.

Pfaffman, C., & Schlosberg, H. The conditioned knee jerk in psychotic and normal individuals. *Journal of Psychology,* 1936, 1, 201-206.

Pinneo, L. R. The effects of induced muscle tension during tracking on level of activation and performance. *Journal of Experimental Psychology*, 1961, 62, 523-531.

Pishkin, V., Armstrong-Ressy, C. T., Aller, R. A., & Comstock, R. L. The effects of temperature on nerve excitability, attention, and reaction time in chronic schizophrenia. *Journal of Nervous and Mental Disease*, 1960, 131, 348-353.

Pishkin, V., & Hershiser, D. Respiration and GSR as functions of white sound in schizophrenia. *Journal of Consulting Psychology*, 1963, 27, 330-337.

Pishkin, V., Smith, T. E., & Leibowitz, H. W. The influence of symbolic stimulus value on perceived size in chronic schizophrenia. *Journal of Consulting Psychology*, 1962, 26, 323-330.

Ramond, C. K. Anxiety and task as determiners of verbal performance. *Journal of Experimental Psychology*, 1953, 46, 120-124.

Reynolds, D. J. An investigation of the somatic response system in chronic schizophrenia. Unpublished doctoral dissertation, Univer. of Pittsburgh, 1962.

Ries, H. A., & Johnson, M. H. Commonality of word associations and good and poor premorbid schizophrenia. *Journal of Abnormal Psychology*, 1967, 72, 487-488.

Rodnick, E. H., & Garmezy, N. An experimental approach to the study of motivation in schizophrenia. In M. R. Jones (Ed.), *Nebraska symposium on motivation*. Lincoln, Nebr.: Nebraska Univer. Press, 1957. Pp. 109-184.

Russell, W. A., & Jenkins, J. J. The complete Minnesota norms for responses to 100 words from the Kent-Rosanoff Word Association Test. Technical Report No. 11, 1954, Univer. of Minnesota, Contract N 8 onr 66216, Office of Naval Research.

Samuels, I. Reticular mechanisms and behavior. *Psychological Bulletin*, 1959, 56, 1-25.

Schnore, M. M. Individual patterns of physiological activity as a function of task differences and degree of arousal. *Journal of Experimental Psychology,* 1959, 58, 117-128.

Schuham, A. I. The double-bind hypothesis a decade later. *Psychological Bulletin*, 1967, 68, 409-416.

Sechahaye, M. *A new psychotherapy in schizophrenia*. New York: Grune & Stratton, 1956.

Shakow, D. Some psychological features of schizophrenia. In M. L. Reymert (Ed.), *Feelings and emotions*. New York: McGraw-Hill, 1950. Pp. 283-290.

Shakow, D. Segmental set. A theory of the formal psychological deficit in schizophrenia. *Archives of General Psychiatry*, 1962, 6, 1-17.

Shakow, D. Psychological deficit in schizophrenia. *Behavioral Science*, 1963, 8, 275-305.

Shipley, W. C. Studies of catatonia. VI. Further investigation of the perseverational tendency. *Psychiatric Quarterly*, 1934, 8, 736-744.

Silverman, J. Psychological deficit reduction in schizophrenia through response contingent noxious reinforcement. *Psychological Reports*, 1963, 13, 187-210.

Silverman, J. The problem of attention in research and theory in schizophrenia. *Psychological Review*, 1964, 71, 352-379. (a)

Silverman, J. Scanning control mechanism and "cognitive filtering" in paranoid and non-paranoid schizophrenia. *Journal of Consulting Psychology*, 1964, 28, 385-393. (b)

Silverman, J. Variations in cognitive control and psychophysiological defense in the schizophrenias. *Psychosomatic Medicine*, 1967, 29, 225-245.

Silverman, J., Berg, P. S. D., & Kantor, R. Some perceptual correlates of institutionalization. *Journal of Nervous and Mental Disease*, 1965, 141, 651-657.

Sommer, R., Dewar, R., & Osmond, H. Is there a schizophrenic language? *Archives of General Psychiatry*, 1960, 3, 665-673.

Spence, J. T., & Lair, C. V. Associative interference in the verbal learning performance of schizophrenics and normals. *Journal of Abnormal and Social Psychology*, 1964, 68, 204-209.

Spence, J. T., & Lair, C. V. Associative interference in paired-associate learning of remitted and nonremitted schizophrenics. *Journal of Abnormal Psychology*, 1965, 70, 119-122.

Spence, K. W. Behavior theory and selective learning. In M. R. Jones (Ed.), *Nebraska symposium on motivation.* Lincoln, Nebr.: Univer. Nebr. Press, 1958. Pp. 73-107.

Spence, K. W., Farber, I. E., & McFann, H. H. The relation of anxiety (drive) level to performance in competitional and non-competitional paired-associate learning. *Journal of Experimental Psychology*, 1956, 52, 296-305.

Spence, K. W., & Taylor, J. A. The relation of conditioned response strength to anxiety in normal, neurotic, and psychotic subjects. *Journal of Experimental Psychology*, 1953, 45, 265-272.

Spence, K. W., Taylor, J. A., & Ketchel, R. Anxiety (drive) level and degree of competition in paired-associate learning. *Journal of Experimental Psychology*, 1956, 52, 306-310.

Stilson, D. W., & Kopell, B. S. The recognition of visual signals in the presence of visual noise by psychiatric patients. *Journal of Nervous and Mental Disease*, 1964, 139, 209-221.

Storms, L. H., & Broen, W. E., Jr. Drive theories and stimulus generalization. *Psychological Review*, 1966, 73, 113-127.

Storms, L. H., Broen, W. E., Jr., & Levin, I. P. Verbal associative stability and commonality as a function of stress in schizophrenics. *Journal of Consulting Psychology*, 1967, 31, 181-187.

Stotsky, B. A. Motivation and task complexity as factors in the psychomotor responses of schizophrenics. *Journal of Personality*, 1957, 25, 327-343.

Sturm, I. E. Overinclusion and concreteness among pathological groups. *Journal of Consulting Psychology*, 1965, 29, 9-18.

Sutton, S., Hakerem, G., Zubin, J., & Portnoy, M. The effect of shift of sensory modality on serial reaction time: a comparison of schizophrenics and normals. *American Journal of Psychology*, 1961, 74, 224-232.

Sutton, S., & Zubin, J. Effect of sequence on reaction time in schizophrenia. In A. T. Welford and J. E. Birren (Eds.), *Behavior, aging and the nervous system.* Springfield, Ill.: Charles C. Thomas, 1965. Pp. 562-597.

Taylor, J. A. Drive theory and manifest anxiety. *Psychological Bulletin*, 1956, 53, 303-321.

Taylor, J. A., & Spence, K. W. Conditioning level in the behavior disorders. *Journal of Abnormal and Social Psychology*, 1954, 49, 497-502.

Taylor, J. N. A comparison of delusional and hallucinatory individuals using field dependency as a measure. Unpublished doctoral dissertation, Purdue Univer. 1956.

Venables, P. H. Stimulus complexity as a determinant of the reaction time of schizophrenics. *Canadian Journal of Psychology*, 1958, 12, 187-190.

Venables, P. H. Selectivity of attention, withdrawal and cortical activation. *Archives of General Psychiatry*, 1963, 9, 74-78.

Venables, P. H. Input dysfunction in schizophrenia. In B. A. Maher (Ed.), *Progress in experimental personality research*. Vol. I. New York: Academic Press, 1964. Pp. 1-47.

Venables, P. H. Slowness in schizophrenia. In A. T. Welford and J. E. Birren (Eds.), *Behavior, aging and the nervous system*. Springfield, Ill.: Charles C. Thomas, 1965. Pp. 598-612.

Weckowicz, T. E. Size constancy in schizophrenic patients. *Journal of Mental Science*, 1957, 103, 475-486.

Weckowicz, T. E. Autonomic activity as measured by the mecholyl test and size constancy in schizophrenic patients. *Psychosomatic Medicine*, 1958, 20, 66-71.

Weckowicz, T. E. Perception of hidden pictures by schizophrenic patients. *Archives of General Psychiatry*, 1960, 2, 521-527.

Weckowicz, T. E., & Blewett, D. B. Size constancy and abstract thinking in schizophrenic patients. *Journal of Mental Science*, 1959, 105, 909-934.

Weinstein, A. D., Goldstone, S., & Boardman, W. K. The effect of recent and remote frames of reference on temporal judgments of schizophrenic patients. *Journal of Abnormal and Social Psychology*, 1958, 57, 241-244.

Whiteman, M. The performance of schizophrenics on social concepts. *Journal of Abnormal and Social Psychology*, 1954, 49, 266-271.

Wilder, J. The law of initial values. *Psychosomatic Medicine*, 1950, 12, 392-401.

Williams, Meyer. Psychophysiological responsiveness to psychological stress in early chronic schizophrenic reactions. *Psychosomatic Medicine*, 1953, 15, 456-462.

Williams, Moyra. The effect of context on schizophrenic speech. *British Journal of Social and Clinical Psychology*, 1966, 5, 161-171.

Willner, A. Impairment of knowledge of unusual meanings of familiar words in brain damage and schizophrenia. *Journal of Abnormal Psychology*, 1965, 70, 405-411.

Yates, A. J. Psychological deficit. In P. R. Farnsworth (Ed.), *Annual Review of Psychology*. Palo Alto: Annual Reviews Inc., 1966. Pp. 111-144.

Zahn, T. P. Acquired and symbolic affective value as determinants of size estimation in schizophrenic and normal subjects. *Journal of Abnormal and Social Psychology*, 1959, 58, 39-47.

Zahn, T. P. Autonomic reactivity and behavior in schizophrenia. *Psychiatric Research Reports*, 1964, 19, 156-173.

Zahn, T. P., Rosenthal, D., & Shakow, D. Reaction time in schizophrenic and normal subjects in relation to the sequence of series of regular preparatory intervals. *Journal of Abnormal and Social Psychology*, 1961, 63, 161-168.

Zahn, T. P., Rosenthal, D., & Shakow, D. Effects of irregular preparatory intervals on reaction time in schizophrenia. *Journal of Abnormal and Social Psychology*, 1963, 67, 44-52.

AUTHOR INDEX

Numbers in italics refer to the pages on which the complete references are listed.

SUBJECT INDEX

A

Acetylcholine (ACH), effects of, 116–119

Activation, see Arousal

Acute schizophrenia, see Schizophrenia, acute

Ambivalence, 111

Anchor effects, time estimation, 145

Anhedonia, 111

Anxiety, see Drive, effects of, Arousal, Arousal effects

Arousal, 84, 186–216, see also Arousal effects, Reticular activating system

  cardiovascular inhibitory processes, 203–216

  general dimension?, 188–192

  inhibitory-homeostatic processes, 158–160, 196–216

  levels in schizophrenia, 84, 99, 100, 157, 175, 187, 193–200, 208, 209, 212–216

  repeated experience, effects of, 204–209, 214–216

  stress effects on level

    normals, 188–191, 195–206, 212–215

    schizophrenics, 193–204, 208, 209, 212–216

Arousal effects, 84, 99–108

  cue utilization, 157–164, 186, 207–216

  response hierarchies, 85, 89, 94, 99, 116–119, 181, 186

Associated intrusions, 1, 3, 21, 22, 27–36, 69–71, 99, see also Response hiearchies, partial collapse

Associative curtain, 100

Associative threads, weakening of, see Information, reduced

Asyndetic thinking, 70

Attention, 4–6, 74, 104–106, 120–131, see also Cue utilization, breadth of, Deficit as function of complexity, stimulus

Audiometric tests, 6, 7, 9

Autokinetic movement, 163

B

Bleuler's theory, 51–55

Brain-damaged patients, 19, 36

Broadbent's model, 179–185

Broen-Storms theory, 76–99

C

Cameron's theory, 69–74